# ALL QUIET
## ON THE
# WESTERN FRONT

WITH RELATED READINGS

Erich Maria Remarque
Translated from the German by
A. W. Wheen

THE EMC MASTERPIECE SERIES

Access Editions

EMC/Paradigm Publishing
St. Paul, Minnesota

**Staff Credits**

Laurie Skiba
*Managing Editor*

Brenda Owens
*High School Editor*

Becky Palmer
*Associate Editor*

Nichola Torbett
*Associate Editor*

Jennifer Anderson
*Assistant Editor*

Paul Spencer
*Art and Photo Researcher*

Valerie Murphy
*Editorial Assistant*

Lori Coleman
*Editorial Consultant*

Christina Bonadio
*Contributing Writer*

Shelley Clubb
*Production Manager*

Jennifer Wreisner
*Senior Designer*

Leslie Anderson
*Senior Electronic Design and Production Specialist*

Parkwood Composition
*Composition*

*All Quiet on the Western Front,* © 1929, 1939, by Little, Brown and Company; renewed copyright 1957, 1958 by Erich Maria Remarque. Published by arrangement with Little, Brown and Company (Inc.). All rights reserved.

Library of Congress Cataloging-in-Publication Data

Remarque, Erich Maria, 1898-1970.
[Im Westen nichts Neues. English]
All quiet on the western front : with related readings / Erich Maria Remarque ; translated from the German by A. W. Wheen.
p. cm. — (EMC masterpiece series access edition)
Summary: A young German soldier of World War I tells of a generation of men who, even though they may have escaped shells, were destroyed by the war.
Contents: All quiet on the western front—Plot analysis of All quiet on the western front—Related Readings—Creative writing activities—Critical writing activities—Projects.
ISBN 0-8219-2420-6
1. World War, 1914-1918—Fiction. [1. World War, 1914-1918—Fiction.
2. Soldiers—Fiction.] I. Wheen, A. W. (Arthur Wesley), 1897-
II. Title. III. EMC masterpiece series access editions.
PT2635.E68 I625
833'.912—dc21                                                                 200202 301

ISBN 0-8219-2420-6

Published by EMC/Paradigm Publishing
875 Montreal Way
St. Paul, Minnesota 55102
www.emcp.com
E-mail: educate@emcp.com

Printed in the United States of America.
1 2 3 4 5 6 7 8 9 10 xxx  08 07 06 05 04 03

# Table of Contents

# Erich Maria Remarque

Erich Maria Remarque was a World War I veteran, a militant pacifist, and a best-selling writer. His works were banned and burned in Germany, but they made him the toast of Hollywood. Throughout Remarque's life, he was driven to realistically portray and condemn a war that nearly annihilated a generation of young people and forever changed its survivors.

Erich Maria Remarque

Remarque was born Erich Paul Remark on June 22, 1898, in Osnabrück, Westphalia, Germany. His father, Peter Franz Remark, and his mother, Anna Maria Remark, were Catholics and of French descent. His father worked as a bookbinder but earned little money, so the Remark family moved many times. Erich had two sisters, Erna and Elfriede, and one brother, Theodor. Theodor died while Erich was still very young. Erich was a talented pianist and gave lessons to earn extra money for clothes and schoolbooks. Erich attended Catholic school, where he sometimes got into trouble with his teachers. He satirized his teachers in his novel *All Quiet on the Western Front*. Although Erich did not always like school, he did like literature and formed a group with his friends to appreciate literature. He also wrote, and a local newspaper published some of Remark's early writings.

In 1916, Erich Remark was drafted as an infantryman, or foot soldier, in the German army. He was sent for basic training. Remark's mother became ill with cancer while he was in the army. Remark was devastated because he had always been especially close to his mother, and he visited her whenever he got leave.

In June of 1917, Remark's regiment was transferred to the Western Front, where Remark experienced the horror of trench warfare. When one of his classmates was wounded in battle, Remark carried his friend to safety, but his friend soon died because of a head injury from grenade splinters that neither Remark nor the doctors initially noticed. In July of 1917, Remark was also injured by grenade splinters and transferred to a Catholic hospital. He was able to visit his mother again before she died in September of that year. After the war ended in 1918, Remark dropped his own middle name, *Paul*, and adopted his mother's middle name, *Maria*, in its place.

After the war, Remark completed his studies to become a teacher. He found he did not enjoy teaching and worked a number of odd jobs. He worked as an organist, a piano teacher, a bookkeeper, and even sold gravestones before landing a position as the editor of a sporting magazine, which Remark enjoyed because he was interested in racing cars. He also married an actress named Jutta Ilse "Jeanne" Zambona.

In 1920, Remark published a novel called *The Dream-Den*. It was so poorly received that an embarrassed Remark later adopted his grandfather's French spelling of the name, *Remarque,* so others would not immediately associate him with the novel. Seven years later, Remark began work on another novel—this one he wrote for himself. He found that the war still deeply disturbed him, so he wrote about how the war affected him and his friends.

In 1929, this novel was published as *Im Westen nichts Neues,* or *All Quiet on the Western Front.* That same year, the novel sold a million and a half copies. It was translated into English and French and was even more popular abroad than it was in Remarque's native Germany. There, the novel drew both critical acclaim and criticism. The National Socialist Party (also known as the Nazis), in particular, was enraged by Remarque's work, and the party's chief propagandist, Josef Goebbels, spread lies about Remarque to discredit him. Hollywood, however, loved Remarque's writing. In 1930, Universal Studios released a film version of *All Quiet on the Western Front.* It received the Academy Award for Best Picture in the United States, but when the film was released in Germany, Nazis disrupted showings of the film. Then, in December of 1930, the German Film Review Office banned the film altogether.

In 1931, Remarque published a sequel to *All Quiet on the Western Front* called *The Road Back.* Nazi reaction to Remarque and his work did not improve. That same year, Remarque and his wife fled to Switzerland. In 1932, German officials seized his German bank account. In 1933, the Nazis held a public book burning. Remarque's novels were tossed into the flames, along with those of other authors of whom the Nazis disapproved.

Meanwhile, Remarque continued writing. In 1936, he published *Three Comrades,* another sequel to *All Quiet on the Western Front.* Both *The Road Back* and *Three Comrades* were released as films. In 1938, Germany revoked Remarque's citizenship, but by then Remarque was already famous in Hollywood, so in 1939, he decided to move there. In 1942, Remarque moved to New York, where he continued to travel in celebrity circles. He counted among his friends actors and actresses like Charlie Chaplin, Marlene Dietrich, and Greta

Garbo and fellow writers like Ernest Hemingway (another World War I veteran) and F. Scott Fitzgerald.

In 1943, Remarque's sister Elfriede was still in Germany. There, the Nazis imprisoned, sentenced, and beheaded her, on the charge that she spread anti-Nazi propaganda. Because World War II raged at that time, Remarque did not learn of her death until 1946. In 1947, Remarque became a U.S. citizen.

Remarque continued to write throughout his life, publishing novels such as *Arch of Triumph* (1945), *Spark of Life* (1952), *A Time to Love and Die* (1954), and *The Black Obelisk* (1956). Many of his novels were made into films, and he became known as the "King of Hollywood." In 1957, he divorced his first wife Jeanne and married a Hollywood actress named Paulette Goddard the following year.

Later in his life, Remarque spent much time traveling around Europe. After he had a series of heart attacks, he spent almost all his time in either Rome or Switzerland. Before he died, Remarque did return to his home country that had renounced him. Much of Germany was destroyed in World War II and had to be rebuilt, so Remarque found much of it unfamiliar. In 1967, The Federal Republic of Germany (then known as West Germany) gave Remarque a medal of honor. He died of heart trouble on September 25, 1970. Films based on Remarque's writings have continued to be made since his death, including a remake of both his most popular novel and film, *All Quiet on the Western Front.*

# Time Line of Remarque's Life

**1898**    Erich Paul Remark is born to Peter Franz Remark and Anna Maria Remark on June 22 in Osnabrück, Westphalia, Germany.

**1898–1912**    The working-class Remark family moves many times during Erich's childhood. Erich attends Catholic school and teaches piano to earn extra money.

**1900**    Erich's sister Erna is born.

**1901**    Erich's older brother Theodor dies.

**1903**    Erich's sister Elfriede is born.

**1913**    Erich Remark enrolls in school to learn to be a teacher.

**1915**    Remark and friends form a literary group.

**1916**    An Osnabrück newspaper publishes an essay, a short story, and a poem by Remark. On November 26, Remark is drafted into Germany's infantry. He goes through basic training.

**1917**    On July 15, Remark's company goes to Flanders. Remark carries one of his friends away from enemy fire, but his friend later dies of a head wound. Remark's mother dies of cancer on September 9. Remark begins writing his first novel.

**1920**    Remark gets his first job as a teacher and goes from teaching job to teaching job before giving up teaching altogether that same year. He works a number of odd jobs. He also publishes a novel called *The Dream-Den,* which is poorly received.

**1921**    Still embarrassed by *The Dream-Den,* Remark begins calling himself Erich Maria Remarque.

**1922**    Remarque moves to Hannover, Germany. He works for a magazine called *Echo Continental.*

**1925**    Remarque gets a job as a writer for *Sport im Bild* magazine. On October 14, he marries actress Jutta Ilse "Jeanne" Zambona.

**1928**    A magazine serially publishes Remarque's first novel, *All Quiet on the Western Front.* Remarque quits his magazine job.

**1929**    Remarque's *All Quiet on the Western Front* is published in novel form in German and English and sells over a million copies.

**1930**    Remarque and his wife separate. Universal Studios releases a film version of *All Quiet on the Western Front.* When the movie premiers in Germany, the Nazis, led by Josef Goebbels, violently protest the film. Germany bans the film.

**1931**    Remarque publishes a sequel to *All Quiet on the Western Front* called *The Road Back.* He is forced to leave Germany for Switzerland because of the Nazis' violent reactions to his work.

| | |
|---|---|
| German officials seize Remarque's bank account. | 1932 |
| Germans publicly ban and burn copies of Remarque's novels, along with works by authors such as Ernest Hemingway, James Joyce, and Albert Einstein. | 1933 |
| Remarque publishes a sequel to *All Quiet on the Western Front* called *Three Comrades*. | 1936 |
| Universal Studios releases a film version of *The Road Back*. | 1937 |
| Remarque remarries his first wife Jeanne so she won't be deported to Germany. Germany revokes Remarque's citizenship. MGM releases a film version of *Three Comrades*. | 1938 |
| Remarque moves to Los Angeles, California. | 1939 |
| Remarque publishes *Flotsam*, and United Artists releases a film version called *So Ends Our Night*. | 1941 |
| Remarque moves to New York City. | 1942 |
| Remarque's sister Elfriede is imprisoned, sentenced to death, and beheaded by the Nazis. | 1943 |
| Remarque publishes *Arch of Triumph*. | 1945 |
| Remarque learns of his sister's execution by the Nazis. | 1946 |
| Remarque becomes a U.S. citizen. | 1947 |
| Remarque returns to Europe, where he travels to Paris, France, and Switzerland. | 1948 |
| Remarque publishes *Spark of Life*. | 1952 |
| Remarque publishes *A Time to Love and Die*. | 1954 |
| Remarque publishes *The Black Obelisk*. | 1956 |
| Remarque divorces his first wife, Jeanne. | 1957 |
| On February 25, Remarque marries American actress Paulette Goddard. | 1958 |
| Remarque publishes *Heaven Has No Favorites*. | 1961 |
| Remarque has his second heart attack and thereafter spends more time in Switzerland and Italy. | 1963 |
| Remarque receives the highest medal of honor from the Federal Republic of Germany. | 1967 |
| Remarque dies of heart trouble in Switzerland on September 25. | 1970 |

# All Quiet on the Western Front

## The Great War

Before World War II, the First World War was known simply as the Great War, or the World War. It was so named because it was the first war to involve many countries from around the world—a total of thirty-two. The war began with Belgium, France, Great Britain, Montenegro, Russia, and Serbia—known as the Allied Powers or the Entente—fighting against the Central Powers, composed of Germany and Austria-Hungary. Soon, however, other countries joined in the war. Italy, Greece, Japan, Romania, and the United States all eventually joined the Allied Powers, while the Ottoman Empire and Bulgaria joined the Central Powers.

The war was different from previous wars because the fighting was intense for so long. The war lasted from 1914 to 1918, a total of four years, but the fighting was nonstop during that period, with thousands of men dying in combat each day. New technologies made the war the bloodiest the world had seen. It was the first war fought on land, sea, and in the air. The only war to foreshadow the ferocity of World War I was the American Civil War. While the American Civil War claimed the lives of about 620,000 men, it is estimated that World War I claimed around 10 million lives.

The war left no aspect of European society unchanged. The main countries involved used all their resources, including their agriculture, their industry, and their people, to fight. When the war ended, a very different Europe emerged. The war destroyed some European empires and generally weakened many European nations. It also witnessed the birth of the Soviet Union and made the United States an economic powerhouse. Many new European countries were formed, claiming their independence from the fallen empires that once ruled them.

## Causes of the War

World War I began with one act of terrorism. In 1914, Austria-Hungary ruled people of many different ethnicities. Some of these people longed to throw off Austrian-Hungarian rule and form their own countries. The Serbs were one such group. On June 28, 1914, a Bosnian Serbian nationalist assassinated Archduke Franz Ferdinand and his wife in Sarajevo, the Bosnian capital. Ferdinand was the heir to the throne of Austria-Hungary. This one act of murder sparked a worldwide war because of various tensions, alliances, and a massive military buildup in Europe.

In 1914, the major powers in Europe were Austria-Hungary, Germany, Great Britain, France, and Russia. Russia felt great sympathy for many of the Slavic people Austria-Hungary held power over, such as the Serbs. France and Germany had a long history of enmity and had fought each other in the previous century. Germany was also interested in Russian resources and had threatened war against Russia. The French and Russians formed an alliance to help each other if they were attacked by Germany. Great Britain was concerned about Germany's growing power in Europe, so it too joined France and Russia in an alliance called the *Triple Entente*. Meanwhile, Germany and Austria-Hungary supported one another.

All these European countries, except for Great Britain, conscripted or drafted large armies. Great Britain had only a volunteer army because it was separated from the other countries by sea and was a great naval power. Led by Kaiser Wilhelm II, who longed to rival other European countries in establishing empires, Germany built up a powerful navy to challenge Great Britain's supremacy at sea. A general arms race was under way in Europe, and each nation had plans in place to mobilize its army should it be attacked. Germany's mobilization plan called for it to sweep through Belgium to attack France, even if war had been declared only against Russia. If war broke out, Germany planned to quickly crush France, so it would not have to fight a war on two fronts.

With a series of alliances and rivalries in place and large armies ready and waiting to be mobilized, Europe was ready to explode into war and the Ferdinand assassination was the spark. After the heir to the Austrian-Hungarian throne was killed, Austria-Hungary sought to crush Serbia. Austria-Hungary asked Germany for its help if the Russians should help the Serbs, and eager to fight with Russia, Kaiser Wilhelm promised Germany's aid. Austria-Serbia sent a harsh and humiliating ultimatum to the Serbs. Both Russia and Great Britain hoped to avoid war and urged Serbia to meet Austria-Hungary's demands. Serbia met most of Austria-Hungary's terms, but Austria-Hungary said the Serbian response was unsatisfactory and declared war against Serbia.

The Russians began to mobilize their army in defense of the Serbs and to fight Austria-Hungary. Germany ordered its armies to mobilize, declared war against Russia on August 1, and sent armies to the east to face Russia and west to face France. Germany asked France to remain neutral in its conflict with Russia. When France refused, Germany declared war on France on August 3 and made ready to move its armies in the west through Belgium to attack France. Belgium was a neutral country and refused to allow Germany to march through its land to attack France. On August 4, Germany invaded Belgium, and Belgium asked Great Britain for help. Great Britain demanded that Germany respect Belgium's neutrality and leave Belgium by midnight on August 4. When Germany refused, Great Britain declared war on Germany.

## A Stalemate at the Western Front

Once the Ottoman Empire joined the Central Powers and Japan joined the Allies, World War I was fought throughout the globe—in Africa, the Pacific, the Atlantic, and the Middle East. While the fighting on Germany's Eastern Front was fierce, most of the warring European nations' forces were spread along the Western Front, where the action in *All Quiet on the Western Front* takes place. Germany swept through Belgium and into northern France but did not quickly conquer France as the nation had planned. Germany met with fierce resistance from France and Great Britain. The two opposing armies were entrenched, facing each other over a long line that stretched from the North Sea to northern France. This line was known as the Western Front. The armies were entrenched and fought each other to gain yards, Germany trying to push its way into Paris to take France, and the Allies trying to push Germany out of France and Belgium.

The armies dug parallel lines of fortified trenches along the Western Front and strung barbed wire to prevent the opposing army from gaining ground. One army would use powerful artillery, or heavy guns, to attack the enemy from afar and kill as many men as possible. They would also use poison gas to attack the enemy from a distance. When the enemy had been thoroughly bombed and gassed, the army would launch an attack using its infantry, who were armed with rifles, bayonets, grenades, and even flame-throwers. The enemy, however, was entrenched and fought back using the same weapons, plus large machine guns. With machine guns, it was easy to kill thousands of the attacking army before they could reach the enemy trenches. Thus, each side would attack one another's trenches and defend their own. The two armies were relatively equal in terms of weapons and numbers of soldiers, so they made little progress. The line shifted first one way and then another by only hundreds of yards at a time. Every hundred yards cost many lives. In a German attack on the French city of Verdun, the Germans began an advance in February 1916 only to be pushed back to the same spot by October 1916—the cost was 700,000 French and German lives.

Another battle along the Somme River was even more costly—in one day, 20,000 British were killed and another 40,000 were injured or lost for a gain of a few yards. By the end of the battle at the Somme, there were over a million casualties—over a million British, French, and German soldiers were killed, injured, captured, or missing. Indeed, throughout World War I, thousands of soldiers were listed as missing. Usually, this meant there was too little left of a soldier to be found and identified, but as the war continued, some soldiers did try to desert, or run away from battle. A deserting soldier who was caught was severely punished.

## Trench Warfare and Life as a Soldier

Much of the action in *All Quiet on the Western Front* takes place in the trenches of the Western Front. Here, soldiers who were lucky enough not to be killed in battle spent years of their lives, either in barracks behind the front or in the trenches themselves. The trenches were dug into the ground, were often filled with mud and rain water, and attracted rats. When they were bombarded by enemy artillery, the soldiers would stay low in their trenches. All they could do was hope a shell wouldn't land on them. While the fortified trenches could stand up to some explosions, they got weaker over time, and a shell that landed just right could completely destroy a trench and every man in it. Soldiers also had to contend with poison gas attacks. The enemy would launch canisters of poison gas that could kill entire divisions if they did not put on their gas masks in time or took them off too soon. Then, when the enemy's army would rush in to attack, the soldiers defended their trench and attacked the enemy soldiers using rifles, machine guns, grenades, and bayonets. Being ordered to attack or counterattack in turn was almost a suicidal mission because the attacking soldiers were certain to meet with great resistance.

Machine guns and flame-throwers were relatively new in battle and cost many lives. Then tanks were introduced into battle, making the war even more terrifying for the average foot soldier. A tank was not stopped by shell holes or barbed wire as soldiers on foot were.

The new weapons used in World War I caused more damage to the human body than weapons used in previous wars. While soldiers had better access to medical care than they did in previous wars, often doctors could do nothing but amputate shattered limbs, and they could do little to help the burned and blinded. Also, millions of soldiers died of disease in the war. Conditions in the trenches were unsanitary, many soldiers had lice, and water was often contaminated, so diseases like dysentery and typhus swept through the armies.

*All Quiet on the Western Front* shows how conditions among the German army deteriorated over time. While all the warring countries used all their resources to provide for their troops in the front lines, Germany was at a disadvantage. The Allies received food and other supplies from the United States and South America and colonies such as India. Once Great Britain secured naval victory over the Germans and the United States entered the war, the Germans were dependent almost entirely on their own resources. As more and more men entered the army and were killed in war, Germans were hard-pressed to keep up the level of industry needed to supply the army. Food was scarce for German soldiers by the end of the war, and many of the civilians in Germany were on the verge of starvation.

## The Russian Revolution

On the Eastern Front, the war was going poorly for the Russians. Germany and Austria-Hungary were able to push back Russia's attacks, and the Allies were not able to get many supplies through to help the Russians. In the Russian capital of Petrograd (now known as Saint Petersburg), the Russian people were starving. *All Quiet on the Western Front* depicts the plight of Russian soldiers taken prisoner by the Germans.

Food riots broke out in Petrograd, and Russian soldiers returned home to protest the war and care for their starving families. The tsar of Russia was forced to abdicate his throne, and the new government of Russia was unable to keep up its war effort. Then, led by Vladimir Lenin, a party of socialists known as the Bolsheviks started a revolution in October of 1917. They seized power, and Lenin negotiated peace with Germany. Russia lost territory and resources to Germany and officially withdrew from the war. This was a terrible blow for the Allies because it meant that Germany could concentrate all its war efforts on the Western Front.

## The United States Enters the War

When World War I first broke out, the United States declared that it would remain neutral. At first, the United States loaned money to both the Allied Powers and the Central Powers and shipped food and supplies to both. But because Great Britain was a strong naval power, much more money and supplies ended up in the hands of the Allies. President Woodrow Wilson campaigned for reelection in 1916 with the promise of keeping the United States out of the war.

The Germans wanted to disrupt Great Britain's trade with the United States and starve Great Britain out of the war. The Germans also had a naval weapon of its own—U-boats, or submarines. Germany used its submarines to attack and sink ships traveling with supplies back to Great Britain. In 1915, the Germans sank a British ship called the *Lusitania*, which had 128 Americans on board. This angered many Americans. Then in January of 1917, Germany declared that it would sink any U.S. boat on site when it entered British or Mediterranean waters, and Germany began sinking Allied and American ships in great numbers. Great Britain also told the United States it had learned that the Germans were trying to ally with Mexico and Japan against the United States. On April 6, 1917, the United States declared war on Germany.

The United States, however, needed time to mobilize its troops. While the first American troops arrived in Europe in 1917, they numbered only a few volunteers and had little effect on the war. In the meantime, the United States adopted a convoy system in which military ships escorted ships bearing goods to the Allies to protect them from the German U-boats. The United States also began a draft and soon had 10 million men ready for duty.

In early 1918, the Germans used the delay before American troops could arrive in Europe to launch a last major offensive on the Western Front. Germany's goal was to capture the French city of Amiens before moving on to Paris. This attack almost succeeded, but the German forces fell short of their goal. The Germans lost many men in their final offensive. With the help of American troops, the Allies launched a counterattack. The German army had already lost many lives, and the Allies had fresh troops, tanks, and more supplies. The Germans fell back, and the Allies began to move forward.

## The War to End All Wars?

As the Allies moved forward on the Western Front, the Central Powers began to crumble. Bulgaria and the Ottoman Empire asked for an armistice, or ending of armed conflict, with the Allied Powers. Italy successfully pushed back the Austrian-Hungarians, and on October 4, 1918, the Austrian-Hungarians also asked for an armistice. Meanwhile, just like the Russians a year earlier, starving Germans were rioting,

German sailors refused to go to sea to fight the British, and the German Social Democratic Party talked of overthrowing Kaiser Wilhelm. On October 4, 1918, Germany also asked for an armistice. Within days, a new government was formed in Germany, and Kaiser Wilhelm was forced to abdicate his throne and flee in exile to the Netherlands. On November 11, 1918, the armistice was signed and the war came to an end.

Leaders from all the Allied nations, except for Russia, met in Paris in January 1919 to create a peace treaty. The Treaty of Versailles blamed Germany for the war. To keep Germany from ever starting another war, the treaty called for Germany to pay reparations for the damage it caused during the war. U.S. president Woodrow Wilson insisted that the treaty include the formation of a League of Nations, an international committee that would work to create a lasting peace and prevent future wars. Because of politics at home, the United States never signed the Treaty of Versailles nor joined the League of Nations, so this international organization was not as powerful as it might have been. The Union of Soviet Socialist Republics (what Russia was now called) also refused to join.

As World War I ended, many new countries emerged, and the European map appeared very different than it did in 1914. Germany lost territory to France, and Poland was carved out of its eastern territory. It also lost all its colonies outside of Europe. Czechoslovakia and Yugoslavia claimed their independence from Austria-Hungary, and Austria-Hungary itself split into two separate countries, Austria and Hungary. The war also helped to create an Arab nationalist movement in the Ottoman Empire.

The war helped spark a revolution in Russia, creating a communist nation, the Soviet Union, that would play a very important role in shaping twentieth-century history. In addition, the war established the United States as an economic powerhouse. Before the war, the United States borrowed money from other nations and imported goods. Now, with its profits from the war, it lent money to help other nations and exported its goods worldwide.

Woodrow Wilson had hoped that the Great War, World War I, would be the war to end all wars. He believed that a lasting peace would follow because of the diligent efforts of the League of Nations to work out peaceable solutions between nations. This vision was not realized. Peace was only temporary. Just about a decade after the Treaty of Versailles was signed, Adolph Hitler was gaining power in Germany. By the end of the 1930, another and even more terrible war would sweep across Europe and then the rest of the world—World War II.

# A Lost Generation

Although nobody knows exactly what World War I cost in terms of human life, it is estimated that about ten million men died in battle. Millions more died of disease. Infant mortality rates increased in Europe as food and doctors were sent to the front. A famine broke out after the war ended, and people starved.

Those soldiers who did return from the war often came home with physical or mental disabilities. Some were missing limbs, some were blind, and others were "shell shocked" or mentally traumatized by the war. Many young people were depressed and disillusioned. They felt they had seen a sad truth about humanity during the war. Gertrude Stein, a French writer, said of the young people who served in World War I, "You're all a lost generation." Hemingway, who served as an ambulance driver in Italy during the war, popularized this quotation, using it as the epigraph in his novel *The Sun Also Rises*. In World War I, a generation of young people lost their lives, their innocence, and their ideals. The idea of a lost generation is an important part of Remarque's *All Quiet on the Western Front*.

# Modernism and Realism

Realism is the attempt to render in art an accurate portrayal of reality. As a literary movement, Realism has its roots in the Victorian period (late nineteenth century), although realistic works were also written before that time. Realistic works depict everyday reality without idealization. While Remarque's *All Quiet on the Western Front* is an example of Realism, it is also associated with a literary movement that arose following World War I—Modernism. Modernist writers expressed the uncertainty of the modern individual who has lost connections to the beliefs and values of preceding generations. Remarque's protagonist, or main character, Paul Baümer, can be seen as a spokesperson for the Modernist movement as he questions traditional beliefs and values and expresses how distant he feels from other generations.

# Characters in
## *All Quiet on the Western Front*

### Major Characters

**Paul Baümer** is a nineteen-year-old German soldier and the narrator of the novel. The novel follows Paul's experiences in the war and how they affect his character.

**Stanislaus Katczinsky** or "Kat" is a German soldier who is older and more experienced than Paul and his classmates. Paul and the other soldiers look up to and depend on Kat. Kat has a unique ability to find food almost anywhere. He becomes Paul's closest friend.

**Albert Kropp** is a German soldier and Paul's friend and fellow classmate. He is injured and his leg is amputated during the war.

**Müller** is a German soldier and one of Paul's friends. He and Paul were in the same class at school. He inherits Kemmerich's boots after Kemmerich dies.

**Tjaden** is a German soldier who formerly worked as a locksmith. He is the same age as Paul and his classmates.

**Haie Westhus** is a German soldier who dug peat for a living before the war. He dreams of becoming a policeman after the war rather than returning to a life digging peat.

**Detering** is a German soldier who is older than Paul and his classmates. He worked as a farmer before the war and has a wife. He would rather be back on his farm than fighting in the war.

**Kantorek** was the schoolteacher in Paul's home town. He encouraged Paul and his classmates to enlist as soldiers in the war to fight for Germany.

**Corporal Himmelstoss** was the officer in charge during Paul's and his companions' basic training. He was cruel and inhumane to the young soldiers, especially to Tjaden.

**Franz Kemmerich** was one of Paul's classmates and a friend of Paul's since they were children. He is injured in the war and dies, giving Müller his boots.

### Minor Characters

**Berger** is a German soldier in Paul's company who risks and loses his own life to aid a wounded messenger dog.

The **chief surgeon** at the hospital uses soldiers with flat feet as guinea pigs for experimental operations.

**Franz Wächter** is a patient at the hospital who is taken to the Dying Room and dies.

**Gérard Duval** is the name of the French solider Paul stabs to death.

**Ginger** is the red-headed cook for Paul's company.

**Josef Hamacher** is in the hospital and has been declared not responsible for his actions because of a head injury. He takes the blame when Paul throws a bottle to stop the sisters at the hospital from praying. He tells the others about the Dying Room. He also warns the others about the chief surgeon.

**Joseph Behm** was one of Paul's classmates. Kantorek encouraged him to enlist in the army. He is one of the first to die in battle.

The **Kaiser**, Wilhelm II, reviews Paul's company. Paul's company is given new uniforms for the Kaiser's visit, but the new uniforms are taken away once the Kaiser leaves.

**Kemmerich's mother** made Paul promise to look after her son. Paul has the unpleasant task of letting her know her son has died. He lies to her about the manner of Kemmerich's death.

**Leer** is a German soldier and was one of Paul's classmates at school. He fancies himself to be a ladies' man.

**Lewandowski** is a patient at the hospital. The other patients give him a chance to have a romantic interlude with his wife Marja.

**Lieutenant Bertinck** is the commander of Paul's company. Unlike Himmelstoss, he earns the respect of his men.

**Marja Lewandowski** is Lewandowski's wife. She visits him at the hospital with her baby.

**Mittelstaedt** was another of Paul's classmates. He trains newly enlisted men. When his former schoolteacher Kantorek is called up on duty, Mittelstaedt seizes the opportunity to make things difficult for his former teacher.

**Paul's father** works hard to take care of his sick wife and his poor family. He wants to hear about the war, but Paul is unable to share his experiences with his father. Paul's father also visits Paul when he is in training camp.

**Paul's mother** is dying of cancer and is impoverished, yet she saves the little food she has for Paul and begs to get him new underpants.

**Paul's sister Erna** greets Paul when he arrives home and later visits him in training camp.

**Peter** is a patient in the hospital who is taken to the Dying Room to die but manages to live.

The **Russian prisoners of war** scrounge for food and live miserable lives imprisoned near Paul's training camp. Paul shares some of his food and cigarettes with them.

**Sergeant Oellerich** is a sharp shooter who guns down the enemy from afar.

**Sister Libertine** is a kind nurse in the hospital.

**Three French girls** have a romantic rendezvous with Paul, Kropp, and Leer. Paul has feelings for the brunette.

# Map of the Western Front

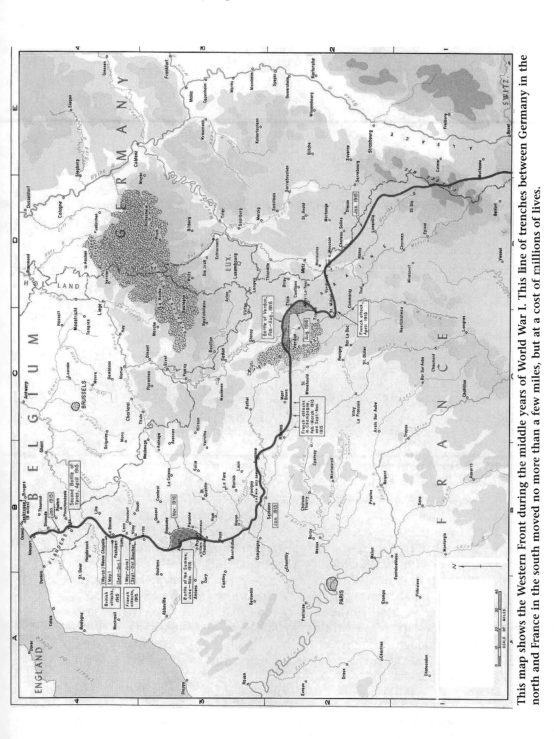

This map shows the Western Front during the middle years of World War I. This line of trenches between Germany in the north and France in the south moved no more than a few miles, but at a cost of millions of lives.

# Echoes:

## Different Perspectives on War

War loves to seek its victims in the young.
—Sophocles (c.496 BC–406 BC)

Arms, and the man I sing.
—Virgil (70–19 BC)

The lamp of war is kindled here, not to be extinguished but by torrents of blood.
Thomas Jefferson (1743–1826)

There never was a good war or a bad peace.
—Benjamin Franklin (1706–1790)

War can only be abolished through war, and in order to get rid of the gun it is necessary to take up the gun.
—Mao Zedong (1893–1976)

War alone brings up to their highest tension all human energies and imposes the stamp of nobility upon the peoples who have the courage to make it.
—Benito Mussolini (1883–1945)

We shall fight on the beaches, we shall fight on the landing grounds, we shall fight in the fields and in the streets, we shall fight in the hills; we shall never surrender.
—Winston Churchill (1874–1965)

More than an end to war, we want an end to the beginnings of all wars. Yes, an end to this brutal, inhuman and thoroughly impractical method of settling the differences between Governments. The once powerful malignant Nazi state is crumbling; the Japanese warlords are receiving in their homelands the retribution for which they asked when they attacked Pearl Harbor. But the mere conquest of our enemies is not enough; we must go on to do all in our power to conquer the doubts and the fears, the ignorance and the greed, which made this horror possible.
—Franklin Delano Roosevelt (1882–1945)

War and culture, those are the two poles of Europe, her heaven and hell, her glory and shame, and they cannot be separated from one another. When one comes to an end, the other will end also and one cannot end without the other. The fact that no war has broken out in Europe for fifty years is connected in some mysterious way with the fact that for fifty years no new Picasso has appeared either.

—Milan Kundera (1929– )

War is always the same. It is young men dying in the fullness of their promise. It is trying to kill a man that you do not even know well enough to hate. Therefore, to know war is to know that there is still madness in this world.

—Lyndon Johnson (1908–1973)

# Images of World War I

Fresh German recruits on their way to the Western Front in 1914. The inscription on the side of the train optimistically proclaims that their destination is Paris, France, the capital of their enemy.

German soldiers on the Western Front rest in a trench between battles.

German soldiers charge across No Man's Land, the area between the opposing trenches, to attack the enemy.

The cemetery for World War I dead at Verdun.

This book is to be neither an accusation nor a confession, and least of all an adventure, for death is not an adventure to those who stand face to face with it. It will try simply to tell of a generation of men who, even though they may have escaped its shells, were destroyed by the war.

# Chapter I

We are at rest five miles behind the front. Yesterday we were relieved,[1] and now our bellies are full of beef and haricot beans.[2] We are satisfied and at peace. Each man has another mess-tin full[3] for the evening; and, what is more, there is a double <u>ration</u> of sausage and bread. That puts a man in fine trim.[4] We have not had such luck as this for a long time. The cook with his carroty head is begging us to eat; he beckons with his ladle to every one that passes, and spoons him out a great <u>dollop</u>. He does not see how he can empty his stew-pot in time for coffee. Tjaden and Müller have produced two washbasins and had them filled up to the brim as a reserve. In Tjaden this is <u>voracity</u>, in Müller it is foresight. Where Tjaden puts it all is a mystery, for he is and always will be as thin as a rake.

What's more important still is the issue of a double ration of smokes. Ten cigars, twenty cigarettes, and two quids of chew[5] per man; now that is decent. I have exchanged my chewing tobacco with Katczinsky for his cigarettes, which means I have forty altogether. That's enough for a day.

It is true we have no right to this <u>windfall</u>. The Prussian[6] is not so generous. We have only a miscalculation to thank for it.

Fourteen days ago we had to go up and relieve the front line. It was fairly quiet on our sector, so the quartermaster[7] who remained in the rear had <u>requisitioned</u> the usual quantity of rations and provided for the full company of one

◀ *What puts the soldiers in a good mood?*

◀ *Who or what do the soldiers have to thank for the extra food and supplies?*

◀ *What happened to seventy men in the narrator's company?*

---

1. **relieved**. Set free from duty
2. **haricot beans**. Kidney beans
3. **mess-tin full**. Full plate of food. Soldiers carried a compact set of metal plates and utensils called a mess kit.
4. **trim**. Condition
5. **quids of chew**. Pieces of chewing tobacco. When this story takes place, people were not aware of the dangers of tobacco.
6. **Prussian**. Northern Germanic people. They were often considered harsh military leaders.
7. **quartermaster**. Officer who provides troops with clothing and equipment

| words for everyday use | |
|---|---|
| **ra • tion** (rash′ ən) *n.*, fixed allowance or allotment of food or provisions. *During World War II, people could buy only <u>rations</u> of meat rather than as much as they wanted.* | **wind • fall** (wind′ fôl′) *n.*, any unexpected gain. *Finding that cool pond to swim in just when we were hot from hiking was a <u>windfall</u>.* |
| **dol • lop** (däl′ əp) *n.*, soft mass or blob, as of some food. *Ramon put a <u>dollop</u> of whip cream on top of his slice of pie.* | **req • ui • si • tion** (rek′ wə zish′ ən) *vt.*, submit a written order or request for (equipment, etc.). *Martin had to <u>requisition</u> his company for office supplies rather than simply ordering them himself.* |
| **vo • rac • i • ty** (vò ras′ ə tē) *n.*, greediness in eating. *The dog revealed its <u>voracity</u> as it gulped down its food.* | |

hundred and fifty men. But on the last day an astonishing number of English heavies[8] opened up on us with high-explosive, drumming ceaselessly on our position, so that we suffered severely and came back only eighty strong.

Last night we moved back and settled down to get a good sleep for once: Katczinsky is right when he says it would not be such a bad war if only one could get a little more sleep. In the line we have had next to none, and fourteen days is a long time at one stretch.

It was noon before the first of us crawled out of our quarters. Half an hour later every man had his mess-tin and we gathered at the cook-house, which smelt greasy and nourishing. At the head of the <u>queue</u> of course were the hungriest—little Albert Kropp, the clearest thinker among us and therefore only a lance-corporal; Müller, who still carries his school textbooks with him, dreams of examinations, and during a <u>bombardment</u> mutters propositions in physics;[9] Leer, who wears a full beard and has a preference for the girls from officers' brothels. He swears that they are obliged by an army order to wear silk chemises and to bathe before entertaining guests of the rank of captain and upwards. And as the fourth, myself, Paul Bäumer. All four are nineteen years of age, and all four joined up from the same class as volunteers for the war.

Close behind us were our friends: Tjaden, a skinny locksmith of our own age, the biggest eater of the company. He sits down to eat as thin as a grasshopper and gets up as big as a bug in the family way; Haie Westhus, of the same age, a peat-digger,[10] who can easily hold a ration-loaf in his hand and say: Guess what I've got in my fist; then Detering, a peasant, who thinks of nothing but his farmyard and his wife; and finally Stainslaus Katczinsky, the leader of our group, <u>shrewd</u>, cunning, and hard-bitten,[11] forty years of age, with a face of the soil, blue eyes, bent shoulders, and a remarkable nose for dirty weather, good food, and soft jobs.

► How does the narrator describe Albert Kropp and Müller?

► Who is the narrator and how does he know Kropp, Müller, and Leer?

► Who is the leader of the group of soldiers? What is he like?

---

8. **heavies.** Heavy artillery, machines that hurl missiles at enemy troops
9. **propositions in physics.** Theories or laws of physics
10. **peat-digger.** Person who digs partly decayed plant matter to burn for fuel
11. **hard-bitten.** Tough and stubborn

**words for everyday use**

queue (kyü) *n.,* line or file of persons, vehicles, etc. waiting as to be served. *Barbara has to wait in a long queue at the department of motor vehicles to renew her driver's license.*

bom • bard • ment (bäm bärd′ mənt) *n.,* attack, especially by bombs or missiles.

*The children launched bombardments of snowballs at each other from behind the cover of trees.*

shrewd (shrüd) *adj.,* keen-witted, clever, or sharp in practical affairs. *Rawana was a shrewd businesswoman who had started her own dog-walking business at fifteen.*

Our gang formed the head of the queue before the cook-house. We were growing impatient, for the cook paid no attention to us.

Finally Katczinsky called to him: "Say, Heinrich, open up the soup-kitchen. Anyone can see the beans are done."

He shook his head sleepily: "You must all be there first." Tjaden grinned: "We are all here."

The sergeant-cook still took no notice. "That may do for you," he said. "But where are the others?"

"They won't be fed by you today. They're either in the dressing-station or pushing up daisies."[12]

The cook was quite disconcerted as the facts dawned on him. He was staggered. "And I have cooked for one hundred and fifty men—"

Kropp poked him in the ribs. "Then for once we'll have enough. Come on, begin!"

Suddenly a vision came over Tjaden. His sharp, mousy features began to shine, his eyes grew small with cunning, his jaws twitched, and he whispered hoarsely: "Man! then you've got bread for one hundred and fifty men too, eh?"

The sergeant-cook nodded absent-minded, and bewildered.

Tjaden seized him by the tunic. "And sausage?"

Ginger nodded again.

Tjaden's chaps[13] quivered. "Tobacco too?"

"Yes, everything."

Tjaden beamed: "What a bean-feast! That's all for us! Each man gets—wait a bit—yes, practically two issues."

Then Ginger stirred himself and said: "That won't do."

We got excited and began to crowd around.

"Why won't that do, you old carrot?" demanded Katczinsky.

"Eighty men can't have what is meant for a hundred and fifty."

"We'll soon show you," growled Müller.

"I don't care about the stew, but I can only issue rations for eighty men," persisted Ginger.

Katczinsky got angry. "You might be generous for once. You haven't drawn food for eighty men. You've drawn it

---

12. **pushing up daisies.** Dead
13. **chaps.** Jaws

---

| words for everyday use | be • wil • der (bē wil' dər) vt., confuse hopelessly. *Because he is usually so polite, we were* bewildered *by John's rude behavior.* |
| --- | --- |

▶ Why don't the men feel kindly toward their cook?

for the Second Company. Good. Let's have it then. We are the Second Company."

We began to jostle the fellow. No one felt kindly toward him, for it was his fault that the food often came up to us in the line too late and cold. Under shellfire he wouldn't bring his kitchen up near enough, so that our soup-carriers had to go much farther than those of the other companies. Now Bulcke of the First Company is a much better fellow. He is as fat as a hamster in winter, but he trundles his pots when it comes to that right up to the very front-line.

We were in just the right mood, and there would certainly have been a dust-up[14] if our company commander had not appeared. He informed himself of the <u>dispute</u>, and only remarked: "Yes, we did have heavy losses yesterday."

He glanced into the dixie. "The beans look good."

Ginger nodded. "Cooked with meat and fat."

▶ What does the lieutenant order the cook to do?

The lieutenant looked at us. He knew what we were thinking. And he knew many other things too, because he came to the company as a non-com.[15] and was promoted from the ranks. He lifted the lid from the dixie[16] again and sniffed. Then passing on he said: "Bring me a plate full. Serve out all the rations. We can do with them."

Ginger looked <u>sheepish</u> as Tjaden danced round him.

"It doesn't cost you anything! Anyone would think the quartermaster's store belonged to him! And now get on with it, you old blubber-sticker, and don't you miscount either."

"You be hanged!" spat out Ginger. When things get beyond him he throws up the sponge altogether; he just goes to pieces. And as if to show that all things were equal to him, of his own free will he issued in addition half a pound of <u>synthetic</u> honey to each man.

\*

▶ What makes today "wonderfully good"?

Today is wonderfully good. The mail has come, and almost every man has a few letters and papers. We stroll over to the meadow behind the billets. Kropp has the round lid of a margarine tub under his arm.

---

14. **dust-up.** Fight
15. **non-com.** Noncombatant, one who does not take part in the fighting
16. **dixie.** Pot

**words for everyday use**

dis • pute (di spyüt') *n.*, quarrel, argument. *The two groups of fans got into a* <u>dispute</u> *about whose team would win on Saturday.*

sheep • ish (shēp' ish) *adj.*, embarrassed. *When Margot finally realized she had for-* gotten Esmerelda's birthday, she looked <u>sheepish</u>.

syn • thet • ic (sin thet' ik) *adj.*, human-made, not natural. *When Rita admired Lucy's fur coat, Lucy quickly said that it was* <u>synthetic</u>, *not real fur.*

On the right side of the meadow a large common latrine[17] has been built, a roofed and durable construction. But that is for recruits who as yet have not learned how to make the most of whatever comes their way. We want something better. Scattered about everywhere there are separate, individual boxes for the same purpose. They are square, neat boxes with wooden sides all round, and have unimpeachably satisfactory seats. On the sides are hand grips enabling one to shift them about.

We move three together in a ring and sit down comfortably. And it will be two hours before we get up again.

I well remembered how embarrassed we were as recruits in barracks[18] when we had to use the general latrine. There were no doors and twenty men sat side by side as in a railway carriage, so that they could be reviewed all at one glance, for soldiers must always be under supervision.

Since then we have learned better than to be shy about such <u>trifling</u> immodesties. In time things far worse than that came easy to us.

◀ What are the soldiers no longer worried about?

Here in the open air though, the business is entirely a pleasure. I no longer understand why we should always have shied at these things before. They are, in fact, just as natural as eating and drinking. We might perhaps have paid no particular attention to them had they not figured so large in our experience, nor been such novelties to our minds—to the old hands they had long been a mere matter of course.

The soldier is on friendlier terms than other men with his stomach and intestines. Three-quarters of his vocabulary is derived from these regions, and they give an intimate flavour to expressions of his greatest joy as well as of his deepest indignation. It is impossible to express oneself in any other way so clearly and <u>pithily</u>. Our families and our teachers will be shocked when we go home, but here it is the universal language.

Enforced publicity[19] has in our eyes restored the character of complete innocence to all these things. More than

---

17. **latrine.** Toilets for the use of a large number of people
18. **barracks.** Buildings for housing soldiers
19. **Enforced publicity.** Lack of privacy

---

**words for everyday use**

tri • fling (trī' fliŋ) *adj.,* having little value or importance. *Although at the time our disagreement seemed serious, later it seemed a <u>trifling</u> matter.*

pi • thi • ly (pi' thi lē) *adv.,* having substance and point. *Our teacher explained the importance of the rules <u>pithily</u>.*

that, they are so much a matter of course that their comfortable performance is fully as much enjoyed as the playing of a safe top running flush. Not for nothing was the word "latrine-rumour" invented; these places are the regimental[20] gossip-shops and common-rooms.

We feel ourselves for the time being better off than in any palatial white-tiled "convenience."[21] *There* it can only be <u>hygienic</u>; *here* it is beautiful.

▶ *What do the men see on the horizon?*

These are wonderfully care-free hours. Over us is the blue sky. On the horizon float the bright yellow, sunlit observation-balloons,[22] and the many little white clouds of the anti-aircraft shells.[23] Often they rise in a sheaf as they follow after an airman. We hear the muffled rumble of the front only as very distant thunder, bumble-bees droning by quite drown it. Around us stretches the flowery meadow. The grasses sway their tall spears; the white butterflies flutter around and float on the soft warm wind of the late summer. We read letters and newspapers and smoke. We take off our caps and lay them down beside us. The wind plays with our hair; it plays with our words and thoughts. The three boxes stand in the midst of the glowing, red field-poppies.

We set the lid of the margarine tub on our knees and so have a good table for a game of skat.[24] Kropp has the cards with him. After every *misère ouverte*[25] we have a round of nap. One could sit like this for ever.

The notes of an accordion float across from the billets.[26] Often we lay aside the cards and look about us. One of us will say: "Well, boys. . . ." Or "It was a near thing that time. . . ." And for a moment we fall silent. There is in each of us a feeling of <u>constraint</u>. We are all sensible of it; it needs no words to communicate it. It might easily have happened that we should not be sitting here on our boxes today; it came damn near to that. And so everything is new and

---

20. **regimental.** Belonging to a military unit
21. **convenience.** Bathroom
22. **observation-balloons.** Balloons for checking out enemy troop movements
23. **anti-aircraft shells.** Explosives launched at aircraft from the ground
24. **skat.** Card game for three people
25. *misère ouverte.* Discussion of hardship or difficulty
26. **billets.** Quarters or lodging for military personnel

---

**words for everyday use**

hy • gi • en • ic (hī jē en' ik) *adj.,* sanitary, clean. *Operating rooms must be kept* <u>hygienic</u> *for the patients' safety.*

con • straint (kən strānt') *n.,* forced, unnatural manner; awkwardness. *When we visited Jules in the hospital, at first we felt* <u>constraint</u>, *but soon we were laughing and joking without restraint.*

brave, red poppies and good food, cigarettes and summer breeze.

Kropp asks: "Anyone seen Kemmerich lately?"

"He's up at St. Joseph's," I tell him.

Müller explains that he has a flesh wound in his thigh; a good blighty.[27]

We decide to go and see him this afternoon.

Kropp pulls out a letter. "Kantorek sends you all his best wishes."

We laugh. Müller throws his cigarette away and says: "I wish he was here."

◀ What has happened to Kemmerich?

◀ From whom does Kropp get a letter? Who was this person?

*

Kantorek had been our schoolmaster, a stern little man in a grey tail-coat, with a face like a shrew mouse. He was about the same size as Corporal Himmelstoss, the "terror of Klosterberg." It is very queer that the unhappiness of the world is so often brought on by small men. They are so much more energetic and uncompromising than the big fellows. I have always taken good care to keep out of sections with small company commanders. They are mostly confounded little martinets.[28]

During drill-time[29] Kantorek gave us long lectures until the whole of our class went, under his shepherding, to the District Commandant and volunteered. I can see him now, as he used to glare at us through his spectacles and say in a moving voice: "Won't you join up, Comrades?"

◀ What did Kantorek urge his students to do?

These teachers always carry their feelings ready in their waistcoat pockets, and trot them out by the hour. But we didn't think of that then.

There was, indeed, one of us who hesitated and did not want to fall into line. That was Joseph Behm, a plump, homely fellow. But he did allow himself to be persuaded, otherwise he would have been <u>ostracized</u>. And perhaps more of us thought as he did, but no one could very well stand out, because at that time even one's parents were ready with the word "coward"; no one had the vaguest idea what we were in for. The wisest were just the poor and

---

27. **blighty.** Terrible wound that prevents a return to battle
28. **martinets.** Strict disciplinarians who uphold rigid rules
29. **drill-time.** Military training or practice

**words for everyday use**   os • tra • cize (ăs' trə sīz') vt., exclude or banish. *We thought it was cruel how the children always ostracized Maria at recess.*

simple people. They knew the war to be a misfortune, whereas those who were better off, and should have been able to see more clearly what the consequences would be, were beside themselves with joy.

Katczinsky said that was a result of their up-bringing. It made them stupid. And what Kat said, he had thought about.

▶ What happened to Joseph Behm, the classmate who hesitated to enlist?

Strange to say, Behm was one of the first to fall. He got hit in the eye during an attack, and we left him lying for dead. We couldn't bring him with us, because we had to come back <u>helter-skelter</u>. In the afternoon suddenly we heard him call, and saw him crawling about in No Man's Land.[30] He had only been knocked unconscious. Because he could not see, and was mad with pain, he failed to keep under cover, and so was shot down before anyone could go and fetch him in.

Naturally we couldn't blame Kantorek for this. Where would the world be if one brought every man to book?[31] There were thousands of Kantoreks, all of whom were convinced that they were acting for the best—in a way that cost them nothing.

And that is why they let us down so badly.

▶ How does Paul feel about Kantorek and the generation that precedes his own?

For us lads of eighteen they ought to have been <u>mediators</u> and guides to the world of maturity, the world of work, of duty, of culture, of progress—to the future. We often made fun of them and played jokes on them, but in our hearts we trusted them. The idea of authority, which they represented, was associated in our minds with a greater insight and a more humane wisdom. But the first death we saw shattered this belief. We had to recognize that our generation was more to be trusted than theirs. They surpassed us only in phrases and in cleverness. The first bombardment showed us our mistake, and under it the world as they had taught it to us broke in pieces.

While they continued to write and talk, we saw the wounded and dying. While they taught that duty to one's country is the greatest thing, we already knew that death-

---

30. **No Man's Land.** Unoccupied region separating opposing armies
31. **brought every man to book.** Held every person accountable (for his or her actions)

---

**words for everyday use**

hel • ter-skel • ter (hel' tər skel' tər) adv., in a disorderly, hurried manner. *The wind blew the leaves <u>helter-skelter</u> across our yard.*

me • di • a • tor (mē' dē āt' ər) n., person who intervenes to resolve a matter. *Our teacher serves as the <u>mediator</u> during our class debates.*

throes are stronger. But for all that we were no <u>mutineers</u>, no deserters, no cowards—they were very free with all these expressions. We loved our country as much as they; we went courageously into every action; but also we distinguished the false from true, we had suddenly learned to see. And we saw that there was nothing of their world left. We were all at once terribly alone; and alone we must see it through.

*

Before going over to see Kemmerich we pack up his things: he will need them on the way back.

In the dressing station[32] there is great activity: it reeks as ever of carbolic,[33] pus, and sweat. We are accustomed to a good deal in the billets, but this makes us feel faint. We ask for Kemmerich. He lies in a large room and receives us with feeble expressions of joy and helpless <u>agitation</u>. While he was unconscious someone had stolen his watch.

Müller shakes his head: "I always told you that nobody should carry as good a watch as that."

◀ Why does Paul think Müller is tactless?

Müller is rather crude and tactless, otherwise he would hold his tongue, for anybody can see that Kemmerich will never come out of this place again. Whether he finds his watch or not will make no difference, at the most one will only be able to send it to his people.

"How goes it, Franz?" asks Kropp.

Kemmerich's head sinks.

"Not so bad . . . but I have such a damned pain in my foot."

We look at his bed covering. His leg lies under a wire basket. The bed covering arches over it. I kick Müller on the shin, for he is just about to tell Kemmerich what the orderlies[34] told us outside: that Kemmerich has lost his foot. The leg is amputated. He looks ghastly, yellow and wan. In his face there are already the strained lines that we know so well, we have seen them now hundreds of times. They are not so much lines as marks. Under the

◀ What has happened to Kemmerich?

---

32. **dressing station.** First-aid tent where injured soldiers are brought before they die or are transferred to military hospitals or rest homes
33. **carbolic.** Antiseptic or disinfectant
34. **orderlies.** Male hospital attendant

| words for everyday use | mu • ti • neer (myü' 'n ir') *n.*, person who revolts against authority. *The captain accused the sailors of being* mutineers *and trying to overthrow his rule aboard ship.* | ag • i • ta • tion (aj' ə tā' shən) *n.*, emotional disturbance or excitement. *Anna's* agitation *was apparent in her flushed face and trembling shoulders.* |

skin the life no longer pulses, it has already pressed out the boundaries of the body. Death is working through from within. It already has command in the eyes. Here lies our comrade, Kemmerich, who a little while ago was roasting horse flesh with us and squatting in the shell-holes. He it is still and yet it is not he any longer. His features have become uncertain and faint, like a photographic plate from which two pictures have been taken. Even his voice sounds like ashes.

I think of the time when we went away. His mother, a good plump matron,[35] brought him to the station. She wept continually, her face was bloated and swollen. Kemmerich felt embarrassed, for she was the least composed of all; she simply dissolved into fat and water. Then she caught sight of me and took hold of my arm again and again, and implored me to look after Franz out there. Indeed he did have a face like a child, and such frail bones that after four weeks' pack-carrying he already had flat feet.[36] But how can a man look after anyone in the field!

"Now you will soon be going home," says Kropp. "You would have had to wait at least three or four months for your leave."

Kemmerich nods. I cannot bear to look at his hands, they are like wax. Under the nails is the dirt of the trenches, it shows through blue-black like poison. It strikes me that these nails will continue to grow like lean fantastic cellar-plants[37] long after Kemmerich breathes no more. I see the picture before me. They twist themselves into corkscrews and grow and grow, and with them the hair on the decaying skull, just like grass in a good soil, just like grass, how can it be possible—

Müller leans over. "We have brought your things, Franz."

Kemmerich signs with his hands. "Put them under the bed."

Müller does so. Kemmerich starts on again about the watch. How can one calm him without making him suspicious?

Müller reappears with a pair of airman's boots. They are fine English boots of soft, yellow leather which reach to

▶ What did Kemmerich's mother ask of Paul?

▶ Which of Kemmerich's possessions do the men covet?

35. **matron.** Woman with a mature appearance
36. **flat feet.** Condition in which the arch of the foot is flattened. Soldiers often got flat feet from marching long distances.
37. **cellar-plants.** Plants that sometimes grow in root cellars or other dark places from bulbs or roots

the knees and lace up all the way—they are things to be
coveted.

Müller is delighted at the sight of them. He matches
their soles against his own clumsy boots and says: "Will
you be taking them with you then, Franz?"

We all three have the same thought; even if he should
get better, he would be able to use only one—they are no
use to him. But as things are now it is a pity that they
should stay here; the orderlies will of course grab them as
soon as he is dead.

"Won't you leave them with us?" Müller repeats.

◀ What does Müller
try to get Kemmerich
to do? Why does
Müller want to visit
again in the
morning?

Kemmerich doesn't want to. They are his most prized
possessions.

"Well, we could exchange," suggests Müller again. "Out
here one can make some use of them." Still Kemmerich is
not to be moved.

I tread on Müller's foot; reluctantly he puts the fine
boots back again under the bed.

We talk a little more and then take our leave.

"Cheerio, Franz."

I promise him to come back in the morning. Müller
talks of doing so, too. He is thinking of the lace-up boots
and means to be on the spot.

Kemmerich groans. He is feverish. We get hold of an
orderly outside and ask him to give Kemmerich a dose of
morphia.[38]

He refuses. "If we were to give morphia to everyone we
would have to have tubs full—"

"You only attend to officers properly," says Kropp
viciously.

I hastily intervene and give him a cigarette. He takes it.

"Are you usually allowed to give it, then?" I ask him.

He is annoyed. "If you don't think so, then why do you
ask?"

I press a few more cigarettes into his hand. "Do us the
favour—"

"Well, all right," he says.

Kropp goes in with him. He doesn't trust him and wants
to see. We wait outside.

---

38. **morphia.** Morphine, a powerful narcotic used to treat pain

---

**words
for
everyday
use**

cov • et (kuv' it) vt., long for with envy. *I have always coveted Anook's skill on the
basketball court.*

Müller returns to the subject of the boots. "They would fit me perfectly. In these boots I get blister after blister. Do you think he will last till tomorrow after drill? If he passes out in the night, we know where the boots—"

Kropp returns. "Do you think—" he asks.

"Done for," says Müller emphatically.

We go back to the huts. I think of the letter that I must write tomorrow to Kemmerich's mother. I am freezing. I could do with a tot of rum. Müller pulls up some grass and chews it. Suddenly little Kropp throws his cigarette away, stamps on it savagely, and looking around him with a broken and distracted face, stammers "Damned shit, the damned shit!"

We walk on for a long time. Kropp has calmed himself; we understand, he saw red; out here every man gets like that sometime.

▶ What does Kantorek call the soldiers in his letter?

"What has Kantorek written to you?" Müller asks him.

He laughs. "We are the Iron Youth."

We all three smile bitterly, Kropp rails: he is glad that he can speak.

▶ What does Paul say about the soldiers' youth?

Yes, that's the way they think, these hundred thousand Kantoreks! Iron Youth. Youth! We are none of us more than twenty years old. But young? Youth? That is long ago. We are old folk.

# Chapter II

It is strange to think that at home in the drawer of my writing table there lies the beginning of a play called "Saul" and a bundle of poems. Many an evening I have worked over them—we all did something of the kind—but that has become so unreal to me I cannot comprehend it any more. Our early life is cut off from the moment we came here, and that without our lifting a hand. We often try to look back on it and to find an explanation, but never quite succeed. For us young men of twenty everything is extraordinarily vague, for Kropp, Müller, Leer, and for me, for all of us whom Kantorek calls the "Iron Youth." All the older men are linked up with their previous life. They have wives, children, occupations, and interests, they have a background which is so strong that the war cannot <u>obliterate</u> it. We young men of twenty, however, have only our parents, and some, perhaps, a girl—that is not much, for at our age the influence of parents is at its weakest and girls have not yet got a hold over us. Besides this there was little else—some enthusiasm, a few hobbies, and our school. Beyond this our life did not extend. And of this nothing remains.

Kantorek would say that we stood on the threshold of life. And so it would seem. We had as yet taken no root. The war swept us away. For the others, the older men, it is but an interruption. They are able to think beyond it. We, however, have been gripped by it and do not know what the end may be. We know only that in some strange and <u>melancholy</u> way we have become a waste land. All the same, we are not often sad.

*

Though Müller would be delighted to have Kemmerich's boots, he is really quite as sympathetic as another who could not bear to think of such a thing for grief. He merely sees things clearly. Were Kemmerich able to make any use of the boots, then Müller would rather go bare-foot over barbed wire than scheme how to get hold of them. But as it is the boots are quite inappropriate to Kemmerich's circumstances, whereas Müller can make good use of them.

◀ What cannot Paul comprehend anymore?

◀ According to Paul, why is the war easier for older men?

◀ What does Paul say the war has done to men of his generation?

◀ In what way does Müller see things clearly?

| words for everyday use | **ob • lit • er • ate** (ə blit' ər āt') *vt.,* blot out or wear away, leaving no traces. *The tombstone was so old that any name inscribed upon it had been <u>obliterated</u> by wind and weather.* | **mel • an • chol • y** (mel' ən käl' ē) *adj.,* sad and depressed; gloomy. *The <u>melancholy</u> music made us sad enough to cry.* |
| --- | --- | --- |

Kemmerich will die; it is <u>immaterial</u> who gets them. Why, then, should Müller not succeed to them? He has more right than a hospital orderly. When Kemmerich is dead it will be too late. Therefore Müller is already on the watch.

We have lost all sense of other considerations, because they are artificial. Only the facts are real and important for us. And good boots are scarce.

\*

Once it was different. When we went to the district commandant to enlist, we were a class of twenty young men, many of whom proudly shaved for the first time before going to the barracks. We had no definite plans for our future. Our thoughts of a career and occupation were as yet of too unpractical a character to furnish[1] any scheme of life. We were still crammed full of vague ideas which gave to life, and to the war also an ideal and almost romantic character. We were trained in the army for ten weeks and in this time more <u>profoundly</u> influenced than by ten years at school. We learned that a bright button is weightier than four volumes of Schopenhauer.[2] At first astonished, then embittered, and finally indifferent, we recognized that what matters is not the mind but the boot brush,[3] not intelligence but the system, not freedom but drill. We became soldiers with eagerness and enthusiasm, but they have done everything to knock that out of us. After three weeks it was no longer incomprehensible to us that a braided postman[4] should have more authority over us than had formerly our parents, our teachers, and the whole <u>gamut</u> of culture from Plato to Goethe.[5] With our young, awakened eyes we saw that the classical conception of the Fatherland[6] held by our teachers resolved itself here

▶ What did the soldiers learn once they enlisted in the army?

▶ What does the concept of Fatherland involve for soldiers?

---

1. **furnish.** Supply
2. **Schopenhauer.** Pessimistic German philosopher who lived from 1788 to 1860
3. **boot brush.** Brush for polishing boots
4. **braided postman.** The narrator is referring to his commanding officer, Corporal Himmelstoss, who once worked as a postman and who has braid on his uniform as a sign of his rank.
5. **Plato to Goethe.** Plato (c.427–c.347 BC) was an ancient Roman philosopher, and Goethe (1749–1832) was a German poet and playwright.
6. **Fatherland.** Person's native land or country

**words for everyday use**

im • ma • te • ri • al (im' mə tir' ē əl) adj., unimportant. *Raisa felt that people's exteriors were immaterial—it was the way they were on the inside that mattered.*

pro • found • ly (prō found' lē) adv., deeply. *Sean was profoundly moved when* he heard the symphony orchestra play for the first time.

gam • ut (gam' ət) n., entire range or extent, as of emotions. *On graduation day, Will's emotions ran the gamut from joy to sadness.*

into a renunciation of personality such as one would not ask of the meanest servants—salutes, springing to attention, parade-marches, presenting arms, right wheel, left wheel, clicking the heels, insults, and a thousand pettifogging[7] details. We had fancied our task would be different, only to find we were to be trained for heroism as though we were circus-ponies. But we soon accustomed ourselves to it. We learned in fact that some of these things were necessary, but the rest merely show. Soldiers have a fine nose for such distinctions.

*

By threes and fours are class was scattered over the platoons amongst Frisian[8] fishermen, peasants, and labourers with whom we soon made friends. Kropp, Müller, Kemmerich, and I went to No. 9 platoon under Corporal Himmelstoss.

He had the reputation of being the strictest disciplinarian in the camp, and was proud of it. He was a small undersized fellow with a foxy, waxed moustache, who had seen twelve years' service and was in civil life a postman. He had a special dislike of Kropp, Tjaden, Westhus, and me, because he sensed a quiet <u>defiance</u>.

I have remade his bed fourteen times in one morning. Each time he had some fault to find and pulled it to pieces. I have kneaded a pair of prehistoric boots that were as hard as iron for twenty hours—with intervals of course—until they became as soft as butter and not even Himmelstoss could find anything more to do to them; under his orders I have scrubbed out the Corporals' Mess[9] with a toothbrush. Kropp and I were given the job of clearing the barrack-square of snow with a hand-broom and a dustpan, and we would have gone on till we were frozen had not a lieutenant accidentally appeared who sent us off, and hauled Himmelstoss over the coals. But the only result of this was to make Himmelstoss hate us more. For six weeks consecutively I did guard every Sunday and was hutorderly for the same length of time. With full pack and

◀ *Who was the new recruits' commanding officer? What is he like? Why does he dislike some of the recruits?*

---

7. **pettifogging.** Unimportant
8. **Frisian.** Person from the Frisian Islands in the North Sea
9. **Corporals' Mess.** Dining hall for officers

---

**words for everyday use**  de • fi • ance (dē fī' əns) *n.*, open, bold resistance to authority or opposition. *Ray soon regretted his act of <u>defiance</u> against his parents.*

rifle I have had to practise on a wet, soft, newly-ploughed field the "Prepare to advance, advance!" and the "Lie down!" until I was one lump of mud and finally collapsed. Four hours later I had to report to Himmelstoss with my clothes scrubbed clean, my hands chafed and bleeding. Together with Kropp, Westhus, and Tjaden I have stood at attention in a hard frost without gloves for a quarter of an hour at a stretch, while Himmelstoss watched for the slightest movement of our bare fingers on the steel barrel of the rifle. I have run eight times from the top floor of the barracks down to the courtyard in my shirt at two o'clock in the morning because my drawers[10] projected three inches beyond the edge of the stool on which one had to stack all one's things. Alongside me ran the corporal, Himmelstoss, and trod on my bare toes. At bayonet-practice[11] I had constantly to fight with Himmelstoss, I with a heavy iron weapon, whilst he had a handy wooden one with which he easily struck my arms till they were black and blue. Once, indeed, I became so <u>infuriated</u> that I ran at him blindly and gave him a mighty jab in the stomach and knocked him down. When he reported me the company commander laughed at him and told him he ought to keep his eyes open; he understood Himmelstoss, and apparently was not displeased at his <u>discomfiture</u>. I became a past master on the parallel bars and excelled at physical jerks;—we have trembled at the mere sound of his voice, but this runaway post-horse[12] never got the better of us.

▶ *What did Kropp and Paul do to Himmelstoss?*

One Sunday as Kropp and I were lugging a latrine-bucket on a pole across the barrack-yard, Himmelstoss came by, all polished up and <u>spry</u> for going out. He planted himself in front of us and asked how we liked the job. In spite of ourselves we tripped and emptied the bucket over his legs. He raved, but the limit had been reached.

"That means clink,"[13] he yelled.

---

10. **drawers.** Underpants
11. **bayonet-practice.** Practice using the weapon of choice—a long, detachable blade put on the end of a rifle for hand-to-hand fighting
12. **post-horse.** The narrator is again referring to Corporal Himmelstoss in a derogatory manner
13. **clink.** Military prison

**words for everyday use**

in • fu • ri • ate (in fyür′ ē āt′) *vt.*, cause to become very angry; enrage. *Rhoda was* *infuriated by her brother's teasing.*

dis • com • fi • ture (dis kum′ fi chər) *n.*, frustration, confusion. *Students who are new to a school often feel* *discomfiture* until they get used to the new building and new faces.

spry (sprī) *adj.*, full of life; active, nimble. *Although our grandfather is eight-five, he is still a* *spry* man.

But Kropp had had enough. "There'll be an inquiry first," he said, "and then we'll unload."[14]

"Mind how you speak to a non-commissioned officer!" bawled Himmelstoss. "Have you lost your senses? You wait till you're spoken to. What will you do, anyway?"

"Show you up,[15] Corporal," said Kropp, his thumbs in line with the seams of his trousers.

Himmelstoss saw that we meant it and went off without saying a word. But before he disappeared he growled: "You'll drink this!"—but that was the end of this authority. He tried it on us once more in the ploughed field with his "Prepare to advance, advance" and "Lie down." We obeyed each order, since an order's an order and has to be obeyed. But we did it so slowly that Himmelstoss became desperate. Carefully we went down on our knees, and then on our hands, and so on; in the meantime, quite infuriated, he had given another command. But before we had even begun to sweat he was hoarse. After that he left us in peace. He did indeed always refer to us as swine, but there was, nevertheless, a certain respect in his tone.

There were many other staff corporals, the majority of whom were more decent. But above all each of them wanted to keep his good job there as long as possible, and this he could do only by being strict with the recruits.

So we were put through every conceivable refinement of parade-ground soldiering[16] till we often howled with rage. Many of us became ill through it; Wolf actually died of inflammation of the lung. But we would have felt ridiculous had we hauled down our colours.[17] We became hard, suspicious, pitiless, vicious, tough—and that was good; for these attributes were just what we lacked. Had we gone into the trenches without this period of training most of us would certainly have gone mad. Only thus were we prepared for what awaited us. We did not break down, but adapted ourselves; our twenty years, which made many another thing so <u>grievous</u>, helped us in this. But by far

◀ *In what did Paul's and Kropp's act of defiance result?*

---

14. **inquiry . . . unload.** Kropp is standing up to Himmelstoss, warning him that if Himmelstoss calls in the authorities to investigate the matter, he and the narrator will tell the authorities what they think of Himmelstoss.
15. **Show you up.** Expose your faults
16. **parade-ground soldiering.** Performing military maneuvers in dress uniforms
17. **hauled down our colours.** Let drop the flag of the regiment

---

words
for
everyday
use

griev • ous (grēv' əs) *adj.,* causing grief. *Maya felt it was <u>grievous</u> to be treated so unfairly.*

▶ What did the soldiers' military training awaken in them?

the most important result was that it awakened in us a strong, practical sense of *esprit de corps*,[18] which in the field developed into the finest thing that arose out of the war—comradeship.[19]

\*

I sit by Kemmerich's bed. He is sinking steadily.[20] Around us is a great commotion. A hospital train has arrived and the wounded fit to be moved are being selected. The doctor passes by Kemmerich's bed without once looking at him.

"Next time, Franz," I say.

He raises himself on the pillow with his elbows. "They have amputated my leg."

He knows it too then. I nod and answer: "You must be thankful you've come off with that."

He is silent.

▶ Where does Paul tell Kemmerich he is going? How does Kemmerich respond?

I resume: "It might have been both legs, Franz. Wegeler has lost his right arm. That's much worse. Besides, you will be going home." He looks at me. "Do you think so?"

"Of course."

"Do you think so?" he repeats.

"Sure, Franz. Once you've got over the operation."

He beckons me to bend down. I stoop over him and he whispers: "I don't think so."

"Don't talk rubbish; Franz, in a couple of days you'll see for yourself. What is it anyway—an amputated leg? Here they patch up far worse things than that."

He lifts one hand. "Look here though, these fingers."

"That's the result of the operation. Just eat decently and you'll soon be well again. Do they look after you properly?"

He points to a dish that is still half full. I get excited. "Franz, you must eat. Eating is the main thing. That looks good too."

He turns away. After a pause he says slowly: "I wanted to become a head-forester[21] once."

"So you may still," I assure him. "There are splendid artificial limbs now, you'd hardly know there was anything missing. They are fixed on to the muscles. You can move the fingers and work and even write with an artificial hand. And besides, they will always be making new improvements."

▶ What does Kemmerich tell Paul to do?

For a while he lies still. Then he says: "You can take my lace-up boots with you for Müller."

---

18. *esprit de corps.* Group spirit or pride
19. **comradeship.** Friendship
20. **sinking steadily.** Becoming more ill
21. **head-forester.** Person in charge of a forest

I nod and wonder what to say to encourage him. His lips have fallen away, his mouth has become larger, his teeth stick out and look as though they were made of chalk. The flesh melts, the forehead bulges more prominently, the cheekbones <u>protrude</u>. The skeleton is working itself through. The eyes are already sunken in. In a couple of hours it will be over.

He is not the first that I have seen thus; but we grew up together and that always makes it a bit different. I have copied his essays. At school he used to wear a brown coat with a belt and shiny sleeves. He was the only one of us, too, who could do the giant's turn on the horizontal bar.[22] His hair flew in his face like silk when he did it. Kantorek was proud of him. But he couldn't stand cigarettes. His skin was very white; he had something of the girl about him.

I glance at my boots. They are big and clumsy, the breeches are tucked into them, and standing up one looks well-built and powerful in these great drainpipes. But when we go bathing and strip, suddenly we have slender legs again and slight shoulders. We are no longer soldiers but little more than boys; no one would believe that we could carry packs. It is a strange moment when we stand naked; then we become civilians, and almost feel ourselves to be so. When bathing Franz Kemmerich looked as slight and frail as a child. There he lies now—but why? The whole world ought to pass by this bed and say: "That is Franz Kemmerich, nineteen and a half years old, he doesn't want to die. Let him not die!"

My thoughts become confused. This atmosphere of carbolic and gangrene[23] clogs the lungs, it is a thick gruel,[24] it suffocates.

It grows dark. Kemmerich's face changes colour, it lifts from the pillow and is so pale that it gleams. The mouth moves slightly. I draw near to him. He whispers: "If you find my watch, send it home—"

◀ *What does Paul think the whole world should do?*

---

22. **giant's turn on the horizontal bar.** Maneuver in gymnastics
23. **gangrene.** Decay in tissue of part of the body when the blood supply is obstructed because of injury or disease
24. **gruel.** Thin porridge

---

**words for everyday use**   pro • trude (prō trüd′) *vt.,* thrust or jut out. *The hikers tripped on the rocks that <u>protrude</u> from the hillside.*

I do not reply. It is no use any more. No one can <u>console</u> him. I am wretched with helplessness. This forehead with its hollow temples, this mouth that now seems all teeth, this sharp nose! And the fat, weeping woman at home to whom I must write. If only the letter were sent off already!

Hospital-orderlies go to and fro with bottles and pails. One of them comes up, casts a glance at Kemmerich and goes away again. You can see he is waiting, apparently he wants the bed.

▶ For what is the hospital orderly waiting?

I bend over Franz and talk to him as though that could save him: "Perhaps you will go to the convalescent home[25] at Klosterberg, among the villas, Franz. Then you can look out from the window across the fields to the two trees on the horizon. It is the loveliest time of the year now, when the corn ripens; at evening the fields in the sunlight look like mother-of-pearl. And the lane of poplars by the Klosterbach, where we used to catch stickle-backs![26] You can build an aquarium again and keep fish in it, and you can go without asking anyone, you can even play the piano if you want to."

I lean down over his face which lies in the shadow. He still breathes, lightly. His face is wet, he is crying. What a fine mess I have made of it with my foolish talk!

"But Franz"—I put my arm round his shoulder and put my face against his. "Will you sleep now?"

He does not answer. The tears run down his cheeks. I would like to wipe them away but my handkerchief is too dirty.

▶ Why does Kemmerich cry?

An hour passes. I sit tensely and watch his every movement in case he may perhaps say something. What if he were to open his mouth and cry out! But he only weeps, his head turned aside. He does not speak of his mother or his brothers and sisters. He says nothing; all that lies behind him; he is entirely alone now with his little life of nineteen years, and cries because it leaves him. This is the most disturbing and hardest parting that I ever have seen, although it was pretty bad too with Tiedjen, who called for

---

25. **convalescent home.** Place where people rest and recuperate from injury or disease
26. **stickle-backs.** Small freshwater fish

**words for everyday use**
con • sole (kən sōl') vt., make feel less sad or disappointed. *I had to <u>console</u> my little brother when his pet parakeet died.*

his mother—a big bear of a fellow who, with wild eyes full of terror, held off the doctor from his bed with a dagger until he collapsed.

Suddenly Kemmerich groans and begins to gurgle.

I jump up, stumble outside and demand: "Where is the doctor? Where is the doctor?"

As I catch sight of the white apron I seize hold of it: "Come quick, Franz Kemmerich is dying."

He frees himself and asks an orderly standing by: "Which will that be?"

He says: "Bed 26, amputated thigh."

He sniffs: "How should I know anything about it, I've amputated five legs to-day"; he shoves me away, says to the hospital-orderly "You see to it," and hurries off to the operating room.

I tremble with rage as I go along with the orderly. The man looks at me and says: "One operation after another since five o'clock this morning. You know, to-day alone there have been sixteen deaths—yours is the seventeenth. There will probably be twenty altogether—"

I become faint, all at once I cannot do any more. I won't <u>revile</u> any more, it is senseless, I could drop down and never rise up again.

We are by Kemmerich's bed. He is dead. The face is still wet from the tears. The eyes are half open and yellow like old horn buttons. The orderly pokes me in the ribs, "Are you taking his things with you?" I nod.

He goes on: "We must take him away at once, we want the bed. Outside they are lying on the floor."

I collect Kemmerich's things, and untie his identification disc. The orderly asks about the pay-book. I say that it is probably in the orderly-room, and go. Behind me they are already hauling Franz on to a waterproof sheet.

Outside the door I am aware of the darkness and the wind as a deliverance. I breathe as deep as I can, and feel the breeze in my face, warm and soft as never before. Thoughts of girls, of flowery meadows, of white clouds suddenly come into my head. My feet begin to move forward in my boots, I go quicker, I run. Soldiers pass by me, I hear their voices without understanding. The earth is streaming with forces which pour into me through the

◀ How do the doctor and orderly respond when Paul asks for help for his friend?

◀ Why does the orderly want Kemmerich's bed?

| words for everyday use | re • vile (ri vīl´) vt., use abusive or scolding language in speaking to or about. *She resisted the temptation to <u>revile</u> the doctor for not saving her son.* |

soles of my feet. The night crackles electrically, the front thunders like a concert of drums. My limbs move supplely, I feel my joints strong, I breathe the air deeply. The night lives, I live. I feel a hunger, greater than comes from the belly alone.

Müller stands in front of the hut waiting for me. I give him the boots. We go in and he tries them on. They fit well.

He roots among his supplies and offers me a fine piece of saveloy.[27] With it goes hot tea and rum.

---

27. **saveloy.** Highly seasoned sausage

## Respond to the Selection

To what extent does the picture of war presented in these two chapters agree or disagree with the way you visualize a war? Are the soldiers like you imagine soldiers to be? Why, or why not?

## Investigate, Inquire, and Imagine

### Recall: GATHERING FACTS

1a. Who is Kantorek? What did he urge his students to do? What does he call the soldiers in his letter?

2a. Who is Corporal Himmelstoss? What are some examples of what he makes his soldiers do? What do Paul and Kropp do to get revenge on Himmelstoss?

3a. What has happened to Kemmerich to separate him from the other soldiers? What does Kemmerich think about his condition at first? What do the other men know? What does Müller want from Kemmerich? What does Kemmerich eventually realize and what happens to him?

### Interpret: FINDING MEANING

1b. How do the soldiers feel about Kantorek? In what way has he and others of his generation let the soldiers down? How does Paul feel about what Kantorek calls the soldiers in his letter?

2b. How do the soldiers feel about Himmelstoss? In what way do the soldiers get the best of him?

3b. Why does Paul think it isn't cruel or unsympathetic for Müller to want this thing? What does it reveal about Kemmerich when he agrees to give this thing to Müller? Why is what happens to Kemmerich particularly hard on Paul? Why isn't it hard on the medical personnel?

### Analyze: TAKING THINGS APART

4a. Compare and contrast how the soldiers feel about the following things:
- The war and their enemy
- Their country
- Kantorek
- Himmelstoss
- Food and clothing

### Synthesize: BRINGING THINGS TOGETHER

4b. Based on your answers to question 4a, explain how the soldiers differ from Kantorek's ideal image of soldiers as "Iron Youth" who feel duty to their country and fight with honor.

**Evaluate:** MAKING JUDGMENTS

5a. Based on what you have read so far, explain whether Paul's critique of the older generation is fair.

**Extend:** CONNECTING IDEAS

➤ 5b. Paul definitely feels a gulf between his generation and the previous generation. Explain a time in your own life when you felt a lack of understanding between generations. What might you have done to help bridge this gap between generations? Is there anything Paul could have done to bridge the gap?

## Understanding Literature

CONFLICT AND CENTRAL CONFLICT. A **conflict** is a struggle between two forces in a literary work. A *plot* involves the introduction, development, and eventual resolution of a conflict. The **central conflict** is the primary struggle dealt with in the plot of a story or novel. One side of the central conflict is taken by the main character. A struggle that takes place between a character and some outside force is called an *external conflict.* A struggle that takes place within a character is called an *internal conflict.* Based on what you have read so far, what is the central conflict in this story? What other conflicts appear in these two chapters? Separate your list of conflicts into two categories: internal and external.

THEME. A **theme** is a central idea in a literary work. One of this novel's major themes is how humans are sometimes inhuman toward each other—how they act callously toward each other and are driven by greed and self-interest. What examples of this theme can you find in this chapter?

AIM. A writer's **aim** is his or her purpose or goal. People may write with the following aims:

- to inform (expository/informational writing)
- to entertain, enrich, enlighten, and/or use an artistic medium to share a perspective (imaginative writing)
- to make a point by sharing a story about an event (narrative writing)
- to reflect (personal/expressive writing)
- to persuade readers or listeners to respond in some way (persuasive/argumentative writing)

At the very beginning of this book, before Chapter 1, Remarque states the aim of his novel. Based on Remarque's own statement, what were his aims in writing this novel? (Choose your aims from the above list.)

# Chapter III

Reinforcements[1] have arrived. The vacancies have been filled and the sacks of straw in the huts are already booked.[2] Some of them are old hands, but there are twenty-five men of a later draft from the base. They are about two years younger than us. Kropp nudges me: "Seen the infants?"

I nod. We stick out our chests, shave in the open, shove our hands in our pockets, inspect the recruits and feel ourselves stone-age veterans.

◀ How much younger than Paul and Kropp are the new recruits? What do they call the new recruits?

◀ What do Paul and his friends feel like in comparison with the new recruits?

Katczinsky joins us. We stroll past the horse-boxes and go over to the reinforcements, who are already being issued with gas masks and coffee.

"Long time since you've had anything decent to eat, eh?" Kat asks one of the youngsters.

He grimaces. "For breakfast, turnip-bread—lunch, turnip-stew—supper, turnip-cutlets and turnip-salad." Kat gives a knowing whistle.

"Bread made of turnips? You've been in luck, it's nothing new for it to be made of sawdust. But what do you say to haricot beans? Have some?"

The youngster turns red: "You can't kid me."

Katczinsky merely says: "Fetch your mess-tin."

We follow curiously. He takes us to a tub beside his straw sack. Sure enough it is half full of beef and beans. Katczinsky plants himself in front of it like a general and says:

◀ What does Kat have hidden away?

"Sharp eyes and light fingers! That's what the Prussians say."

We are surprised. "Great guts, Kat, how did you come by that?" I ask him.

"Ginger was glad I took it. I gave him three pieces of parachute-silk for it. Cold beans taste fine, too."

Patronizingly he gives the youngster a portion and says:

"Next time you come with your mess-tin have a cigar or a chew of tobacco in your other hand. Get me?" Then he turns to us. "You get off scot free,[3] of course."

◀ What does Kat ask for in return for beans from the new recruit? What does he ask for in return from his friends?

---

1. **Reinforcements.** Additional troops of soldiers
2. **sacks . . . booked.** The soldiers stuff sacks with straw and use them for beds
3. **scot free.** Free from payment

**words for everyday use**    pa • tron • iz • ing • ly (pā′ trən īz′ iŋ lē) *adv.*, in a helpful but snobbish way, as if dealing with an inferior. *Marla was angry when the storekeeper spoke to her <u>patronizingly</u>, as if she were a baby.*

*

We couldn't do without Katczinsky; he has a sixth sense.[4] There are such people everywhere but one does not appreciate it at first. Every company has one or two. Katczinsky is the smartest I know. By trade he is a cobbler,[5] I believe, but that hasn't anything to do with it; he understands all trades. It's a good thing to be friends with him, as Kropp and I are, and Haie Westhus too, more or less. But Haie is rather the executive arm, operating under Kat's orders when things come to blows. For that he has his qualifications.

For example, we land at night in some entirely unknown spot, a sorry hole, that has been eaten out to the very walls. We are quartered in a small dark factory adapted to the purpose. There are beds in it, or rather bunks—a couple of wooden beams over which wire netting is stretched.

▶ What are the soldiers' beds made from? What does Kat do to make them more comfortable?

Wire netting is hard. And there's nothing to put on it. Our waterproof sheets are too thin. We use our blankets to cover ourselves.

Kat looks at the place and then says to Haie Westhus: "Come with me." They go off to explore. Half an hour later they are back again with arms full of straw. Kat has found a horse-box with straw in it. Now we might sleep if we weren't so terribly hungry.

▶ What does the artilleryman tell Kat he won't be able to find?

Kropp asks an artilleryman[6] who has been some time in this neighbourhood: "Is there a canteen[7] anywhere abouts?"

"Is there a what?" he laughs. "There's nothing to be had here. You won't find so much as a crust of bread here."

"Aren't there any inhabitants here at all then?"

He spits. "Yes, a few. But they hang round the cookhouse and beg."

"That's a bad business!—Then we'll have to pull in our belts and wait till the rations come up in the morning."

But I see Kat has put on his cap.

"Where to, Kat?" I ask.

---

4. **sixth sense.** Special power of perception or intuition in addition to the five senses
5. **cobbler.** Person whose work is mending or making shoes
6. **artilleryman.** Person who works heavy guns used in battle
7. **canteen.** Place outside a military camp where food and other supplies can be bought

---

**words for everyday use**

qual • i • fi • ca • tion (kwŏl' i fi kā' shən) n., any quality, skill, knowledge, or experience that fits a person for a position, office, or profession. *Sam thought the summer he spent babysitting was a qualification he could put on his resume to show his reliability.*

"Just to explore the place a bit." He strolls off. The artilleryman grins scornfully. "Go ahead and explore. But don't strain yourself in carrying what you find."

Disappointed we lie down and consider whether we couldn't have a go at the iron rations. But it's too risky; so we try to get a wink of sleep.

Kropp divides a cigarette and hands me half. Tjaden gives an account of his national dish—broad-beans and bacon. He despises it when not flavoured with bog-myrtle,[8] and, "for God's sake, let it all be cooked together, not the potatoes, the beans, and the bacon separately." Someone growls that he will pound Tjaden into bog-myrtle if he doesn't shut up. Then all becomes quiet in the big room—only the candles flickering from the necks of a couple of bottles and the artilleryman spitting every now and then.

We are just dozing off when the door opens and Kat appears. I think I must be dreaming; he has two loaves of bread under his arm and a blood-stained sandbag full of horse flesh[9] in his hand.

◄ With what does Kat return?

The artilleryman's pipe drops from his mouth. He feels the bread. "Real bread, by God, and still hot too?"

Kat gives no explanation. He has the bread, the rest doesn't matter. I'm sure that if he were planted down in the middle of the desert, in half an hour he would have gathered together a supper of roast meat, dates, and wine.

◄ What does Paul think Kat could do if he were stranded in a desert?

"Cut some wood," he says <u>curtly</u> to Haie.

Then he hauls out a frying pan from under his coat, and a handful of salt as well as a lump of fat from his pocket. He has thought of everything. Haie makes a fire on the floor. It lights up the empty room of the factory. We climb out of bed.

The artilleryman hesitates. He wonders whether to praise Kat and so perhaps gain a little for himself. But Katczinsky doesn't even see him, he might as well be thin air. He goes off cursing.

◄ With whom won't Kat share his food?

Kat knows the way to roast horse-flesh so that it's tender. It shouldn't be put straight into the pan, that makes it

---

8. **bog-myrtle.** Berries from an evergreen that can be used as a flavoring
9. **horse-flesh.** People usually eat horses only in times of great hardship, such as famines

---

**words for everyday use**

**curt • ly** (kurt′ lē) *adv.,* in a manner that is brief to the point of rudeness. *When my father is driving in traffic, he always answers us <u>curtly</u> until he reaches emptier roads and can relax.*

tough. It should be boiled first in a little water. With our knives we squat round in a circle and fill our bellies.

That is Kat. If for one hour in a year something eatable were to be had in some one place only, within that hour, as if moved by a vision, he would put on his cap, go out and walk directly there, as though following a compass, and find it.

He finds everything—if it is cold, a small stove and wood, hay and straw, a table and chairs—but above all food. It is <u>uncanny</u>; one would think he conjured it out of the air. His masterpiece was four boxes of lobsters. Admittedly we would rather have had a good beef steak.

▶ What was Kat's "masterpiece"?

\*

We have settled ourselves on the sunny side of the hut. There is a smell of tar, of summer, and of sweaty feet. Kat sits beside me. He likes to talk. Today we have done an hour's saluting drill because Tjaden failed to salute a major smartly enough. Kat can't get it out of his head.

▶ According to Kat, why are the Germans losing the war?

"You take it from me, we are losing the war because we can salute too well," he says.

Kropp stalks up, with his breeches rolled up and his feet bare. He lays out his washed socks to dry on the grass. Kat turns his eyes to heaven, lets off a mighty fart, and says meditatively: "Every little bean must be heard as well as seen."

The two begin to argue. At the same time they lay a bottle of beer on the result of an air-fight[10] that's going on above us. Katczinsky won't budge from the opinion which as an old Front-hog,[11] he rhymes:

> Give 'em hell all the same grub and all the same pay
> And the war would be over and done in a day.

▶ How does Kropp think a war should be fought? What is wrong with the way the war is fought now?

Kropp on the other hand is a thinker. He proposes that a declaration of war should be a kind of popular festival with entrance-tickets and bands, like a bull fight. Then in the arena the ministers[12] and generals of the two countries,

---

10. **air-fight.** Battles between planes for air superiority
11. **Front-hog.** Someone who has spent a lot of time at the war's front. Katczinsky is older and more experienced than Paul and his friends.
12. **ministers.** Persons appointed by the head of a government to take charge of specific departments

---

**words for everyday use**

**un • can • ny** (un kan′ ē) *adj.,* so remarkable or acute as to seem supernatural. *My twin sister's ability to complete my sentences is <u>uncanny</u>.*

dressed in bathing-drawers[13] and armed with clubs, can have it out among themselves. Whoever survives, his country wins. That would be much simpler and more just than this arrangement, where the wrong people do the fighting.

The subject is dropped. Then the conversation turns to drill.

A picture comes before me. Burning midday in the barrack-yard.[14] The heat hangs over the square. The barracks are deserted. Every thing sleeps. All one hears is the drummers practising; they have installed themselves somewhere and practise brokenly, dully, <u>monotonously</u>. What a <u>concord</u>! Midday heat, barrack square, and drummers beating!

The windows of the barracks are empty and dark. From some of them trousers are hanging to dry. The rooms are cool and one looks toward them longingly.

O dark, musty platoon huts,[15] with the iron bedsteads, the chequered bedding, the lockers and the stools! Even you can become the object of desire; out here you have a faint resemblance to home; your rooms, full of the smell of stale food, sleep, smoke, and clothes.

◀ What is the "home" to which the soldiers long to return?

Katczinsky paints it all in lively colours. What would we not give to be able to return to it! Farther back than that our thoughts dare not go.

Those early morning hours of instruction—"What are the parts of the 98 rifle?"[16]—the midday hours of physical training—"Pianist forward! By the right, quick march. Report to the cook-house for potato-peeling."

We indulge in <u>reminiscences</u>. Kropp laughs suddenly and says: "Change at Löhne!"

That was our corporal's favourite game. Löhne is a railway junction. In order that our fellows going on shouldn't get lost there, Himmelstoss used to practise the change in

◀ What was Himmelstoss's favorite game?

---

13. **bathing-drawers.** Loose bathing suit
14. **barrack-yard.** Yard outside the building where the soldiers live
15. **platoon huts.** Small, crude cabin in which soldiers live
16. **98 rifle.** Type of rifle used in the Germany military in the first decades of the twentieth century

---

**words for everyday use**

mo • not • o • nous • ly (mə nät′ 'n əs lē) *adv.,* going on in the same tone without variation. *Carla is a good public speaker because she varies her tone and pitch, rather than droning on <u>monotonously</u>.*

con • cord (kän′ kôrd′) *n.,* combination of simultaneous and harmonious tones. *Werner loved to hear the brass section of a band play together in <u>concord</u>.*

rem • i • nis • cence (rem′ ə nis′ əns) *n.,* act of remembering past experiences. *Visiting her old hometown, Viola was filled with <u>reminiscences</u> of her old school and friends.*

the barrack-room. We had to learn that at Löhne, to reach the branch-line, we must pass through a subway. The beds represented the subway and each man stood at attention on the left side of his bed. Then came the command: "Change at Löhne!" and like lightning everyone scrambled under the bed to the opposite side. We practised this for hours on end.

Meanwhile the German aeroplane has been shot down. Like a comet it bursts into a streamer of smoke and falls <u>headlong</u>. Kropp has lost the bottle of beer. Disgruntled he counts out the money from his wallet.

▶ What does Paul wonder about?

"Surely Himmelstoss was a very different fellow as a postman," say I, after Albert's disappointment has <u>subsided</u>. "Then how does it come that he's such a bully as a drill-sergeant?"

The question revives Kropp, more particularly as he hears there's no more beer in the canteen. "It's not only Himmelstoss, there are lots of them. As sure as they get a stripe or a star they become different men, just as though they'd swallowed concrete."

"That's the uniform," I suggest.

▶ To what does Kat attribute Himmelstoss's cruel behavior?

"Roughly speaking it is," says Kat, and prepares for a long speech; "but the root of the matter lies somewhere. For instance, if you train a dog to eat potatoes and then afterwards put a piece of meat in front of him, he'll snap at it, it's his nature. And if you give a man a little bit of authority he behaves just the same way, he snaps at it too. The things are precisely the same. In himself man is essentially a beast, only he butters it over like a slice of bread with a little <u>decorum</u>. The army is based on that; one man must always have power over the other. The mischief[17] is merely that each one has much too much power. A non-com. can torment a private, a lieutenant a non-com., a captain a lieutenant, until he goes mad. And because they know they can, they all soon acquire the habit more or less. Take a simple case: we are marching back from the parade-ground dog-tired. Then comes the order to sing. We sing spiritlessly, for

---

17. **mischief.** Trouble

---

**words for everyday use**

**head • long** (hed' lòŋ') adv., with uncontrolled speed and force. Jeanine was lucky that she didn't break any bones when she fell headlong down the stairs.

**sub • side** (səb sīd') vi., become less active or intense. The president waited until the applause subsided before beginning to speak.

**de • co • rum** (di kō' rəm) n., propriety and good behavior. Mother warned us that she expected us to behave with decorum when she had guests over for dinner.

it is all we can do to <u>trudge</u> along with our rifles. At once the company is turned about and has to do another hour's drill as punishment. On the march back the order to sing is given again, and once more we start. Now what's the use of all that? It's simply that the company commander's head has been turned by having so much power. And nobody blames him. On the contrary, he is praised for being strict. That, of course, is only a trifling instance, but it holds also in very different affairs. Now I ask you: Let a man be whatever you like in peace-time, what occupation is there in which he can behave like that without getting a crack[18] on the nose? He can only do that in the army. It goes to the heads of them all, you see. And the more insignificant a man has been in civil life the worse it takes him."

"They say, of course, there must be discipline," <u>ventures</u> Kropp meditatively.

"True," growls Kat, "they always do. And it may be so; still it oughtn't to become an abuse. But you try to explain that to a black-smith or a labourer or a workman, you try to make that clear to a peasant—and that's what most of them are here. All he sees is that he has been put through the mill[19] and sent to the front, but he knows well enough what he must do and what not. It's simply amazing, I tell you, that the ordinary tommy[20] sticks it[21] all up here in the front-line. Simply amazing!"

No one protests. Everyone knows that drill ceases only in the front-line and begins again a few miles behind, with all absurdities of saluting and parade. It is an Iron law that the soldier must be employed under every circumstance.

Here Tjaden comes up with a flushed face. He is so excited that he stutters. Beaming with satisfaction he stammers out: "Himmelstoss is on his way. He's coming to the front!"

◀ What news does Tjaden bring?

*

Tjaden has a special grudge against Himmelstoss, because of the way he educated him in the barracks.

◀ What problem does Tjaden have? Why does he have a special grudge against Himmelstoss?

18. **crack.** Punch or hit
19. **put through the mill.** Put through a hard and painful but instructive experience
20. **tommy.** Man
21. **sticks it.** Carries on or endures

Tjaden wets his bed, he does it at night in his sleep. Himmelstoss maintained that it was sheer laziness and invented a method worthy of himself for curing Tjaden.

He hunted up another piss-a-bed, named Kindervater, from a neighbouring hut, and quartered him with Tjaden. In the huts there were the usual bunks, one above the other in pairs, with mattresses of wire netting. Himmelstoss put these two so that one occupied the upper and the other the lower bunk. The man underneath of course had a vile time. The next night they were changed over and the lower one put on top so that he could <u>retaliate</u>. That was Himmelstoss's system of self-education.

The idea was not low but ill-conceived. Unfortunately it accomplished nothing because the first assumption was wrong: it was not laziness in either of them. Anyone who looked at their sallow skin could see that. The matter ended in one of them always sleeping on the floor, where he frequently caught cold.

Meanwhile Haie sits down beside us. He winks at me and rubs his paws thoughtfully. We once spent the finest day of our army-life together—the day before we left for the front. We had been allotted to one of the recently formed regiments, but were first to be sent back for equipment to the garrison, not to the reinforcement-depot, of course, but to another barracks.[22] We were due to leave next morning early. In the evening we prepared ourselves to square accounts[23] with Himmelstoss.

▶ *What does Kropp plan to do when the war is over?*

We had sworn for weeks past to do this. Kropp had even gone so far as to propose entering the postal service in peacetime in order to be Himmelstoss's superior when he became a postman again. He revelled in the thought of how he would grind him. It was this that made it impossible for him to crush us altogether—we always reckoned that later, at the end of the war, we would have our revenge on him.

---

22. **We had been . . . barracks.** Paul and Haie were assigned to one military unit and then sent to soldiers' quarters to get equipment, rather than to a reinforcement-depot, or central place for holding supplies.
23. **square accounts.** Get even

---

**words for everyday use**   re • tal • i • ate (ri tal′ ē āt′) *vi.,* return like for like, especially to pay back injury for injury. *We admired Sophie because she would never <u>retaliate</u> when insulted but continued to be kind, even to people who were not kind to her.*

In the meantime we decided to give him a good hiding.[24] What could he do to us anyhow if he didn't recognize us and we left early in the morning?

We knew which pub he used to visit every evening. Returning to the barracks he had to go along a dark, uninhabited road. There we waited for him behind a pile of stones. I had a bed-cover with me. We trembled with suspense, hoping he would be alone. At last we heard his footstep, which we recognized easily, so often had we heard it in the mornings as the door flew open and he bawled: "Get up!"

"Alone?" whispered Kropp.

"Alone."

I slipped round the pile of stones with Tjaden.

Himmelstoss seemed a little elevated;[25] he was singing. His belt-buckle gleamed. He came on unsuspectingly.

We seized the bed-cover, made a quick leap, threw it over his head from behind and pulled it round him so that he stood there in a white sack unable to raise his arms. The singing stopped. The next moment Haie Westhus was there, and spreading his arms he shoved us back in order to be first in. He put himself in position with evident satisfaction, raised his arm like a signal-mast[26] and his hand like a coal-shovel and fetched such a blow on the white sack as would have felled an ox.

◀ What do Paul and his friends do to Himmelstoss?

Himmelstoss was thrown down, he rolled five yards and started to yell. But we were prepared for that and had brought a cushion. Haie squatted down, laid the cushion on his knees, felt where Himmelstoss's head was and pressed it down on the pillow. Immediately his voice was muffled. Haie let him get a gasp of air every so often, when he would give a mighty yell that was immediately hushed.

Tjaden unbuttoned Himmelstoss's braces[27] and pulled down his trousers, holding the whip meantime in his teeth. Then he stood up and set to work.

It was a wonderful picture: Himmelstoss on the ground; Haie bending over him with a fiendish grin and his mouth open with bloodlust, Himmelstoss's head on his knees; then the convulsed[28] striped drawers, the knock knees,[29]

---

24. **hiding.** Severe beating or whipping
25. **elevated.** Intoxicated
26. **like a signal-mast.** Straight overhead
27. **braces.** Suspenders
28. **convulsed.** Shaking
29. **knock knees.** Condition in which the legs bend inward so that the knees knock together or touch

executing at every blow most original movements in the lowered breeches, and towering over them like a wood-cutter the indefatigable Tjaden. In the end we had to drag him away to get our turn.

Finally Haie stood Himmelstoss on his feet again and gave one last personal remonstrance. As he stretched out his right arm preparatory to giving him a box on the ear he looked as if he were going to reach down a star.

Himmelstoss toppled over. Haie stood him up again, made ready and fetched him a second, well-aimed beauty with the left hand. Himmelstoss yelled and made off on all fours. His striped postman's backside gleamed in the moonlight.

We disappeared at full speed.

Haie looked round once again and said wrathfully, satisfied and rather mysteriously:

"Revenge is black-pudding."[30]

▶ According to Paul, why should Himmelstoss be pleased?

Himmelstoss ought to have been pleased; his saying that we should each educate one another had borne fruit for himself. We had become successful students of his method.

He never discovered whom he had to thank for the business. At any rate he scored a bed-cover out of it; for when we returned a few hours later to look for it, it was no longer to be found.

▶ What does an older man call Paul and his friends?

That evening's work made us more or less content to leave next morning. And an old buffer[31] was pleased to describe us as "young heroes."

---

30. **black-pudding.** Spicy sausage made of blood, lard, and flavorings
31. **buffer.** Fellow, man

| words for everyday use | ex • e • cute (ek' si kyüt') vt., follow out or carry out; do; perform. *The soldier performed his duty, faithfully executing his commanding officer's orders.*<br><br>in • de • fat • i • ga • ble (in' di fat' i gə bəl) adj., cannot be tired out; untiring. *Although we were ready to sleep, Kyle was indefatigable and kept us awake by talking all night.* | re • mon • strance (ri män' strəns) n., protest or complaint. *Even though she could have said, "I told you so," Beth didn't utter a single remonstrance when I got the group lost by ignoring her advice.*<br><br>wrath • ful • ly (rath' fəl lē) adv., in a very angry manner. *"I will have my revenge!" shouted the villain wrathfully.* |

# Chapter IV

We have to go up on wiring fatigue.[1] The motor lorries[2] roll up after dark. We climb in. It is a warm evening and the twilight seems like a canopy under whose shelter we feel drawn together. Even the stingy Tjaden gives me a cigarette and then a light.

We stand jammed in together, shoulder to shoulder, there is no room to sit. But we do not expect that. Müller is in a good mood for once; he is wearing his new boots.

The engines drone, the lorries bump and rattle. The roads are worn and full of holes. We dare not show a light so we <u>lurch</u> along and are often almost pitched out.[3] That does not worry us, however. It can happen if it likes; a broken arm is better than a hole in the guts, and many a man would be thankful enough for such a chance of finding his way home again.

Beside us stream the munition-columns[4] in long files. They are making the pace, they overtake us continually. We joke with them and they answer back.

A wall becomes visible, it belongs to a house which lies on the side of the road. I suddenly prick up my ears. Am I deceived? Again I hear distinctly the cackle of geese. A glance at Katczinsky—a glance from him to me; we understand one another.

"Kat, I hear some aspirants for[5] the frying-pan over there."

He nods. "It will be attended to when we come back. I have their number."

Of course Kat has their number. He knows all about every leg of goose within a radius of fifteen miles.

The lorries arrive at the artillery lines. The gun-emplacements are camouflaged with bushes against aerial observation, and look like a kind of military Feast of

◀ *What are Paul and the other soldiers being sent to do?*

◀ *Why is Müller in a good mood?*

◀ *What do Paul and Kat hear? What do they plan to do later?*

---

1. **on wiring fatigue.** On duty laying barbed wire to slow the enemy's advance
2. **lorries.** Motor trucks
3. **pitched out.** Thrown out
4. **munition-columns.** Columns of men who supply weapons and ammunition to the soldiers
5. **aspirants for.** Creatures that are eager to go into

---

**words for everyday use**

lurch (lŭrch) *vi.,* roll or sway suddenly forward or to one side. *Kayla <u>lurched</u> from side to side as she walked aboard ship for the first time.*

the Tabernacles.[6] These branches might seem gay and cheerful were not cannon embowered[7] there.

The air becomes <u>acrid</u> with the smoke of the guns and the fog. The fumes of powder taste bitter on the tongue. The roar of the guns makes our lorry stagger, the <u>reverberation</u> rolls raging away to the rear, everything quakes. Our faces change <u>imperceptibly</u>. We are not, indeed, in the front-line, but only in the reserves, yet in every face can be read: This is the front, now we are within its embrace.

▶ What changes the soldiers' faces?

It is not fear. Men who have been up as often as we have become thick-skinned. Only the young recruits are agitated. Kat explains to them: "That was a twelve-inch. You can tell by the report; now you'll hear the burst."

But the muffled thud of the burst does not reach us. It is swallowed up in the general murmur of the front: Kat listens: "There'll be a bombardment tonight."

We all listen. The front is restless. "The Tommies[8] are firing already," says Kropp.

The shelling can be heard distinctly. It is the English batteries[9] to the right of our section. They are beginning an hour too soon. According to us they start punctually at ten o'clock.

"What's got them?" says Müller, "their clocks must be fast."

▶ What does Kat predict?

"There'll be a bombardment, I tell you. I can feel it in my bones." Kat shrugs his shoulders.

Three guns open fire close beside us. The burst of flame shoots across the fog, the guns roar and boom. We shiver and are glad to think that we shall be back in the huts early in the morning.

Our faces are neither paler nor more flushed than usual; they are not more tense nor more flabby—and yet they are changed. We feel that in our blood a contact has shot

---

6. **gun-emplacements . . . Feast of the Tabernacles.** The narrator is comparing how the large stationary guns are camouflaged with bushes to a Jewish festival celebrating the fall harvest.
7. **embowered.** Sheltered
8. **Tommies.** Tommy guns, submachine guns
9. **batteries.** Heavy guns

---

**words for everyday use**

ac • rid (ak′ rid) *adj.,* sharp, bitter, stinging, or irritating to the taste or smell. *You could smell the forest fire from miles away because of the acrid smoke.*

re • ver • ber • a • tion (ri vʉr′ bə rā′ shən) *n.,* reechoing or reflection of light or sound waves, deflection of heat or flame. *In the valley, we could hear the reverberation of the thunder off the hills in the distance.*

im • per • cep • ti • bly (im′ pər sep′ tə blē) *adv.,* in a manner so slight, gradual, or subtle as not to be easily perceived. *Hours before dawn the sky becomes almost imperceptibly brighter.*

home. That is no figure of speech; it is fact. It is the front, the consciousness of the front, that makes this contact. The moment that the first shells whistle over and the air is <u>rent</u> with the explosions there is suddenly in our veins, in our hands, in our eyes a tense waiting, a watching, a heightening alertness, a strange sharpening of the senses. The body with one bound is in full readiness.

◀ *In what way do the soldiers feel different at the front?*

It often seems to me as though it were the vibrating, shuddering air that with a noiseless leap springs upon us; or as though the front itself emitted an electric current which awakened unknown nerve-centres.

Every time it is the same. We start out for the front plain soldiers, either cheerful or gloomy: then come the first gun-emplacements and every word of our speech has a new ring.

When Kat stands in front of the hut and says: "There'll be a bombardment," that is merely his own opinion; but if he says it here, then the sentence has the sharpness of a bayonet in the moonlight, it cuts clean through the thought, it thrusts nearer and speaks to this unknown thing that is awakened in us, a dark meaning—"There'll be a bombardment." Perhaps it is our inner and most secret life that shivers and falls on guard.

*

To me the front is a mysterious whirlpool. Though I am in still water far away from its centre, I feel the whirl of the <u>vortex</u> sucking me slowly, irresistibly, inescapably into itself.

From the earth, from the air, sustaining forces pour into us—mostly from the earth. To no man does the earth mean so much as to the soldier. When he presses himself down upon her long and powerfully, when he buries his face and his limbs deep in her from the fear of death by shell-fire, then she is his only friend, his brother, his mother; he <u>stifles</u> his terror and his cries in her silence and her security; she shelters him and releases him for ten seconds to live, to run, ten seconds of life; receives him again and often for ever.

◀ *What means a lot to the soldiers?*

Earth!—Earth!—Earth!

Earth with thy folds, and hollows, and holes, into which a man may fling himself and crouch down. In the

---

**words for everyday use**

**rent** (rent) *adj.*, pierced with sound. *The quiet evening was suddenly <u>rent</u> by the screaming siren.*

**vor • tex** (vòr′ teks′) *n.*, whirling mass of water forming a vacuum at its center, into which anything caught in the motion is drawn. *The biggest danger when caught in a <u>vortex</u> is drowning.*

**sti • fle** (stī′ fəl) *vt.*, repress; hold back. *The class could barely <u>stifle</u> a laugh at the melodramatic and overly sentimental play.*

spasm of terror, under the hailing of <u>annihilation</u>, in the bellowing death of the explosions, O Earth, thou grantest us the great resisting surge of new-won life. Our being, almost utterly carried away by the fury of the storm, streams back through our hands from thee, and we, thy redeemed ones, bury ourselves in thee, and through the long minutes in a mute agony of hope bite into thee with our lips!

▶ *What protects the soldiers at the front?*

At the sound of the first droning of the shells we rush back, in one part of our being, a thousand years. By the animal instinct that is awakened in us we are led and protected. It is not conscious; it is far quicker, much more sure, less <u>fallible</u>, than consciousness. One cannot explain it. A man is walking along without thought or heed;—suddenly he throws himself down on the ground and a storm of fragments flies harmlessly over him;—yet he cannot remember either to have heard the shell coming or to have thought of flinging himself down. But had he not abandoned himself to the impulse he would now be a heap of mangled flesh. It is this other, this second sight[10] in us, that has thrown us to the ground and saved us, without our knowing how. If it were not so, there would not be one man alive from Flanders to the Vosges.[11]

▶ *What do the soldiers become at the front?*

We march up, moody or good-tempered soldiers—we reach the zone where the front begins and become on the instant human animals.

\*

An <u>indigent</u> looking wood receives us. We pass by the soup-kitchens. Under cover of the wood we climb out. The lorries turn back. They are to collect us again in the morning before dawn.

Mist and the smoke of guns lie breast-high over the fields. The moon is shining. Along the road troops file. Their helmets gleam softly in the moonlight. The heads and the rifles stand out above the white mist, nodding heads, rocking barrels.

---

10. **second sight.** Supposed ability to see things not physically present or to foretell events
11. **from Flanders to Vosges.** From a region in northwestern Europe on the North Sea to a mountain range in northeastern France

**words for everyday use**

an • ni • hi • la • tion (ə nī′ ə lā′ shən) *n.*, complete destruction. *The anthropologist studied the <u>annihilation</u> of the civilization, determined to discover what caused the collapse.*

fal • li • ble (fal′ ə bəl) *adj.*, liable to be mistaken or deceived. *Shana told me,* "Don't beat yourself up when you make a mistake. Everyone is <u>fallible</u>."

in • di • gent (in′ di jənt) *adj.*, in poverty; poor; needy. *Every Thanksgiving, Carla spends the day feeding homeless and <u>indigent</u> people.*

Farther on the mist ends. Here the heads become figures; coats, trousers, and boots appear out of the mist as from a milky pool. They become a column. The column marches on, straight ahead, the figures resolve themselves into a block, individuals are no longer recognizable, the dark wedge presses onward, fantastically topped by the heads and weapons floating on the milky pool. A column—not men at all.

Guns and munition wagons[12] are moving along a cross-road. The backs of the horses shine in the moonlight, their movements are beautiful, they toss their heads, and their eyes gleam. The guns and the wagons float past the dim background of the moonlit landscape, the riders in their steel helmets resemble knights of a forgotten time; it is strangely beautiful and arresting.

◀ *What do the riders of the horse-drawn munition wagons look like in the dim light?*

We push on to the pioneer dump.[13] Some of us load our shoulders with pointed and twisted iron stakes; others thrust smooth iron rods through rolls of wire and go off with them. The burdens are awkward and heavy.

The ground becomes more broken. From ahead come warnings: "Look out, deep shell-hole on the left"—"Mind, trenches"—

Our eyes peer out, our feet and our sticks feel in front of us before they take the weight of the body. Suddenly the line halts; I bump my face against the roll of wire carried by the man in front and curse.

There are some shell-smashed lorries in the road. Another order: "Cigarettes and pipes out." We are near the line.

In the meantime it has become pitch dark. We skirt a small wood and then have the front-line immediately before us.

An uncertain red glow spreads along the skyline from one end to the other. It is in perpetual movement, punctuated with the bursts of flame from the nozzles of the batteries. Balls of light rise up high above it, silver and red spheres which explode and rain down in showers of red, white, and green stars. French rockets go up, which unfold a silk parachute to the air and drift slowly down. They light up everything as bright as day, their light shines on us and we see our shadows sharply outlined on the ground. They hover for the space of a minute before they burn out. Immediately fresh ones shoot up in the sky, and again green, red, and blue stars.

---

12. **munition wagons.** Horse-drawn wagons in which weapons and ammunition are carried
13. **pioneer dump.** Supply source for infantrymen

▶ What happens to the soldiers once they reach the front?

"Bombardment," says Kat.

The thunder of the guns swells to a single heavy roar and then breaks up again into separate explosions. The dry bursts of the machine-guns rattle. Above us the air teems with invisible swift movement, with howls, pipings, and hisses. They are smaller shells;—and amongst them, booming through the night like an organ, go the great coal-boxes[14] and the heavies. They have a hoarse, distant bellow like a rutting stag[15] and make their way high above the howl and whistle of the smaller shells. It reminds me of flocks of wild geese when I hear them. Last autumn the wild geese flew day after day across the path of the shells.

The searchlights begin to sweep the dark sky. They slide along it like gigantic tapering[16] rulers. One of them pauses, and quivers a little. Immediately a second is beside him, a black insect is caught between them and tries to escape—the airman. He hesitates, is blinded and falls.

\*

At regular intervals we ram in the iron stakes. Two men hold a roll and the others spool off the barbed wire. It is that awful stuff with close-set, long spikes. I am not used to unrolling it and tear my hand.

After a few hours it is done. But there is still some time before the lorries come. Most of us lie down and sleep. I try also, but it has turned too chilly. We know we are not far from the sea because we are constantly waked by the cold.

▶ What does Paul see when he wakes? Where does he think he is for a moment?

Once I fall fast asleep. Then wakening suddenly with a start I do not know where I am. I see the stars, I see the rockets, and for a moment have the impression that I have fallen asleep at a garden fête.[17] I don't know whether it is morning or evening, I lie in the pale cradle of the twilight, and listen for soft words which will come, soft and near—am I crying? I put my hand to my eyes, it is so fantastic, am I a child? Smooth skin;—it lasts only a second, then I recognize the silhouette of Katczinsky. The old veteran, he sits quietly and smokes his pipe—a covered pipe[18] of course. When he sees I am awake, he says: "That gave you a fright. It was only a nose-cap,[19] it landed in the bushes over there."

---

14. **coal-boxes.** Type of German shell, or explosive, that emitted dark smoke
15. **rutting stag.** Male deer in mating season
16. **tapering.** Gradually decreasing in width or thickness
17. **fête.** Party
18. **covered pipe.** Katczinsky is covering his pipe so the light from it doesn't alert the enemy to their whereabouts.
19. **nose-cap.** Metal tip of a bomb

I sit up, I feel myself strangely alone. It's good Kat is there. He gazes thoughtfully at the front and says:

"Mighty fine fire-works if they weren't so dangerous."

One lands behind us. Some recruits jump up terrified. A couple of minutes later another comes over, nearer this time. Kat knocks out his pipe. "We're in for it."

Then it begins in earnest. We crawl away as well as we can in our haste. The next lands fair amongst us. Two fellows cry out. Green rockets shoot up on the sky-line. Barrage.[20] The mud flies high, fragments whizz past. The crack of the guns is heard long after the roar of the explosions.

Beside us lies a fair-headed recruit in <u>utter</u> terror. He has buried his face in his hands, his helmet has fallen off. I fish hold of it and try to put it back on his head. He looks up, pushes the helmet off and like a child creeps under my arm, his head close to my breast. The little shoulders heave. Shoulders just like Kemmerich's. I let him be. So that the helmet should be of some use I stick it on his behind;—not for a <u>jest</u>, but out of consideration, since that is his highest part. And though there is plenty of meat there, a shot in it can be damned painful. Besides, a man has to lie for months on his belly in the hospital, and afterwards he would be almost sure to have a limp.

It's got someone pretty badly. Cries are heard between the explosions.

At last it grows quiet. The fire has lifted over us and is now dropping on the reserves. We risk a look. Red rockets shoot up to the sky. Apparently there's an attack coming.

Where we are it is still quiet. I sit up and shake the recruit by the shoulder. "All over, kid! It's all right this time."

He looks round him dazedly. "You'll get used to it soon," I tell him.

He sees his helmet and puts it on. Gradually he comes to. Then suddenly he turns fiery red and looks confused. Cautiously he reaches his hand to his behind and looks at me dismally.

I understand at once: Gun-shy. That wasn't the reason I had stuck his helmet over it. "That's no disgrace," I reassure

◀ What does Paul do for the terrified new recruit?

---

20. **Barrage.** Curtain of artillery fire laid down to keep enemy forces from moving, or to cover or prepare the way for one's own forces

**words for everyday use**

ut • ter (ut' ər) *adj.*, complete; total. *We wept with <u>utter</u> joy at graduation.*

jest (jest) *n.*, joke; witticism. *Chris was the class clown, always quick with a <u>jest</u> or a practical joke.*

him: "Many's the man before you has had his pants full after the first bombardment. Go behind that bush there and throw your underpants away. Get along—"

*

He goes off. Things become quieter, but the cries do not cease. "What's up, Albert?" I ask.

"A couple of columns over there have got it in the neck."

The cries continued. It is not men, they could not cry so terribly.

"Wounded horses," says Kat.

It's unendurable. It is the moaning of the world, it is the <u>martyred</u> creation, wild with anguish, filled with terror, and groaning.

We are pale. Detering stands up. "God! For God's sake! Shoot them."

He is a farmer and very fond of horses. It gets under his skin. Then as if deliberately the fire dies down again. The screaming of the beasts becomes louder. One can no longer distinguish whence in this now quiet silvery landscape it comes; ghostly, invisible, it is everywhere, between heaven and earth it rolls on <u>immeasurably</u>. Detering <u>raves</u> and yells out: "Shoot them! Shoot them, can't you? Damn you again!"

"They must look after the men first," says Kat quietly.

We stand up and try to see where it is. If we could only see the animals we should be able to endure it better. Müller has a pair of glasses. We see a dark group, bearers with stretchers, and larger black clumps moving about. Those are the wounded horses. But not all of them. Some gallop away in the distance, fall down, and then run on farther. The belly of one is ripped open, the guts trail out. He becomes tangled in them and falls, then he stands up again.

Detering raises up his gun and aims. Kat hits it in the air. "Are you mad—?"

Detering trembles and throws his rifle on the ground.

We sit down and hold our ears. But this <u>appalling</u> noise, these groans and screams penetrate, they penetrate everywhere.

▶ What is making the terrible cries?

▶ What does Detering scream? Why is he especially upset by the horses' plight? What does Kat tell him?

**words for everyday use**

**mar • tyr** (märt' ər) vt., torture; make suffer greatly; persecute. *Many people of many religions have been <u>martyred</u> for their beliefs.*

**im • meas • ur • a • bly** (im mezh' ər ə blē) adv., without bounds; vastly. *The wide open sea lay <u>immeasurably</u> before us.*

**rave** (rāv) vi., speak out wildly; talk irrationally. *Ryan <u>raves</u> angrily whenever he talks about the time his car was hijacked.*

**ap • pall • ing** (ə pòl' iŋ) adj., causing horror, shock, or dismay. *We were shocked by the pictures in the news showing the <u>appalling</u> destruction in the war-torn country.*

We can bear almost anything. But now the sweat breaks out on us. We must get up and run no matter where, but where these cries can no longer be heard. And it is not men, only horses.

From the dark group stretchers move off again. Then single shots crack out. The black heap convulses and then sinks down. At last! But still it is not the end. The men cannot overtake the wounded beasts which fly in their pain, their wide open mouths full of anguish. One of the men goes down on his knee, a shot—one horse drops—another. The last one props itself on its forelegs and drags itself round in a circle like a merry-go-round; squatting, it drags round in circles on its stiffened forelegs, apparently its back is broken. The soldier runs up and shoots it. Slowly, humbly, it sinks to the ground.

◀ What do the soldiers do to the wounded horses?

We take our hands from our ears. The cries are silenced. Only a long-drawn, dying sigh still hangs on the air.

Then only again the rockets, the singing of the shells and the stars there—most strange.

Detering walks up and down cursing: "Like to know what harm they've done." He returns to it once again. His voice is agitated, it sounds almost dignified as he says: "I tell you it is the <u>vilest</u> baseness to use horses in the war."

◀ According to Detering, what is the vilest baseness?

\*

We go back. It is time we returned to the lorries. The sky has become brighter. Three o'clock in the morning. The breeze is fresh and cool, the pale hour makes our faces look grey.

We trudge onward in single file through the trenches and shell-holes and come again to the zone of mist. Katczinsky is <u>restive</u>, that's a bad sign.

◀ According to Paul, what is a bad sign?

"What's up, Kat?" says Kropp.

"I wish I were back home." Home—he means the huts.

"We'll soon be out of it, Kat."

He is nervous. "I don't know, I don't know—"

We come to the communication-trench[21] and then to the open fields. The little wood reappears; we know every foot of ground here. There's the cemetery with the mounds and the black crosses.

---

21. **communication-trench.** Deep ditch in which communication officers, who are in charge of sending messages, are located

---

**words for everyday use**

vile (vīl) *adj.*, morally base or evil; wicked. *The senator promised that the state would punish the <u>vilest</u> criminals to the full extent of the law.*

res • tive (res' tiv) *adj.*, nervous or impatient under pressure or restraint. *Sitting on the sidelines, Jenny felt <u>restive</u>—she wanted the coach to put her into the game.*

That moment it breaks out behind us, swells, roars, and thunders. We duck down—a cloud of flame shoots up a hundred yards ahead of us.

The next minute under a second explosion part of the wood rises slowly in the air, three or four trees sail up and then crash to pieces. The shells begin to hiss like safety-valves—heavy fire—

"Take cover!" yells somebody—"Cover!"

▶ Where do the soldiers take cover from the attack?

The fields are flat, the wood is too distant and danger-ous—the only cover is the graveyard and the mounds. We stumble across in the dark and as though he had been spat there every man lies glued behind a mound.

Not a moment too soon. The dark goes mad. It heaves and raves. Darknesses blacker than the night rush on us with giant strides, over us and away. The flames of the explosion light up the graveyard.

There is no escape anywhere. By the light of the shells I try to get a view of the fields. They are a surging sea, dag-gers of flame from the explosions leap up like fountains. It is impossible for anyone to break through it.

The wood vanishes, it is pounded, crushed, torn to pieces. We must stay here in the graveyard.

▶ What happens to Paul?

The earth bursts before us. It rains clods.[22] I feel a smack. My sleeve is torn away by a splinter. I shut my fist. No pain. Still that does not reassure me: wounds don't hurt till afterwards. I feel the arm all over. It is grazed but sound. Now a crack on the skull, I begin to lose con-sciousness. Like lightning the thought comes to me: Don't faint! I sink down in the black broth[23] and immediately come up to the top again. A splinter slashes into my hel-met, but has already travelled so far that it does not go through. I wipe the mud out of my eyes. A hole is torn up in front of me. Shells hardly ever land in the same hole twice, I'll get into it. With one lunge, I shoot as flat as a fish over the ground; there it whistles again, quickly I crouch together, claw for cover, feel something on the left, shove in beside it, it gives way, I groan, the earth leaps, the blast thunders in my ears, I creep under the yielding thing, cover myself with it, draw it over me, it is wood, cloth, cover, cover, miserable cover against the whizzing splinters.

▶ Where does Paul take shelter?

I open my eyes—my fingers grasp a sleeve, an arm. A wounded man? I yell to him—no answer—a dead man. My

---

22. **clods.** Clumps of earth
23. **black broth.** The narrator is describing unconsciousness figuratively as a black broth.

hand gropes farther, splinters of wood—now I remember again that we are lying in the graveyard.

But the shelling is stronger than everything. It wipes out the sensibilities, I merely crawl still farther under the coffin, it shall protect me, though Death himself lies in it.

Before me gapes the shell-hole. I grasp it with my eyes as with fists. With one leap I must be in it. There, I get a smack in the face, a hand clamps onto my shoulder—has the dead man waked up?—The hand shakes me, I turn my head, in the second of light I stare into the face of Katczinsky, he has his mouth wide open and is yelling. I hear nothing, he rattles me, comes nearer, in a momentary <u>lull</u> his voice reaches me: "Gas—Gaas—Gaaas—Pass it on."

◀ What warning does Katczinsky give Paul?

I grab for my gas-mask. Some distance from me there lies someone. I think of nothing but this: That fellow there must know: Gaaas—Gaaas—

I call, I lean toward him, I swipe at him with the satchel, he doesn't see—once again, again—he merely ducks—it's a recruit—I look at Kat desperately, he has his mask on—I pull out mine, too, my helmet falls to one side, it slips over my face, I reach the man, his satchel is on the side nearest me, I seize the mask, pull it over his head, he understands, I let go and with a jump drop into the shell-hole.

The dull thud of the gas-shells mingles with the crashes of the high explosives. A bell sounds between the explosions, gongs, and metal clappers warning everyone—Gas—Gas—Gaas.

Someone plumps down behind me, another. I wipe the goggles of my mask clear of the moist breath. It is Kat, Kropp, and someone else. All four of us lie there in heavy, watchful suspense and breathe as lightly as possible.

These first minutes with the mask decide between life and death: is it air-tight? I remember the awful sights in the hospital: the gas patients who in day-long suffocation cough up their burnt lungs in clots.

◀ What happens to people who breathe in the gas?

Cautiously, the mouth applied to the valve, I breathe. The gas still creeps over the ground and sinks into all hollows. Like a big, soft jelly-fish it floats into our shell-hole and lolls there obscenely.[24] I nudge Kat, it is better to crawl

---

24. **obscenely.** Disgustingly

---

**words for everyday use**     **lull** (lul) *n.,* short period of quiet or of comparative calm. *There was a <u>lull</u> among the crowd as the band began playing, but soon they roared their appreciation.*

out and lie on top than to stay where the gas collects most. But we don't get as far as that; a second bombardment begins. It is no longer as though shells roared; it is the earth itself raging.

With a crash something black bears down on us. It lands close beside us; a coffin thrown up.

I see Kat move and I crawl across. The coffin has hit the fourth man in our hole on his out-stretched arm. He tries to tear off his gas-mask with the other hand. Kropp seizes him just in time, twists the hand sharply behind his back and holds it fast.

Kat and I proceed to free the wounded arm. The coffin lid is loose and bursts open, we are easily able to pull it off, we toss the corpse out, it slides down to the bottom of the shell-hole, then we try to loosen the under-part.

Fortunately the man swoons[25] and Kropp is able to help us. We no longer have to be careful, but work away till the coffin gives with a sigh before the spade that we have dug in under it.

It has grown lighter. Kat takes a piece of the lid, places it under the shattered arm, and we wrap all our bandages round it. For the moment we can do no more.

Inside the gas-mask my head booms and roars—it is nigh bursting. My lungs are tight, they breathe always the same hot, used-up air, the veins on my temples are swollen. I feel I am suffocating.

A grey light filters through to us. I climb out over the edge of the shell-hole. In the dirty twilight lies a leg torn clean off; the boot is quite whole, I take that all in at a glance. Now something stands up a few yards distant. I polish the windows, in my excitement they are immediately dimmed again. I peer through them, the man there no longer wears his mask.

I wait some seconds—he has not collapsed—he looks around and makes a few paces—rattling in my throat I tear my mask off too and fall down, the air streams into me like cold water, my eyes are bursting the wave sweeps over me and extinguishes me.

*

The shelling has ceased, I turn towards the crater beckoning to the others. They take off their masks. We lift up the wounded man, one taking his splinted arm. And so we stumble off hastily.

The graveyard is a mass of wreckage. Coffins and corpses lie strewn about. They have been killed once

▶ What traps one of the men? What does the trapped man try to do? What do Kat and Paul do to help him?

▶ What has happened to the graveyard? Whom did the corpses save?

---

25. **swoons.** Faints

again; but each of them that was flung up saved one of us.

The hedge is destroyed, the rails of the light railway are torn up and rise stiffly in the air in great arches. Someone lies in front of us. We stop; Kropp goes on alone with the wounded man.

The man on the ground is a recruit. His hip is covered with blood; he is so exhausted that I feel for my water-bottle where I have rum and tea. Kat restrains my hand and stoops over him.

"Where's it got you comrade?"

His eyes move. He is too weak to answer.

We slit open his trousers carefully. He groans. "Gently, gently, it is much better—"

If he has been hit in the stomach he oughtn't to drink anything. There's no vomiting, that's a good sign. We lay the hip bare. It is one mass of mincemeat and bone splinters. The joint has been hit. This lad won't walk any more.

I wet his temples with a moistened finger and give him a swig. His eyes move again. We see now that the right arm is bleeding as well.

Kat spreads out two wads of dressing[26] as wide as possible so that they will cover the wound. I look for something to bind loosely round it. We have nothing more, so I slip up the wounded man's trouser leg still farther in order to use a piece of his underpants as a bandage. But he is wearing none. I now look at him closely. He is the fair-headed boy of a little while ago.

◄ Who has been wounded?

In the meantime Kat has taken a bandage from a dead man's pocket and we carefully bind the wound. I say to the youngster who looks at us fixedly: "We're going for a stretcher now—"

Then he opens his mouth and whispers: "Stay here—"

"We'll be back again soon," says Kat. "We are only going to get a stretcher for you."

We don't know if he understands. He <u>whimpers</u> like a child and plucks at us: "Don't go away—"

Kat looks around and whispers: "Shouldn't we just take a revolver and put an end to it?"

◄ What does Kat suggest they do to the wounded solider? What do they believe will happen to the soldier if they get a stretcher for him?

---

26. **dressing.** Bandages

**words for everyday use**    whim • per (hwim' pər) vi., make low, whining, broken sounds, as in crying or in fear. *Our new puppy <u>whimpers</u> when we leave him alone in his kennel.*

The youngster will hardly survive the carrying, and at the most he will only last a few days. What he has gone through so far is nothing to what he's in for till he dies. Now he is numb and feels nothing. In an hour he will become one screaming bundle of <u>intolerable</u> pain. Every day that he can live will be a howling torture. And to whom does it matter whether he has them or not—

I nod. "Yes, Kat, we ought to put him out of his misery."

He stands still a moment. He has made up his mind. We look round—but we are no longer alone. A little group is gathering, from the shell-holes and trenches appear heads.

We get a stretcher.

Kat shakes his head. "Such a kid—" He repeats it. "Young innocents—"

*

Our losses are less than was to be expected—five killed and eight wounded. It was in fact quite a short bombardment. Two of our dead lie in the upturned graves. We merely throw the earth in on them.

We go back. We trot off silently in single file one behind the other. The wounded are taken to the dressing-station. The morning is cloudy. The bearers make a fuss about numbers and tickets, the wounded whimper. It begins to rain.

An hour later we reach our lorries and climb in. There is more room now than there was.

The rain becomes heavier. We take out waterproof sheets and spread them over our heads. The rain rattles down, and flows off at the sides in streams. The lorries bump through the holes, and we rock to and fro in a half-sleep.

Two men in the front of the lorry have long forked poles. They watch for telephone wires which hang cross-wise over the road so low that they might easily pull our heads off. The two fellows take them at the right moment on their poles and lift them over behind us. We hear their call "Mind—wire—," dip the knee in a half-sleep and straighten up again.

Monotonously the lorries sway, monotonously come the calls, monotonously falls the rain. It falls on our heads and on the heads of the dead up in the line, on the body

▶ What happens to change Kat and Paul's plan?

▶ What is different about the trip back?

**words for everyday use**

**in • tol • er • a • ble** (in täl′ ər ə bəl) *adj.*, too severe, painful, or cruel to be endured. *When he first sprained his ankle, Maurice felt walking was <u>intolerable</u>, but within a week he could put more pressure on it.*

of the little recruit with the wound that is so much too big for his hip; it falls on Kemmerich's grave; it falls in our hearts.

An explosion sounds somewhere. We wince, our eyes become tense, our hands are ready to vault over the side of the lorry into the ditch by the road.

Nothing happens—only the monotonous cry: "Mind—wire,"—our knees bend—we are again half asleep.

◀ Where does the rain fall?

## Respond to the Selection

Many of the images of war presented in Chapter 4 are vivid and horrifying. What scene stands out most in your mind?

## Investigate, Inquire, and Imagine

**Recall:** GATHERING FACTS

1a. What special ability does Kat seem to have? What does Kat do to provide the soldiers with food and physical comfort? What does he do to take care of the other soldiers in battle?

**Interpret:** FINDING MEANING

➤ 1b. In what way is Kat different from the other soldiers? How do the other soldiers seem to feel about him? How does he discriminate about whom he chooses to help? Explain why you think Kat discriminates among the soldiers in this way?

2a. What are some examples of the way Himmelstoss was cruel to the soldiers he trained? What did the soldiers do to get revenge on Himmelstoss before they left for the front? Behind the front, why are the soldiers made to perform an hour of saluting drill?

➤ 2b. To what would Kat attribute Himmelstoss's behavior toward the soldiers? Why do you think the officers make soldiers perform seemingly pointless tasks? What does Kat mean when he says, "You take it from me, we are losing the war because we can salute too well"? Explain what you thought about the soldiers taking revenge on Himmelstoss.

3a. What happens to the soldiers while they are laying barbed wire? Whom does Paul comfort? What happens to the horses that drew the munition wagons? As the men return through the woods and a cemetery, what again happens to them? What provides the men with cover? Who is injured, and what do Kat and Paul plan to do to this person? What stops them?

➤ 3b. Explain how what happens to the horses is similar to what happens to the new recruit. Explain whether or not you feel Kat and Paul are justified in their decision about how to treat the new recruit. What do the events in this chapter reveal about the value of human life in the war?

**Analyze:** TAKING THINGS APART

4a. Analyze the soldiers' thoughts about the war itself, looking specifically at their reaction to the air fight overhead, Kropp's thoughts about how wars should be fought, and the soldiers' reactions to the front. What do these soldiers seem to think of the war and their role in it?

**Synthesize:** BRINGING THINGS TOGETHER

4b. Nationalism is the idea that you owe your loyalty to your nation, first and foremost, and that your nation's interests are more important than international interests. Nationalism was a leading force behind World War I. Based on what you have read so far, what do you think Remarque's attitude toward nationalism might have been? When might nationalism be beneficial and when might it be harmful?

**Evaluate:** MAKING JUDGMENTS

5a. What does Paul mean when he says, after the soldiers beat Himmelstoss, "Himmelstoss ought to have been pleased; his saying that we should educate one another had borne fruit for himself. We had become successful students of his method." In what way have the soldiers been affected by what they experienced under Himmelstoss's command? To what extent has the war and their training dehumanized the soldiers?

**Extend:** CONNECTING IDEAS

5b. What are some other situations in which an experience changes a person's behavior for the worse? for the better?

# Understanding Literature

HERO AND CHIVALRY. A **hero** is a character whose actions are inspiring and courageous. **Chivalry** was the code of conduct of the medieval knight. According to the code of chivalry, a knight exemplified such virtues as loyalty, bravery, courage, courtesy, honesty, faith, and gentleness. Knights obeyed strict codes of behavior even in battle; for example, if a knight was unhorsed another knight might let him get back on his horse before resuming the fight, rather than pressing his advantage. Knights were often heroes in medieval writing. At one point in Chapter 4, Remarque writes, "The riders in their steel helmets resemble knights of a forgotten time." Earlier in the novel, Paul blamed Kantorek for filling his own and his classmates' heads with notions about the honor and glory of war and for telling them that it was their duty to fight—ideals left over from more chivalric times. Explain how the war being fought on the front differs from the type of battle that knights likely knew. Explain whether or not Kat is a hero in this novel. In what way is he both similar to and different from a knight out of the chivalric period?

MOTIF, FOIL, AND STYLE. A **motif** is any element that recurs in one or more works of literature or art. A **foil** is a character or thing whose attributes, or characteristics, contrast with and therefore throw into relief the attributes of another character or thing. **Style** is the manner in which something is said or written. Traditionally, critics and scholars have referred to three levels of style: high style, for formal occasions or lofty subjects; middle style, for ordinary occasions or subjects; and low style, for extremely informal occasions and subjects. Nature, and people's relationship with nature, is a motif in this work. In Chapter 4, on pages 37–38, Paul describes the soldier's relationship to the earth. Using examples from the text, explain the way in which the style of writing changes in this passage. Why do you think the author chose to adopt a different style at this point in the novel? Why do you think Remarque uses nature as a motif? The nature motif serves as a foil in this novel. What does it contrast with and throw into relief? What does the use of this foil emphasize about war?

IRONY. **Irony** is a difference between appearance and reality. Explain why the following lines are ironic:

- "It is the vilest baseness to use horses in the war."
- "Coffins and corpses lie strewn about. They have been killed once again; but each of them that was flung up saved one of us."

# Chapter V

Killing each separate louse[1] is a tedious business when a man has hundreds. The little beasts are hard and the ever-lasting cracking with one's fingernails very soon becomes wearisome. So Tjaden has rigged up the lid of a boot-polish tin with a piece of wire over the lighted stump of a candle. The lice are simply thrown into this little pan. Crack! and they're done for.

◀ What do the soldiers have?

We sit around with our shirts on our knees, our bodies naked to the warm air and our hands at work. Haie has a particularly fine brand of louse: they have a red cross on their heads. He suggests that he brought them back with him from the hospital at Thourhout, where they attended personally on a surgeon-general. He says he means to use the fat that slowly accumulates in the tin-lid for polishing his boots, and roars with laughter for half an hour at his own joke.

But he gets little response today; we are too <u>preoccupied</u> with another affair.

The rumour has materialized. Himmelstoss has come. He appeared yesterday; we've already heard the well-known voice. He seems to have overdone it with a couple of young recruits on the ploughed field at home and unknown to him the son of the local magistrate[2] was watching. That cooked his goose.[3]

◀ Who has arrived at the front?

He will get some surprises here. Tjaden has been meditating for hours what to say to him. Haie gazes thoughtfully at his great paws and winks at me. The thrashing was the high water mark[4] of his life. He tells me he often dreams of it. Kropp and Müller are amusing themselves. From somewhere or other, probably the pioneer-cookhouse, Kropp has bagged for himself a mess-tin full of beans. Müller squints hungrily into it but checks himself and says: "Albert, what would you do if it were suddenly peace-time again?"

◀ What is Kropp's first response when Müller asks him what he would do if it were peacetime?

"There won't be any peace-time," says Albert bluntly.

---

1. **louse.** Insect that lives on humans' skin or hair and drinks their blood
2. **magistrate.** Minor officer with judicial powers
3. **cooked his goose.** Spoiled things for him
4. **high water mark.** Highest point

---

**words for everyday use**

pre • oc • cu • pied (prē ăk' yü pīd') *adj.*, wholly occupied with or absorbed in one's thoughts. *Jana was so <u>preoccupied</u> with worry that she didn't even hear me when I told her she had made the team.*

"Well, but if—" persists Müller, "what would you do?"

"Clear out of this!" growls Kropp.

"Of course. And then what?"

"Get drunk," says Albert.

"Don't talk rot, I mean seriously—"

"So do I," says Kropp, "what else should a man do?"

Kat becomes interested. He levies tribute[5] on Kropp's tin of beans, swallows some, then considers for a while and says: "You might get drunk first, of course, but then you'd take the next train for home and mother. Peace-time, man, Albert—"

He fumbles in his oil-cloth pocket-book[6] for a photograph and suddenly shows it all round. "My old woman!" Then he puts it back and swears: "Damned lousy war—"

"It's all very well for you to talk," I tell him. "You've a wife and children."

"True," he nods, "and I have to see to it that they've something to eat."

We laugh. "They won't lack for that, Kat, you'd scrounge it from somewhere."

Müller is <u>insatiable</u> and gives himself no peace. He wakes Haie Westhus out of his dream. "Haie, what would you do if it was peace-time?"

"Give you a kick in the backside for the way you talk," I say. "How does it come about exactly?"

"How does the cow-shit come on the roof?" retorts Müller <u>laconically</u>, and turns to Haie Westhus again.

It is too much for Haie. He shakes his freckled head:

"You mean when the war's over?"

"Exactly. You've said it."

"Well, there'd be women of course, eh?"—Haie licks his lips.

"Sure."

"By Jove, yes," says Haie, his face melting, "then I'd grab some good buxom dame, some real kitchen wench with plenty to get hold of, you know, and jump straight into bed. Just you think, boys, a real feather-bed with a spring mattress; I wouldn't put trousers on again for a week."

---

5. **levies tribute.** Takes a portion of
6. **oil-cloth pocket-book.** Wallet made of cloth that has been made waterproof with oil

**words for everyday use**

in • sa • ti • a • ble (in sā' shə bəl) *adj.*, constantly wanting more. *Ramon was an* *insatiable reader who always had a book in his hands.*

la • con • i • cal • ly (lə kän' ik ə lē) *adv.*, using few words; concisely. *When asked what he thought about the chances for a victory in Sunday's game, the player* *laconically responded, "We'll win."*

Everyone is silent. The picture is too good. Our flesh creeps. At last Müller pulls himself together and says:

"And then what?"

A pause. Then Haie explains rather awkwardly: "If I were a non-com. I'd stay with the Prussians and serve out my time."

◀ What would Haie do if the war were over?

"Haie, you've got a screw loose, surely!" I say.

"Have you ever dug peat?" he retorts good-naturedly. "You try it."

Then he pulls a spoon out of the top of his boot and reaches over into Kropp's mess-tin.

"It can't be worse than digging trenches," I venture.

Haie chews and grins: "It lasts longer though. And there's no getting out of it either."

"But, man, surely it's better at home."

"Some ways," says he, and with open mouth sinks into a day-dream.

◀ In what way is Haie's home life difficult?

You can see what he is thinking. There is the mean little hut on the moors,[7] the hard work on the heath from morning till night in the heat, the miserable pay, the dirty labourer's clothes.

"In the army in peace-time you've nothing to trouble about," he goes on, "your food's found every day, or else you kick up a <u>row</u>; you've a bed, every week clean underwear like a perfect gent, you do your non-com.'s duty, you have a good suit of clothes; in the evening you're a free man and go off to the pub."

◀ According to Haie, what is good about being in the army in peacetime?

Haie is extraordinarily set on his idea. He's in love with it.

"And when your twelve years are up you get your pension and become the village bobby,[8] and you can walk about the whole day."

He's already sweating on it. "And just you think how you'd be treated. Here a dram, there a pint.[9] Everybody wants to be well in with a bobby."

"You'll never be a non-com. though, Haie," interrupts Kat.

---

7. **moors.** Tract of open, rolling wasteland, usually covered with heather and often marshy or peaty

8. **bobby.** Policeman

9. **dram . . . pint.** Drinks of various sizes

**words for everyday use**   row (rou) *n.*, noisy quarrel, dispute, or disturbance. *The children were having a <u>row</u> about who got to play the new game first.*

Haie looks at him sadly and is silent. His thoughts still linger over the clear evenings in autumn, the Sundays in the heather, the village bells, the afternoons and evenings with the servant girls, the fried bacon and barley, the carefree hours in the ale-house—

He can't part with all these dreams so abruptly; he merely growls: "What silly questions you do ask."

He pulls his shirt over his head and buttons up his tunic.

▶ What would Tjaden do if the war were over?

"What would you do, Tjaden!" asks Kropp.

Tjaden thinks of one thing only. "See to it that Himmelstoss didn't get past me."

Apparently he would like most to have him in a cage and sail into him with a club every morning. To Kropp he says warmly: "If I were in your place I'd see to it that I became a lieutenant. Then you could grind him till the water in his backside boils."

"And you, Detering!" asks Müller like an inquisitor.[10] He's a born schoolmaster with all his questions.

▶ What would Detering do if the war were over? Why is Detering worried?

Detering is <u>sparing</u> with his words. But on this subject he speaks. He looks at the sky and says only the one sentence: "I would go straight on with the harvesting."

Then he gets up and walks off.

He is worried. His wife has to look after the farm. They've already taken away two more of his horses. Every day he reads the papers that come, to see whether it is raining in his little corner of Oldenburg. They haven't brought in the hay yet.

At this moment Himmelstoss appears. He comes straight up to our group. Tjaden's face turns red. He stretches his length on the grass and shuts his eyes in excitement.

Himmelstoss is a little hesitant, his <u>gait</u> becomes slower. Then he marches up to us. No one makes any motion to stand up. Kropp looks up at him with interest.

He continues to stand in front of us and wait. As no one says anything he launches a "Well!"

A couple of seconds go by. Apparently Himmelstoss doesn't quite know what to do. He would like most to set

---

10. **inquisitor.** Harsh or prying questioner

| **words for everyday use** | **spar • ing** (sper' iŋ) *adj.*, careful in spending or using; frugal. *Kaitlin is <u>sparing</u> in her use of butter because she is concerned about cholesterol.* | **gait** (gāt) *n.*, manner of walking or running. *The pony's rapid <u>gait</u> made her almost impossible to catch.* |
| --- | --- | --- |

us all on the run again. But he seems to have learned already that the front-line isn't a parade ground. He tries it on though, and by addressing himself to one instead of to all of us hopes to get some response. Kropp is nearest, so he favours him.

"Well, you here too?"

But Albert's no friend of his. "A bit longer than you, I fancy," he <u>retorts</u>.

The red moustache twitches: "You don't recognize me any more, what?"

Tjaden now opens his eyes. "I do though."

Himmelstoss turns to him: "Tjaden, isn't it?"

Tjaden lifts his head. "And do you know what you are?"

Himmelstoss is <u>disconcerted</u>. "Since when have we become so familiar? I don't remember that we ever slept in the gutter together?"

◀ What surprises Himmelstoss?

He has no idea what to make of the situation. He didn't expect this open hostility. But he is on his guard: he has already had some rot dinned into him[11] about getting a shot in the back.

The question about the gutter makes Tjaden so mad that he becomes almost witty: "No you slept there by yourself."

Himmelstoss begins to boil. But Tjaden gets in ahead of him. He must bring off his insult: "Wouldn't you like to know what you are? A dirty hound, that's what you are. I've been wanting to tell you that for a long time."

The satisfaction of months shines in his dull pig's eyes as he spits out: "Dirty hound!"

Himmelstoss lets fly too, now. "What's that, you muck-rake, you dirty peat-stealer? Stand up there, bring your heels together when your superior officer speaks to you."

Tjaden waves him off. "You take a run and jump at yourself, Himmelstoss."

Himmelstoss is a raging book of army regulations. The Kaiser[12] couldn't be more insulted. "Tjaden, I command you, as your superior officer: Stand up!"

"Anything else you would like?" asks Tjaden.

◀ What does Himmelstoss order Tjaden to do? What does he do instead?

---

11. **rot dinned into him.** Untrue information repeated to him
12. **Kaiser.** Ruler of Germany, Wilhelm II (1859–1941)

---

**words for everyday use**

re • tort (ri tòrt') *vi.*, reply, esp. in a sharp, quick, or witty way. *Laura <u>retorts</u> quickly to Tim's insult, making us all laugh.*

dis • con • cert (dis' kən surt') *vt.*, upset the composure of; embarrass. *Jill was <u>disconcerted</u> when the teacher told her that her answer was incorrect.*

"Will you obey my order or not?"

Tjaden replies, without knowing it, in the well-known classical phrase.

At the same time he ventilates his backside.[13]

"I'll have you court-martialled,"[14] storms Himmelstoss.

We watch him disappear in the direction of the Orderly Room.[15] Haie and Tjaden burst into a regular peat-digger's bellow. Haie laughs so much that he dislocates his jaw, and suddenly stands there helpless with his mouth wide open. Albert has to put it back again by giving it a blow with his fist.

Kat is troubled: "If he reports you, it'll be pretty serious."

"Do you think he will?" asks Tjaden.

"Sure to," I say.

"The least you'll get will be five days close arrest," says Kat.

That doesn't worry Tjaden. "Five days clink are five days rest."

"And if they send you to the Fortress?"[16] urges the thoroughgoing Müller.

"Well, for the time being the war will be over so far as I am concerned."

Tjaden is a cheerful soul. There aren't any worries for him. He goes off with Haie and Leer so that they won't find him in the first flush of excitement.

*

Müller hasn't finished yet. He tackles Kropp again.

"Albert, if you were really at home now, what would you do?"

Kropp is contented now and more accommodating:

"How many of us were there in the class exactly?"

We count up: out of twenty, seven are dead, four wounded, one in a mad-house. That makes twelve.

"Three of them are lieutenants," says Müller. "Do you think they would still let Kantorek sit on them?"[17]

We guess not: we wouldn't let ourselves be sat on for that matter.

▶ *Why isn't Tjaden worried about being sent to "the clink" or to military prison?*

▶ *How many classmates of Paul's enlisted? How many are left?*

---

13. **ventilates his backside.** Moons him
14. **court-martialled.** Brought to a military court for breaking a military law
15. **Orderly Room.** Room where military orders are recorded and transmitted
16. **the Fortress.** Military prison
17. **sit on them.** Give them an examination

---

**words for everyday use**

storm (stòrm) *vt.*, attack or direct something at (someone) in a vigorous or angry outburst. *"I'll never speak to you again as long as I live," storms Jacob.*

"What do you mean by the three-fold theme in 'William Tell'?"[18] says Kropp reminiscently, and roars with laughter.

"What was the purpose of the Poetic League of Göttingen?"[19] asked Müller suddenly and earnestly.

"How many children had Charles the Bald?"[20] I interrupt gently.

"You'll never make anything of your life, Bäumer," croaks Müller.

"When was the battle of Zama?"[21] Kropp wants to know.

"You lack the studious mind, Kropp, sit down, three minus—" I say.

"What offices did Lycurgus[22] consider the most important for the state?" asks Müller, pretending to take off his pince-nez.[23]

"Does it go: 'We Germans fear God and none else in the whole world,' or We, the Germans, fear God and—'" I submit.

"How many inhabitants has Melbourne?"[24] asks Müller.

"How do you expect to succeed in life if you don't know that?" I ask Albert hotly.

Which he caps[25] with: "What is meant by Cohesion?"

We remember mighty little of all that rubbish. Anyway, it has never been the slightest use to us. At school nobody ever taught us how to light a cigarette in a storm of rain, nor how a fire could be made with wet wood—nor that it is best to stick a bayonet in the belly because there it doesn't get jammed, as it does in the ribs.

Müller says thoughtfully: "What's the use? We'll have to go back and sit on the forms again."[26]

I consider that out of the question. "We might take a special exam."

◀ *What don't the soldiers remember? What knowledge is of use to them in war?*

---

18. **William Tell.** Swiss hero who was forced on pain of death to shoot an apple off his son's head. The German poet Johann Schiller wrote a dramatic poem about him.
19. **Poetic League of Göttingen.** Group of German university students who appreciated Romantic poetry
20. **Charles the Bald.** Charles I (823–877), king of France and the Holy Roman Emperor
21. **battle of Zama.** Zama is an ancient town in North Africa, southwest of Carthage and the scene of a battle (202 BC) in which Scipio defeated Hannibal, ending the Second Punic War.
22. **Lycurgus.** Spartan lawgiver of the ninth century BC
23. **pince-nez.** Eyeglasses without temples held in place by a spring gripping the bridge of the nose
24. **Melbourne.** Seaport in southeastern Australia
25. **caps.** Tops
26. **sit on the forms again.** Take examinations or tests again

"That needs preparation. And if you do get through, what then? A student's life isn't any better. If you have no money, you have to work like the devil."

"It's a bit better. But it's rot all the same, everything they teach you."

Kropp supports me: "How can a man take all that stuff seriously when he's once been out here?"

"Still you must have an occupation of some sort," insists Müller, as though he were Kantorek himself.

▶ What will Kat, Detering, and Haie do after the war? According to Albert Kropp, why can't he and his classmates do the same thing?

▶ What is Paul's first thought about what he and his classmates should do after the war?

Albert cleans his nails with a knife. We are surprised at this delicacy. But it is merely <u>pensiveness</u>. He puts the knife away and continues: "That's just it. Kat and Detering and Haie will go back to their jobs because they had them already. Himmelstoss too. But we never had any. How will we ever get used to one after this, here?"—he makes a gesture toward the front.

"What we'll want is a private income, and then we'll be able to live by ourselves in a wood," I say, but at once feel ashamed of this absurd idea.

"But what will really happen when we go back?" wonders Müller, and even he is troubled.

Kropp gives a shrug, "I don't know. Let's get back first, then we'll find out."

We are all utterly at a loss. "What could we do?" I ask.

"I don't want to do anything," replies Kropp wearily. "You'll be dead one day, so what does it matter? I don't think we'll ever go back."

"When I think about it, Albert," I say after a while rolling over on my back, "when I hear the word 'peacetime,' it goes to my head: and if it really came, I think I would do some unimaginable thing—something, you know, that it's worth having lain here in the muck for. But I can't even imagine anything. All I do know is that this business about professions and studies and salaries and so on—it makes me sick, it is and always was disgusting. I don't see anything at all, Albert."

All at once everything seems to me confused and hopeless.

Kropp feels it too. "It will go pretty hard with us all. But nobody at home seems to worry much about it. Two years of shells and bombs—a man won't peel that off as easy as a sock."

---

**words for everyday use**    **pen • sive • ness** (pen' siv nəs) *n.*, filled with deep or serious thoughts, often of sad or melancholy things. *Brenda was the picture of <u>pensiveness</u>—her chin on one hand and a troubled expression in her eyes.*

We agree that it's the same for everyone; not only for us here, but everywhere, for everyone who is of our age; to some more, and to others less. It is the common fate of our generation.

◄ What is the common fate of Paul's generation?

Albert expresses it: "The war has ruined us for everything."

He is right. We are not youth any longer. We don't want to take the world by storm. We are fleeing. We fly from ourselves. From our life. We were eighteen and had begun to love life and the world; and we had to shoot it to pieces. The first bomb, the first explosion, burst in our hearts. We are cut off from activity, from striving, from progress. We believe in such things no longer, we believe in the war.

*

The Orderly Room shows signs of life. Himmelstoss seems to have stirred them up. At the head of the column trots the fat sergeant-major. It is queer that almost all of the regular sergeant-majors are fat.

Himmelstoss follows him, thirsting for vengeance. His boots gleam in the sun.

We get up.

"Where's Tjaden?" the sergeant puffs.

No one knows, of course. Himmelstoss <u>glowers</u> at us wrathfully. "You know very well. You won't say, that's the fact of the matter. Out with it!"

Fatty looks round enquiringly; but Tjaden is not to be seen. He tries another way.

"Tjaden will report at the Orderly Room in ten minutes."

Then he steams off with Himmelstoss in his wake.

"I have a feeling that next time we go up wiring I'll be letting a bundle of wire fall on Himmelstoss's leg," hints Kropp.

"We'll have quite a lot of jokes with him," laughs Müller.—

That is our sole ambition: to knock the conceit out of a postman.

◄ What is the soldiers' sole ambition?

I go into the hut and put Tjaden wise. He disappears.

Then we change our possy[27] and lie down again to play cards. We know how to do that: to play cards, to swear, and

---

27. **possy.** Position

| words for everyday use | **glow • er** (glou′ ər) *vi.*, stare with sullen anger; scowl. *By the way his father glowers at him, Louis knows he is in trouble.* |
|---|---|

to fight. Not much for twenty years;—and yet too much for twenty years.

Half an hour later Himmelstoss is back again. Nobody pays any attention to him. He asks for Tjaden. We shrug our shoulders.

"Then you'd better find him," he persists. "Haven't you been to look for him?"

Kropp lies back on the grass and says: "Have you ever been out here before?"

▶ What does Kropp say rather than telling Himmelstoss where Tjaden is? What does he sarcastically suggest the soldiers will do next time they are at the front?

"That's none of your business," retorts Himmelstoss. "I expect an answer."

"Very good," says Kropp, getting up. "See up there where those little white clouds are. Those are anti-aircraft. We were over there yesterday. Five dead and eight wounded. And that's a <u>mere</u> nothing. Next time, when you go up with us, before they die the fellows will come up to you, click their heels, and ask stiffly: 'Please may I go? Please may I hop it? We've been waiting here a long time for someone like you.'"

He sits down again and Himmelstoss disappears like a comet.

"Three days C.B.,"[28] conjectures Kat.

"Next time I'll let fly,"[29] I say to Albert.

But that is the end. The case comes up for trial in the evening. In the Orderly Room sits our Lieutenant, Bertink, and calls us in one after another.

I have to appear as a witness and explain the reason of Tjaden's <u>insubordination</u>.

The story of the bed-wetting makes an impression. Himmelstoss is recalled and I repeat my statement.

"Is that right?" Bertink asks Himmelstoss.

He tries to <u>evade</u> the question, but in the end has to confess, for Kropp tells the same story.

"Why didn't someone report the matter, then?" asks Bertink.

We are silent: he must know himself how much use it is in reporting such things. It isn't usual to make complaints

---

28. **C.B.** Confinement to barracks
29. **let fly.** Tell him off

<u>words for everyday use</u>

**mere** (mir) *adj.*, nothing more or other than; only. *The little boy was determined not to let a mere shadow frighten him during the night.*

**in • sub • or • di • na • tion** (in' sə bòrd' 'n ā shən) *n.*, disobedience. *Because of Philip's insubordination, the coach kept him* out of the game, so Philip would learn not to question his judgment.

**e • vade** (ē vād') *vi.*, avoid doing or answering directly. *When the teacher asked a difficult question, Craig tried to evade answering him.*

in the army. He understands it all right though, and lectures Himmelstoss, making it plain to him that the front isn't a parade-ground. Then comes Tjaden's turn, he gets a long sermon and three days' open arrest. Bertink gives Kropp a wink and one day's open arrest. "It can't be helped," he says to him regretfully. He is a decent fellow.

Open arrest is quite pleasant. The clink was once a fowl-house; there we can visit the prisoners, we know how to manage it. Close arrest would have meant the cellar.

They used to tie us to a tree, but that is forbidden now. In many ways we are treated quite like men.

An hour later after Tjaden and Kropp are settled in behind their wire-netting we make our way into them. Tjaden greets us crowing. Then we play skat far into the night. Tjaden wins of course, the lucky wretch.

*

When we break it up Kat says to me: "What do you say to some roast goose?"

"Not bad," I agree.

We climb up on a munition-wagon. The ride costs us two cigarettes. Kat has marked the spot exactly. The shed belongs to a regimental headquarters. I agree to get the goose and receive my instructions. The outhouse is behind the wall and the door shuts with just a peg.

Kat hoists me up. I rest my foot in his hands and climb over the wall. Kat keeps watch below.

I wait a few moments to accustom my eyes to the darkness. Then I recognize the shed. Softly I steal across, lift the peg, pull it out and open the door.

I distinguish two white patches. Two geese, that's bad: if I grab one the other will cackle. Well, both of them—if I'm quick, it can be done.

I make a jump. I catch hold of one and the next instant the second. Like a madman I bash their heads against the wall to stun them. But I haven't quite enough weight. The beasts cackle and strike out with their feet and wings. I fight desperately, but Lord! what a kick a goose has! They struggle and I stagger about. In the dark these white patches are terrifying. My arms have grown wings and I'm almost afraid of going up into the sky, as though I held a couple of captive balloons in my fists.

Then the row begins; one of them gets his breath and goes off like an alarm clock. Before I can do anything, something comes in from outside; I feel a blow, lie outstretched on the floor, and hear awful growls. A dog. I steal a glance to the side, he makes a snap at my throat. I lie still and tuck my chin into my collar.

◀ About what does Lieutenant Bertink lecture Himmelstoss? How does he punish Tjaden and Kropp?

◀ What are Kat and Paul planning to do?

It's a bull dog. After an eternity he withdraws his head and sits down beside me. But if I make the least movement he growls. I consider. The only thing to do is to get hold of my small revolver, and that too before anyone arrives. Inch by inch I move my hand toward it.

I have the feeling that it lasts an hour. The slightest movement and then an awful growl; I lie still, then try again. When at last I have the revolver my hand starts to tremble. I press it against the ground and say over to myself: Jerk the revolver up, fire before he has a chance to grab, and then jump up.

Slowly I take a deep breath and become calmer. Then I hold my breath, whip up the revolver, it cracks, the dog leaps howling to one side, I make for the door of the shed and fall head over heels over one of the scuttering[30] geese.

At full speed I seize it again, and with a swing toss it over the wall and clamber up. No sooner am I on top than the dog is up again as lively as ever and springs at me. Quickly I let myself drop. Ten paces away stands Kat with the goose under his arm. As soon as he sees me we run.

At last we can take a breather. The goose is dead, Kat saw to that in a moment. We intend to roast it at once so that nobody will be any wiser. I fetch a dixie and wood from the hut and we crawl into a small deserted lean-to[31] which we use for such purposes. The single window space is heavily curtained. There is a sort of hearth, an iron plate set on some bricks. We kindle a fire.

Kat plucks and cleans the goose. We put the feathers carefully to one side. We intend to make two cushions out of them with the inscription: "Sleep soft under shell-fire." The sound of the gunfire from the front penetrates into our refuge. The glow of the fire lights up our faces, shadows dance on the wall. Sometimes a heavy crash and the lean-to shivers. Aeroplane bombs. Once we hear a stifled cry. A hut must have been hit.

Aeroplanes drone; the tack-tack of machine-guns breaks out. But no light that could be observed shows from us.

▶ How does Paul feel about Kat?

We sit opposite one another, Kat and I, two soldiers in shabby coats, cooking a goose in the middle of the night. We don't talk much, but I believe we have a more complete communion with one another than even lovers have.

We are two men, two minute sparks of life; outside is the night and the circle of death. We sit on the edge of it

---

30. **scuttering.** Scurrying or bustling about
31. **lean-to.** Shed with a one-slope roof

crouching in danger, the grease drips from our hands, in our hearts we are close to one another, and the hour is like the room: flecked over with the lights and shadows of our feelings cast by a quiet fire. What does he know of me or I of him? Formerly we should not have had a single thought in common—now we sit with a goose between us and feel in <u>unison</u>, are so intimate that we do not even speak.

It takes a long time to roast a goose, even when it is young and fat. So we take turns. One bastes it while the other lies down and sleeps. A grand smell gradually fills the hut.

The noises without increase in volume, pass into my dream and yet linger in my memory. In a half sleep I watch Kat dip and raise the ladle. I love him, his shoulders, his angular, stooping figure—and at the same time I see behind him woods and stars, and a clear voice utters words that bring me peace, to me, a soldier in big boots, belt, and knapsack, taking the road that lies before him under the high heaven, quickly forgetting and seldom sorrowful, for ever pressing on under the wide night sky.

A little soldier and a clear voice, and if anyone were to caress him he would hardly understand, this soldier with the big boots and the shut heart, who marches because he is wearing his boots, and has forgotten all else but marching. Beyond the sky-line is a country with flowers, lying so still that he would like to weep. There are sights there that he has not forgotten, because he never possessed them—<u>perplexing</u>, yet lost to him. Are not his twenty summers there?

Is my face wet, and where am I? Kat stands before me, his gigantic, stooping shadow falls upon me, like home. He speaks gently, he smiles and goes back to the fire.

Then he says: "It's done."

"Yes, Kat."

I stir myself. In the middle of the room shines the brown goose. We take our collapsible forks and our pocket-knives and each cuts off a leg. With it we have army bread dipped in gravy. We eat slowly and with gusto.

"How does it taste, Kat?"

"Good! And yours?"

"Good, Kat."

---

**words for everyday use**

u • ni • son (yün′ ə sən) *adj.*, uttering the same words, or producing the same sound, at the same time. *Every morning, our class says the pledge of allegiance in <u>unison</u>.*

per • plex • ing (pər pleks′ iŋ) *adj.*, confusing; puzzling. *Bernard found algebra <u>perplexing</u>, but one day the equations began to make sense to him.*

▶ What does Paul
say he and Kat are?


▶ To whom do Kat
and Paul wish to
bring goose?

We are brothers and press on one another the choicest pieces. Afterwards I smoke a cigarette and Kat a cigar. There is still a lot left.

"How would it be, Kat if we took a bit to Kropp and Tjaden?"

"Sure," says he.

We carve off a portion and wrap it up carefully in newspaper. The rest we thought of taking over to the hut. Kat laughs, and simply says: "Tjaden."

I agree, we will have to take it all.

So we go off to the fowl-house to waken them. But first we pack away the feathers.

Kropp and Tjaden take us for magicians. Then they get busy with their teeth. Tjaden holds a wing in his mouth with both hands like a mouth-organ, and gnaws. He drinks the gravy from the pot and smacks his lips:

"May I never forget you!"

We go to our hut. Again there is the lofty sky with the stars and the oncoming dawn, and I pass beneath it, a soldier with big boots and a full belly, a little soldier in the early morning—but by my side, stooping and angular, goes Kat, my comrade.

The outlines of the huts are upon us in the dawn like a dark, deep sleep.

# Chapter VI

There are rumours of an offensive.[1] We go up to the front two days earlier than usual. On the way we pass a shelled school-house. Stacked up against its longer side is a high double wall of yellow, unpolished, brand-new coffins. They still smell of resin,[2] and pine, and the forest. There are at least a hundred.

◀ What is stacked against the bombed-out schoolhouse?

"That's a good preparation for the offensive," says Müller astonished.

"They're for us," growls Detering.

"Don't talk rot," says Kat to him angrily.

"You be thankful if you get so much as a coffin," grins Tjaden, "they'll slip you a waterproof sheet for your old Aunt Sally[3] of a carcase."[4]

The others jest too, unpleasant jests, but what else can a man do?—The coffins are really for us. The organization surpasses itself in that kind of thing.

◀ For whom are the coffins intended?

Ahead of us everything is shimmering. The first night we try to get our bearings. When it is fairly quiet we can hear the transports[5] behind the enemy lines rolling ceaselessly until dawn. Kat says that they do not go back but are bring up troops—troops, munitions, and guns.

◀ What is happening behind enemy lines? What has happened to the English artillery?

The English artillery has been strengthened, that we can detect at once. There are at least four more batteries of nine-inch guns to the right of the farm, and behind the poplars they have put in trench-mortars.[6] Beside these they have brought up a number of those little French beasts with instantaneous fuses.[7]

We are now in low spirits. After we have been in the dug-outs two hours our own shells begin to fall in the trench. This is the third time in four weeks. If it were simply a mistake in aim no one would say anything, but the truth is that the barrels are worn out. The shots are often so uncertain that they land within our own lines. Tonight two of our men were wounded by them.

◀ What causes the German's own shells to fall in their trenches?

*

The front is a cage in which we must await fearfully whatever may happen. We lie under the network of arching shells and live in a suspense of uncertainty. Over us,

---

1. **offensive.** Attack by hostile armed forces
2. **resin.** Sticky substance produced by plants and trees
3. **Aunt Sally.** Person set up as an easy target for criticism
4. **carcase.** Carcass, the dead body of an animal
5. **transports.** Train or other vehicle used to move soldiers
6. **trench-mortars.** Short-barreled canon that hurls explosive shells in a high trajectory
7. **instantaneous fuses.** Explosives that explode immediately upon impact

▶ What makes the
soldiers indifferent?

Chance hovers. If a shot comes, we can duck, that is all; we neither know nor can determine where it will fall.

It is this Chance that makes us <u>indifferent</u>. A few months ago I was sitting in a dug-out playing skat; after a while I stood up and went to visit some friends in another dug-out. On my return nothing more was to be seen of the first one, it had been blown to pieces by a direct hit. I went back to the second and arrived just in time to lend a hand digging it out. In the <u>interval</u> it had been buried.

It is just as much a matter of chance that I am still alive as that I might have been hit. In a bomb-proof dug-out I may be smashed to atoms and in the open may survive ten hours' bombardment <u>unscathed</u>. No soldier outlives a thousand chances. But every soldier believes in Chance and trusts his luck.

*

▶ Why must the
soldiers look out for
their bread?

We must look out for our bread. The rats have become much more numerous lately because the trenches are no longer in good condition. Detering says it is a sure sign of a coming bombardment.

▶ What do they call
the rats?

The rats here are particularly repulsive, they are so fat— the kind we all call corpse-rats. They have shocking, evil, naked faces, and it is nauseating to see their long, nude tails.

They seem to be mighty hungry. Almost every man has had his bread gnawed. Kropp wrapped his in his water-proof sheet and put it under his head, but he cannot sleep because they run over his face to get at it. Detering meant to outwit them: he fastened a thin wire to the roof and sus-pended his bread from it. During the night when he switched on his pocket-torch he saw the wire swing to and fro. On the bread was riding a fat rat.

At least we put a stop to it. We cannot afford to throw the bread away, because then we should have nothing left to eat in the morning, so we carefully cut off the bits of bread that the animals have gnawed.

The slices we cut off are heaped together in the middle of the floor. Each man takes out his spade and lies down

---

**words for everyday use**

in • dif • fer • ent (in dif' ər ənt) adj., having or showing no interest, concern, or feeling. Although James loves that television show and Wanda hates it, I am *indifferent* to it.

in • ter • val (in' tər vəl) n., period of time between two points of time. The *interval* between acts in a play is called an intermission.

un • scathed (un skāthd') adj., not hurt; unharmed. We were amazed that people at the circus could breathe fire and swallow swords yet remain *unscathed*.

prepared to strike. Detering, Kropp, and Kat hold their pocket-torches[8] ready.

After a few minutes we hear the first shuffling and tugging. It grows, now it is the sound of many little feet. Then the torches switch on and every man strikes at the heap, which scatters with a rush. The result is good. We toss the bits of rat over the parapet[9] and again lie in wait.

Several times we repeat the process. At last the beasts get wise to it, or perhaps they have scented the blood. They return no more. Nevertheless, before morning the remainder of the bread on the floor has been carried off.

In the adjoining sector they attacked two large cats and a dog, bit them to death and devoured them.

Next day there was an issue of Edamer cheese. Each man gets almost a quarter of a cheese. In one way that is all to the good, for Edamer is tasty—but in another way it is vile, because the fat red balls[10] have long been a sign of a bad time coming. Our <u>forebodings</u> increase as rum is served out. We drink it of course; but are not greatly comforted.

◀ Of what is Edamer cheese a sign?

During the day we loaf about and make war on the rats. Ammunition and hand-grenades become more plentiful. We overhaul the bayonets—that is to say, the ones that have a saw on the blunt edge. If the fellows over there catch a man with one of those he's killed at sight. In the next sector some of our men were found whose noses were cut off and their eyes poked out with their own sawbayonets. Their mouths and noses were stuffed with sawdust so that they suffocated.

◀ Why do the men overhaul their bayonets?

Some of the recruits have bayonets of this sort; we take them away and give them the ordinary kind.

But the bayonet has practically lost its importance. It is usually the fashion now to charge with bombs and spades[11] only. The sharpened spade is a more handy and many-sided weapon; not only can it be used for jabbing a man under the chin, but it is much better for striking with

---

8. **pocket-torches.** Flashlights
9. **parapet.** Wall or bank used to screen troops from frontal enemy fire
10. **fat red balls.** Edamer cheese comes in round wheels covered with red wax
11. **spades.** Shovels

---

**words for everyday use**

fore • bod • ing (fôr bōd′ iŋ) n., prediction, especially of something bad or harmful.
*Raoul's <u>forebodings</u> before the game proved well-founded because we lost.*

because of its greater weight; and if one hits between the neck and shoulder it easily cleaves as far down as the chest. The bayonet frequently jams on the thrust and then a man has to kick hard on the other fellow's belly to pull it out again; and in the interval he may easily get one himself. And what's more the blade often gets broken off.

At night they send over gas. We expect the attack to follow and lie with our masks on, ready to tear them off as soon as the first shadow appears.

Dawn approaches without anything happening—only the everlasting, <u>nerve-wracking</u> roll behind the enemy lines, trains, trains, lorries, lorries; but what are they concentrating? Our artillery fires on it continually, but still it does not cease.

▶ What does Kat think will happen to them?

We have tired faces and avoid each other's eyes. "It will be like the Somme,"[12] says Kat gloomily. "There we were shelled steadily for seven days and nights." Kat has lost all his fun since we have been here, which is bad, for Kat is an old front-hog, and can smell what is coming. Only Tjaden seems pleased with the good rations and the rum; he thinks we might even go back to rest without anything happening at all.

It almost looks like it. Day after day passes. At night I squat in the listening-post.[13] Above me the rockets and parachute-lights shoot up and float down again. I am cautious and tense, my heart thumps. My eyes turn again and again to the <u>luminous</u> dial of my watch; the hands will not budge. Sleep hangs on my eyelids, I work my toes in my boots in order to keep awake. Nothing happens till I am relieved;—only the everlasting rolling over there. Gradually we grow calmer and play skat and poker continually. Perhaps we will be lucky.

All day the sky is hung with observation balloons. There is a rumour that the enemy are going to put tanks over and use low-flying planes for the attack. But that interests us less than what we hear of the new flame-throwers.

---

12. **the Somme.** River in France and the site of a major battle during World War I
13. **listening-post.** Position near the enemy's lines for detecting the enemy's movements by listening

---

**words for everyday use**

nerve-wrack • ing (nŭrv rak′ iŋ) *adj.*, very trying to one's patience or calm. *Yolanda found it <u>nerve-wracking</u> to sit back stage before the show, but once she got on stage her fears disappeared.*

lu • mi • nous (lü′ mə nəs) *adj.*, giving off light; shining; bright. *We stared at the <u>luminous</u> reflection of the moon shining off the water.*

We wake up in the middle of the night. The earth booms. Heavy fire is falling on us. We crouch into corners. We distinguish shells of every calibre.[14]

Each man lays hold of his things and looks again every minute to reassure himself that they are still there. The dug-out heaves, the night roars and flashes. We look at each other in the momentary flashes of light, and with pale faces and pressed lips shake our heads.

◀ What is happening to the soldiers' dugout?

Every man is aware of the heavy shells tearing down the parapet, rooting up the embankment and demolishing the upper layers of concrete. When a shell lands in the trench we note how the hollow, furious blast is like a blow from the paw of a raging beast of prey. Already by morning a few of the recruits are green and vomiting. They are too inexperienced.

Slowly the grey light trickles into the post and pales the flashes of the shells. Morning is come. The explosion of mines mingles with the gun-fire. That is the most <u>dementing</u> convulsion of all. The whole region where they go up becomes one grave.

The reliefs go out, the observers stagger in, covered with dirt, and trembling. One lies down in silence in the corner and eats, the other, an older man of the new draft, sobs; twice he has been flung over the parapet by the blast of the explosions without getting any more than shell-shock.

The recruits are eyeing him. We must watch them, these things are catching, already some lips begin to quiver. It is good that it is growing daylight; perhaps the attack will come before noon.

The bombardment does not diminish. It is falling in the rear too. As far as one can see spout fountains of mud and iron. A wide belt is being raked.

The attack does not come, but the bombardment continues. We are gradually benumbed. Hardly a man speaks. We cannot make ourselves understood.

◀ What is the effect of the continued bombardment on the soldiers' trench?

Our trench is almost gone. At many places it is only eighteen inches high, it is broken by holes, and craters, and mountains of earth. A shell lands square in front of our post. At once it is dark. We are buried and must dig

---

14. **calibre.** Size of a shell or bullet

---

**words for everyday use**
de • ment (dē ment') vt., make insane. The accused's <u>dementing</u> childhood was used as part of the defense in his trial.

▶ What does the commander say he will try to do?

▶ What is even Kat unable to do?

ourselves out. After an hour the entrance is clear again, and we are calmer because we have had something to do.

Our Company Commander scrambles in and reports that two dug-outs are gone. The recruits calm themselves when they see him. He says that an attempt will be made to bring up food this evening.

That sounds reassuring. No one had thought of it except Tjaden. Now the outside world seems to draw a little nearer: if food can be brought up, think the recruits, then it can't really be so bad.

We do not <u>disabuse</u> them; we know that food is as important as ammunition and only for that reason must be brought up.

But it miscarries.[15] A second party goes out, and it also turns back. Finally Kat tries, and even he reappears without accomplishing anything. No one gets through, not even a fly is small enough to get through such a barrage.

We pull in our belts tighter and chew every mouthful three times as long. Still the food does not last out; we are damnably hungry. I take out a scrap of bread, eat the white and put the crust back in my knapsack; from time to time I nibble at it.

*

The night is unbearable. We cannot sleep, but stare ahead of us and doze. Tjaden regrets that we wasted the gnawed pieces of bread on the rats. We would gladly have them again to eat now. We are short of water, too, but not seriously yet.

Towards morning, while it is still dark, there is some excitement. Through the entrance rushes in a swarm of fleeting rats that try to storm the walls. Torches light up the confusion. Everyone yells and curses and slaughters. The madness and despair of many hours unloads itself in this outburst. Faces are distorted, arms strike out, the beasts scream; we just stop in time to avoid attacking one another.

The onslaught has exhausted us. We lie down to wait again. It is a marvel that our post has had no casualties so far. It is one of the less deep dug-outs.

---

15. **miscarries.** Goes wrong

**words for everyday use**
dis • a • buse (dis' ə byüz') *vt.*, rid of false ideas. *The coach tried to <u>disabuse</u> us of the notion that volleyball would be all fun and no hard work.*

A corporal creeps in; he has a loaf of bread with him. Three people have had the luck to get through during the night and bring some provisions. They say the bombardment extends undiminished as far as the artillery lines. It is a mystery where the enemy gets all his shells.

We wait and wait. By midday what I expected happens. One of the recruits has a fit. I have been watching him for a long time, grinding his teeth and opening and shutting his fists. These hunted, protruding eyes, we know them too well. During the last few hours he has had merely the appearance of calm. He had collapsed like a rotten tree.

◀ What happens to one of the recruits?

Now he stands up, stealthily creeps across the floor, hesitates a moment and then glides towards the door. I intercept him and say: "Where are you going?"

"I'll be back in a minute," says he, and tries to push past me.

"Wait a bit, the shelling will stop soon."

He listens for a moment and his eyes become clear. Then again he has the glowering eyes of a mad dog, he is silent, he shoves me aside.

"One minute, lad," I say. Kat notices. Just as the recruit shakes me off Kat jumps in and we hold him.

Then he begins to rave: "Leave me alone, let me go out, I will go out!"

He won't listen to anything and hits out, his mouth is wet and pours out words, half choked, meaningless words. It is a case of <u>claustrophobia</u>, he feels as though he is suffocating here and wants to get out at any price. If we let him go he would run about everywhere regardless of cover. He is not the first.

Though he raves and his eyes roll, it can't be helped, we have to give him a hiding to bring him to his senses. We do it quickly and mercilessly, and at last he sits down quietly. The others have turned pale; let's hope it <u>deters</u> them. This bombardment is too much for the poor devils, they have been sent straight from a recruiting-depot into a barrage that is enough to turn an old soldier's hair grey.

◀ What do Paul and his friends do to bring the recruit back to his senses?

After this affair the sticky, close atmosphere works more than ever on our nerves. We sit as if in our graves waiting only to be closed in.

---

**words for everyday use**

claus • tro • pho • bi • a (klòs' trə fō' bē ə) *n.*, abnormal fear of being in an enclosed or confined place. *People who have <u>claustrophobia</u> often find it hard to be in elevators or restrooms on airplanes.*

de • ter (dē tʉr') *vt.*, keep or discourage (a person, group, or nation) from doing something by instilling fear, anxiety, or doubt. *Joel's fear of water <u>deters</u> him from learning to swim.*

Suddenly it howls and flashes terrifically, the dug-out cracks in all its joints under a direct hit, fortunately only a light one that the concrete blocks are able to withstand. It rings metallically, the walls reel, rifles, helmets, earth, mud, and dust fly everywhere. Sulphur fumes pour in.

If we were in one of those light dug-outs that they have been building lately instead of this deeper one, none of us would be alive.

But the effect is bad enough even so. The recruit starts to rave again and two others follow suit. One jumps up and rushes out, we have trouble with the other two. I start after the one who escapes and wonder whether to shoot him in the leg—then it shrieks again, I fling myself down and when I stand up the wall of the trench is plastered with smoking splinters, lumps of flesh, and bits of uniform. I scramble back.

▶ What seems to have happened to the frightened recruit?

The first recruit seems actually to have gone insane. He butts his head against the wall like a goat. We must try tonight to take him to the rear. Meanwhile we bind him, but in such a way that in case of attack he can be released at once.

Kat suggests a game of skat: it is easier when a man has something to do. But it is no use, we listen for every explosion that comes close, miscount the tricks, and fail to follow suit. We have to give it up. We sit as though in a boiler[16] that is being belaboured from without on all sides.

Night again. We are deadened by the strain—a deadly tension that scrapes along one's spine like a gapped knife.[17] Our legs refuse to move, our hands tremble, our bodies are a thin skin stretched painfully over repressed madness, over an almost irresistible, bursting roar. We have neither flesh nor muscles any longer, we dare not look at one another for fear of some incalculable thing. So we shut our teeth—it will end—it will end—perhaps we will come through.

▶ What change has occurred at the front?

Suddenly the nearer explosions cease. The shelling continues but it has lifted and falls behind us, our trench is free. We seize the hand-grenades pitch them out in front of the dug-out and jump after them. The bombardment has stopped and a heavy barrage now falls behind us. The attack has come.

No one would believe that in this howling waste there could still be men; but steel helmets now appear on all

16. **boiler.** Container in which things are boiled or heated
17. **gapped knife.** Serrated knife

sides out of the trench, and fifty yards from us a machine-gun is already in position and barking.

The wire entanglements are torn to pieces. Yet they offer some obstacle. We see the storm-troops[18] coming. Our artillery opens fire. Machine-guns rattle, rifles crack. The charge works its way across. Haie and Kropp begin with the hand-grenades. They throw as fast as they can, others pass them, the handles with the strings already pulled. Haie throws seventy-five yards, Kropp sixty, it has been measured, the distance is important. The enemy as they run cannot do much before they are within forty yards.

We recognize the smooth distorted faces, the helmets: they are French. They have already suffered heavily when they reach the <u>remnants</u> of the barbed wire entanglements. A whole line has gone down before our machine-guns; then we have a lot of stoppages and they come nearer.

I see one of them, his face upturned, fall into a wire cradle. His body collapses, his hands remain suspended as though he were praying. Then his body drops clean away and only his hands with the stumps of his arms, shot off, now hang in the wire.

The moment we are about to retreat three faces rise up from the ground in front of us. Under one of the helmets a dark pointed beard and two eyes that are fastened on me. I raise my hand, but I cannot throw into those strange eyes; for one mad moment the whole slaughter whirls like a circus round me, and these two eyes alone are motionless; then the head rises up, a hand, a movement, and my hand-grenade flies through the air and into him.

We make for the rear, pull wire cradles into the trench and leave bombs behind us with the strings pulled, which ensures us a fiery retreat. The machine-guns are already firing from the next position.

We have become wild beasts. We do not fight, we defend ourselves against annihilation. It is not against men that we fling our bombs, what do we know of men in this moment when Death is hunting us down—now, for the first time in three days we can see his face, now for the first time in

◀ *What do the German soldiers do to stop the enemy soldiers who lead the attack?*

◀ *What do the soldiers leave behind when they retreat?*

---

18. **storm-troops.** Soldiers in the first wave of an attack

three days we can oppose him; we feel a mad anger. No longer do we lie helpless, waiting on the <u>scaffold</u>, we can destroy and kill, to save ourselves, to save ourselves and to be revenged.

We crouch behind every corner, behind every barrier of barbed wire, and hurl leaps of explosives at the feet of the advancing enemy before we run. The blast of the hand-grenades <u>impinges</u> powerfully on our arms and legs; crouching like cats we run on, overwhelmed by this wave that bears us along, that fills us with ferocity, turns us into thugs, into murderers, into God only knows what devils; this wave that multiplies our strength with fear and madness and greed of life, seeking and fighting for nothing but our deliverance. If your own father came over with them you would not hesitate to fling a bomb at him.

▶ What does Paul say you would not hesitate to do?

The forward trenches have been abandoned. Are they still trenches? They are blown to pieces, annihilated—there are only broken bits of trenches, holes linked by cracks, nests of craters, that is all. But the enemy's casualties increase. They did not count on so much resistance.

*

It is nearly noon. The sun blazes hotly, the sweat stings in our eyes, we wipe it off on our sleeves and often blood with it. At last we reach a trench that is in a somewhat better condition. It is manned and ready for the counter-attack, it receives us. Our guns open in full blast and cut off the enemy attack.

▶ What has happened to the enemy attack?

The lines behind us stop. They can advance no farther. The attack is crushed by our artillery. We watch. The fire lifts a hundred yards and we break forward. Beside me a lance-corporal has his head torn off. He runs a few steps more while the blood spouts from his neck like a fountain.

It does not come quite to hand-to-hand fighting; they are driven back. We arrive once again at our shattered trench and pass on beyond it.

Oh, this turning back again! We reach the shelter of the reserves and yearn to creep in and disappear;—but instead we must turn round and plunge again into the horror. If we were not <u>automata</u> at that moment we would continue

---

**words for everyday use**

scaf • fold (skaf′ əld) *n.*, raised platform on which criminals are executed, as by hanging. *Many towns in the American West had scaffolds for executions because there were many outlaws who committed violent crimes.*

im • pinge (im pinj′) *vi.*, strike, hit, or dash (*on, upon,* or *against* something). *The steady thump of the basketball impinges against the concrete, luring us outside to play.*

au • tom • a • ton (pl. automata) (ȯ täm′ ə tän′) *n.*, person or animal acting in an automatic or mechanical way. *After a long day of backbreaking work in the hot sun, the farm hands stumbled toward home like automata, not even speaking.*

lying there, exhausted, and without will. But we are swept forward again, powerless, madly savage and raging; we will kill, for they are still our mortal enemies, their rifles and bombs are aimed against us, and if we don't destroy them, they will destroy us.

The brown earth, the torn, blasted earth, with a greasy shine under the sun's rays; the earth is the background of this restless, gloomy world of automatons, our gasping is the scratching of a quill, our lips are dry, our heads are debauched with stupor[19]—thus we stagger forward, and into our pierced and shattered souls bores the torturing image of the brown earth with the greasy sun and the convulsed and dead soldiers, who lie there—it can't be helped—who cry and clutch at our legs as we spring away over them.

◀ What happens as the soldiers stagger forward?

We have lost all feeling for one another. We can hardly control ourselves when our glance lights on the form of some other man. We are <u>insensible</u>, dead men, who through some trick, some dreadful magic, are still able to run and to kill.

◀ What does Paul say they are?

A young Frenchman lags behind, he is overtaken, he puts up his hands, in one he still holds his revolver—does he mean to shoot or to give himself!—a blow from a spade cleaves through his face. A second sees it and tries to run farther; a bayonet jabs into his back. He leaps in the air, his arms thrown wide, his mouth wide open, yelling; he staggers, in his back the bayonet quivers. A third throws away his rifle, cowers down with his hands before his eyes. He is left behind with a few other prisoners to carry off the wounded.

Suddenly in the pursuit we reach the enemy line.

We are so close on the heels of our retreating enemies that we reach it almost at the same time as they. In this way we suffer few casualties. A machine-gun barks, but is silenced with a bomb. Nevertheless, the couple of seconds has sufficed to give us five stomach wounds. With the butt of his rifle Kat smashes to pulp the face of one of the unwounded machine-gunners. We bayonet the others before they have time to get out their bombs. Then thirstily we drink the water they have for cooling the gun.

---

19. **debauched with stupor.** Corrupted by mental dullness

**words for everyday use**     in • sen • si • ble (in sen' sə bəl) *adj.*, lacking sensation; unaware; indifferent. *After spending all afternoon skiing, Linda's hands and toes were <u>insensible</u> because of the cold.*

Everywhere wire-cutters are snapping, planks are thrown across the entanglements, we jump through the narrow entrances into the trenches. Haie strikes his spade into the neck of a gigantic Frenchman and throws the first hand-grenade; we duck behind a breastwork for a few seconds, then the straight bit of trench ahead of us is empty. The next throw whizzes obliquely over the corner and clears a passage; as we run past we toss handfuls down into the dug-outs, the earth shudders, it crashes, smokes and groans, we stumble over slippery lumps of flesh, over yielding bodies; I fall into an open belly on which lies a clean, new officer's cap.

The fight ceases. We lose touch with the enemy. We cannot stay here long but must retire under cover of our artillery to our own position. No sooner do we know this than we dive into the nearest dug-outs, and with the utmost haste seize on whatever <u>provisions</u> we can see, especially the tins of corned beef and butter, before we clear out.

We get back pretty well. There is no further attack by the enemy. We lie for an hour panting and resting before anyone speaks. We are so completely played out[20] that in spite of our great hunger we do not think of the provisions. Then gradually we become something like men again.

The corned beef over there is famous along the whole front. Occasionally it has been the chief reason for a flying raid on our part, for our nourishment is generally very bad; we have a constant hunger.

We bagged five tins altogether. The fellows over there are well looked after; they fare magnificently, as against us, poor starving wretches, with our turnip jam; they can get all the meat they want. Haie has scored a thin loaf of white French bread, and stuck it in behind his belt like a spade. It is a bit bloody at one corner, but that can be cut off.

It is a good thing we have something decent to eat at last; we still have a use for all our strength. Enough to eat is just as valuable as a good dug-out; it can save our lives; that is the reason we are so greedy for it.

▶ *What do the soldiers seize before they leave to return to their position?*

▶ *What has caused the German soldiers to make a raid on the enemy?*

▶ *How does the enemy's food compare with what the soldiers usually get?*

---

20. **played out.** Exhausted

**words for everyday use**

pro • vi • sions (prō vizh′ əns) *n.,* stock of food and other supplies assembled for future needs. *Pioneers moving out west in covered wagons carried with them all their possessions and the <u>provisions</u> they would need for the journey.*

Tjaden has captured two water-bottles full of cognac. We pass them round.

*

The evening benediction[21] begins. Night comes, out of the craters rise the mists. It looks as though the holes were full of ghostly secrets. The white vapour creeps painfully round before it ventures to steal away over the edge. Then long streaks stretch from crater to crater.

It is chilly. I am on sentry[22] and stare into the darkness. My strength is exhausted as always after an attack, and so it is hard for me to be alone with my thoughts. They are not properly thoughts; they are memories which in my weakness haunt me and strangely move me.

The parachute-lights[23] soar upwards—and I see a picture, a summer evening, I am in the cathedral cloister[24] and look at the tall rose trees that bloom in the middle of the little cloister garden where the monks lie buried. Around the walls are the stone carvings of the Stations of the Cross.[25] No one is there. A great quietness rules in this blossoming quadrangle,[26] the sun lies warm on the heavy grey stones, I place my hand upon them and feel the warmth. At the right-hand corner the green cathedral spire ascends into the pale blue sky of the evening. Between the glowing columns of the cloister is the cool darkness that only churches have, and I stand there and wonder whether, when I am twenty, I shall have experienced the bewildering emotions of love.

◀ What does Paul wonder?

The image is alarmingly near; it touches me before it dissolves in the light of the next star-shell.

I lay hold of my rifle to see that it is in trim.[27] The barrel is wet, I take it in my hands and rub off the moisture with my fingers.

Between the meadows behind our town there stands a line of old poplars by a stream. They were visible from a great distance, and although they grew on one bank only, we called them the poplar avenue. Even as children we had a great love for them, they drew us vaguely thither,

---

21. **benediction.** Blessing
22. **on sentry.** On guard duty
23. **parachute-lights.** Parachutes that were launched with lights to illuminate the movements of enemy troops
24. **cloister.** Covered walk along the inside wall of a church
25. **Stations of the Cross.** Series of fourteen crosses, as along the walls of a church, typically placed above representations of the stages of Jesus' final sufferings and of his death and burial
26. **quadrangle.** Area surrounded on four sides by buildings
27. **trim.** Good condition

we played <u>truant</u> the whole day by them and listened to their rustling. We sat beneath them on the bank of the stream and let our feet hang in the bright, swift waters. The pure fragrance of the water and the melody of the wind in the poplars held our fancies. We loved them dearly, and the image of those days still makes my heart pause in its beating.

It is strange that all the memories that come have these two qualities. They are always completely calm, that is <u>predominant</u> in them; and even if they are not really calm, they become so. They are soundless apparitions that speak to me, with looks and gestures silently, without any word—and it is the alarm of their silence that forces me to lay hold of my sleeve and my rifle lest I should abandon myself to the liberation and <u>allurement</u> in which my body would dilate[28] and gently pass away into the still forces that lie behind these things.

*▶ Why are all Paul's memories quiet?*

They are quiet in this way, because quietness is so unattainable for us now. At the front there is no quietness and the curse of the front reaches so far that we never pass beyond it. Even in the remote depots and rest-areas the droning and the muffled noise of shelling is always in our ears. We are never so far off that it is no more to be heard. But these last few days it has been unbearable.

Their stillness is the reason why these memories of former times do not awaken desire so much as sorrow—a vast, <u>inapprehensible</u> melancholy. Once we had such desires—but they return not. They are past, they belong to another world that is gone from us. In the barracks they called forth a rebellious, wild craving for their return; for then they were still bound to us, we belonged to them and they to us, even though we were already absent from them. They appeared in the soldiers' songs which we sang as we marched between the glow of the dawn and the

---

28. **dilate.** Expand or swell

black silhouettes of the forests to drill on the moor, they were a powerful remembrance that was in us and came from us.

But here in the trenches they are completely lost to us. They arise no more; we are dead and they stand remote on the horizon, they are a mysterious reflection, an apparition,[29] that haunts us, that we fear and love without hope. They are strong and our desire is strong—but they are unattainable, and we know it.

And even if these scenes of our youth were given back to us we would hardly know what to do. The tender, secret influence that passed from them into us could not rise again. We might be amongst them and move in them; we might remember and love them and be stirred by the sight of them. But it would be like gazing at the photograph of a dead comrade; those are his features, it is his face, and the days we spent together take on a mournful life in the memory; but the man himself it is not.

◀ What does Paul say would happen if they were given back scenes from their youth?

We could never regain the old intimacy with those scenes. It was not any recognition of their beauty and their significance that attracted us, but the communion, the feeling of a comradeship with the things and events of our existence, which cut us off and made the world of our parents a thing incomprehensible to us—for then we surrendered ourselves to events and were lost in them, and the least little thing was enough to carry us down the stream of eternity. Perhaps it was only the privilege of our youth, but as yet we recognized no limits and saw nowhere an end. We had that thrill of expectation in the blood which united us with the course of our days.

Today we would pass through the scenes of our youth like travellers. We are burnt up by hard facts; like tradesmen we understand distinctions, and like butchers, necessities. We are no longer untroubled—we are indifferent. We might exist there; but should we really live there?

We are <u>forlorn</u> like children, and experienced like old men, we are crude and sorrowful and <u>superficial</u>—I believe we are lost.

◀ In what way are the soldiers like children? In what way are they like old men?

---

29. **apparition.** Ghost

**words for everyday use**

for • lorn (fòr lòrn') adj., without hope; desperate. *We knew from Ben's forlorn expression that he did not do well on the test.*

su • per • fi • cial (sü' pər fish' əl) adj., concerned with and understanding only the easily apparent and obvious; shallow. *Hannah found girls who cared only about hair and makeup to be superficial.*

*

My hands grow cold and my flesh creeps; and yet the night is warm. Only the mist is cold, this mysterious mist that trails over the dead and sucks from them their last, creeping life. By morning they will be pale and green and their blood congealed and black.

Still the parachute-rockets shoot up and cast their pitiless light over the stony landscape, which is full of craters and frozen lights like a moon. The blood beneath my skin brings fear and restlessness into my thoughts. They become feeble and tremble, they want warmth and life. They cannot persist without <u>solace</u>, without illusion, they are disordered before the naked picture of despair.

I hear the rattle of the mess-tins and immediately feel a strong desire for warm food; it would do me good and comfort me. Painfully I force myself to wait until I am relieved.

Then I go into the dug-out and find a mug of barley. It is cooked in fat and tastes good, I eat it slowly. I remain quiet, though the others are in a better mood, for the shelling has died down.

*

The days go by and the incredible hours follow one another as a matter of course. Attacks alternate with counter-attacks and slowly the dead pile up in the field of craters between the trenches. We are able to bring in most of the wounded that do not lie too far off. But many have long to wait and we listen to them dying.

For one of them we search two days in vain. He must be lying on his belly and unable to turn over. Otherwise it is hard to understand why we cannot find him; for it is only when a man has his mouth close to the ground that it is impossible to gauge the direction of his cry.

He must have been badly hit—one of those nasty wounds neither so severe that they exhaust the body at once and a man dreams on in a half-swoon, nor so light that a man endures the pain in the hope of becoming well again. Kat thinks he has either a broken pelvis or a shot through the spine. His chest cannot have been injured otherwise he would not have such strength to cry out. And if it were any other kind of wound it would be possible to see him moving.

▶ *To what do the soldiers have to listen?*

▶ *Why do they think the lost injured man is lying on his belly?*

---

**words for everyday use**   sol • ace (säl' is) *n.*, something that eases or relieves; comfort. *When his cat died, Hank was so upset he could draw no <u>solace</u> from his family or friends.*

He grows gradually hoarser. The voice is so strangely pitched that it seems to be everywhere. The first night some of our fellows go out three times to look for him. But when they think they have located him and crawl across, next time they hear the voice it seems to come from somewhere else altogether.

We search in vain until dawn. We scrutinized the field all day with glasses, but discover nothing. On the second day the calls are fainter; that will be because his lips and mouth have become dry.

Our Company Commander has promised next turn of leave with three days extra to anyone who finds him. That is a powerful <u>inducement</u>, but we would do all that is possible without that for his cry is terrible. Kat and Kropp even go out in the afternoon, and Albert gets the lobe of his ear shot off in consequence. It is to no purpose, they come back without him.

◀ What does the commander offer the soldiers if they can find the injured man?

It is easy to understand what he cries. At first he called only for help—the second night he must have had some <u>delirium</u>, he talked with his wife and his children, we often detected the name Elise. Today he merely weeps. By evening the voice dwindles to a croaking. But it persists still through the whole night. We hear it so distinctly because the wind blows toward our line. In the morning when we suppose he must already have long gone to his rest, there comes across to us one last gurgling rattle.

◀ How have the injured man's cries changed over time?

The days are hot and the dead lie unburied. We cannot fetch them all in, if we did we should not know what to do with them. The shells will bury them. Many have their bellies swollen up like balloons. They hiss, belch, and make movements. The gases in them make noises.

◀ What are the soldiers unable to do?

The sky is blue and without clouds. In the evening it grows <u>sultry</u> and the heat rises from the earth. When the wind blows toward us it brings the smell of blood, which is very heavy and sweet. This deathly exhalation from the shell-holes seems to be a mixture of chloroform and <u>putrefaction</u>, and fills us with nausea and retching.

---

**words for everyday use**

in • duce • ment (in düs' mənt) *n.*, motive; incentive. *Our dog's inducement to learn to sit and stay was a small dog biscuit every time he obeyed the command correctly.*

de • lir • i • um (di lir' ē əm) *n.*, temporary state of extreme mental excitement, marked by restlessness, confused speech, and hallucinations. *When Curtis had a high fever he was in a state of delirium and kept mistaking his family members for his classmates.*

sul • try (sul' trē) *adj.*, oppressively hot and moist. *On sultry summer days nothing is as refreshing as a glass of lemonade.*

pu • tre • fac • tion (pyü' trə fak' shən) *n.*, decomposition of organic matter by bacteria, fungi, and oxidation, resulting in the formation of foul-smelling products. *The forgotten banana in the back of the refrigerator had entered a state of putrefaction.*

*

The nights become quiet and the hunt for copper driving-bands and the silken parachutes of the French star-shells[30] begins. Why the driving-bands are so desirable no one knows exactly. The collectors merely assert that they are valuable. Some have collected so many that they will stoop under the weight of them when we go back.

But Haie at least gives a reason. He intends to give them to his girl to supplement her garters. At this the Friesians explode with mirth. They slap their knees: "By Jove though, he's a wit, Haie is, he's got brains." Tjaden especially can hardly contain himself; he takes the largest of the rings in his hand and every now and then puts his leg through it to show how much slack there is.

"Haie, man, she must have legs like, legs—" his thoughts mount somewhat higher "and a behind too she must have, like a—like an elephant!"

He cannot get over it. "I wish I could play hothand with her once, my hat—"

Haie beams, proud that his girl should receive so much appreciation.

"She's a nice bit," he says with self-satisfaction.

The parachutes are turned to more practical uses. According to the size of the bust three or perhaps four will make a blouse. Kropp and I use them as handkerchiefs. The others send them home. If the women could see at what risk these bits of rag are often obtained, they would be horrified.

Kat surprised Tjaden endeavouring with perfect <u>equanimity</u> to knock the driving-band off a dud.[31] If anyone else had tried it the thing would have exploded, but Tjaden always has his luck with him.

▶ What do the butterflies do?

One morning two butterflies play in front of our trench. They are brimstone-butterflies, with red spots on their yellow wings. What can they be looking for here? There is not a plant nor a flower for miles. They settle on the teeth of a skull. The birds too are just as carefree, they have long

---

30. **copper driving-bands . . . French star-shells.** The soldiers take bits from exploded and unexploded bombs and other military devices for souvenirs.
31. **dud.** Bomb that fails to explode

since accustomed themselves to the war. Every morning larks ascend from No Man's Land. A year ago we watched them nesting; the young ones grew up too.

◄ Where have all the rats gone?

We have a spell from the rats in the trench. They are in No Man's Land—we know what for. They grow fat; when we see one we have a crack at it. At night we hear again the rolling behind the enemy lines. All day we have only the normal shelling, so that we are able to repair the trenches. There is always plenty of amusement, the airmen see to that. There are countless fights for us to watch every day.

Battle planes don't trouble us, but the observation planes we hate like the plague; they put the artillery to us. A few minutes after they appear, <u>shrapnel</u> and high-explosives begin to drop on us. We lose eleven men in one day that way, and five of them stretcher-bearers. Two are smashed so that Tjaden remarks you could scrape them off the wall of the trench with a spoon and bury them in a mess-tin. Another has the lower part of his body and his legs torn off. Dead, his chest leans against the side of the trench, his face is lemon-yellow, in his beard still burns a cigarette. It glows until it dies out on his lips.

We put the dead in a large shell-hole. So far there are three layers, one on top of the other.

*

Suddenly the shelling begins to pound again. Soon we are sitting up once more with the rigid tenseness of blank anticipation.

Attack, counter-attack, charge, repulse—these are words, but what things they signify! We have lost a good many men, mostly recruits. Reinforcements have again been sent up to our sector. They are one of the new regiments, composed almost entirely of young fellows just called up. They have had hardly any training, and are sent into the field with only a theoretical knowledge. They do know what a hand-grenade is, it is true, but they have very little idea of cover, and what is most important of all, have no eye for it. A fold in the ground has to be quite eighteen inches high before they can see it.

◄ What type of reinforcements are they sent?

Although we need reinforcement, the recruits give us almost more trouble than they are worth. They are helpless in this grim fighting area, they fall like flies. Modern

◄ What happens to the reinforcements?

**words for everyday use**  shrap • nel (shrap′ nəl) *n.,* artillery shell filled with an explosive charge and many small metal balls designed to explode in the air over the objective; any fragments scattered by such an explosion. *More soldiers died from the jagged bits of <u>shrapnel</u> from the explosion than from the shell's impact.*

trench-warfare demands knowledge and experience; a man must have a feeling for the contours of the ground, an ear for the sound and character of the shells, must be able to decide beforehand where they will drop, how they will burst, and how to shelter from them.

The young recruits of course know none of these things. They get killed simply because they hardly can tell shrapnel from high-explosive, they are mown down because they are listening anxiously to the roar of the big coalboxes falling in the rear, and miss the light, piping whistle of the low spreading daisy-cutters.[32] They flock together like sheep instead of scattering, and even the wounded are shot down like hares by the airmen.

Their pale turnip faces, their pitiful clenched hands, the fine courage of these poor devils, the desperate charges and attacks made by the poor brave wretches, who are so terrified that they dare not cry out loudly, but with battered chests, with torn bellies, arms and legs only whimper softly for their mothers and cease as soon as one looks at them.

▶ What do the dead faces of the reinforcements look like?

▶ What does Paul want to do to the new recruits?

Their sharp, downy, dead faces have the awful expressionlessness of dead children.

It brings a lump into the throat to see how they go over, and run and fall. A man would like to spank them, they are so stupid, and to take them by the arm and lead them away from here where they have no business to be. They wear grey coats and trousers and boots, but for most of them the uniform is far too big, it hangs on their limbs, their shoulders are too narrow, their bodies too slight; no uniform was ever made to these childish measurements.

Between five and ten recruits fall to every old hand.

A surprise gas-attack carries off a lot of them. They have not yet learned what to do. We found one dug-out full of them, with blue heads and black lips. Some of them in a shell-hole took off their masks too soon; they did not know that the gas lies longest in the hollows; when they saw others on top without masks they pulled theirs off too and swallowed enough to scorch their lungs. Their condition is hopeless, they choke to death with haemorrhages[33] and suffocation.

\*

▶ Whom does Paul find in one trench?

In one part of the trench I suddenly run into Himmelstoss. We dive into the same dug-out. Breathless we are all lying one beside the other waiting for the charge.

---

32. **daisy-cutters.** Type of explosive device that has a scattering-type of explosion, used to kill enemy soldiers
33. **haemorrhages.** Hemorrhages, heavy bleeding (in the lungs)

When we run out again, although I am very excited, I suddenly think: "Where's Himmelstoss?" Quickly I jump back into the dug-out and find him with a small scratch lying in a corner pretending to be wounded. His face looks <u>sullen</u>. He is in a panic; he is new to it too. But it makes me mad that the young recruits should be out there and he here.

◀ What is Himmelstoss doing?

"Get out!" I spit.

He does not stir, his lips quiver, his moustache twitches. "Out!" I repeat.

◀ What does Paul force Himmelstoss to do?

He draws up his legs, crouches back against the wall, and shows his teeth like a cur.[34]

I seize him by the arm and try to pull him up. He barks. This is too much for me. I grab him by the neck and shake him like a sack, his head jerks from side to side.

"You lump, will you get out—you hound, you skunk, sneak out of it, would you?" His eye becomes glassy, I knock his head against the wall—"You cow"—I kick him in the ribs—"You swine"—I push him toward the door and shove him out head first.

Another wave of our attack has just come up. A lieutenant is with them. He sees us and yells: "Forward, forward, join in, follow." And the word of command does what all my banging could not. Himmelstoss hears the order, looks round him as if awakened, and follows on.

I come after and watch him go over. Once more he is the smart Himmelstoss of the parade-ground, he has even outstripped the lieutenant and is far ahead.

◀ What does Himmelstoss do once he is out of the trench?

Bombardment, barrage, curtain-fire, mines, gas, tanks, machine-guns, hand-grenades—words, words, but they hold the horror of the world.

Our faces are encrusted, our thoughts are devastated, we are weary to death; when the attack comes we shall have to strike many of the men with our fists to waken them and make them come with us—our eyes are burnt, our hands are torn, our knees bleed, our elbows are raw.

How long has it been? Weeks—months—years? Only days. We see time pass in the colourless faces of the dying, we cram food into us, we run, we throw, we shoot, we kill,

---

34. **cur.** Dog

**words for everyday use**  sul • len (sul' ən) *adj.,* showing resentment and ill humor by morose, unsociable withdrawal. *I hoped that despite his <u>sullen</u> expression I would be able to convince him to cheer up and join me for a walk.*

we lie about, we are feeble and spent, and nothing supports us but the knowledge that there are still feebler, still more spent, still more helpless ones there who, with staring eyes, look upon us as gods that escape death many times.

▶ What do the soldiers try to teach the new recruits?

In the few hours of rest we teach them. "There, see that waggle-top?[35] That's a mortar coming. Keep down, it will go clean over. But if it comes this way, then run for it. You can run from a mortar."

We sharpen their ears to the malicious, hardly audible buzz of the smaller shells that are not easily distinguishable. They must pick them out from the general din by their insect-like hum—we explain to them that these are far more dangerous than the big ones that can be heard long beforehand.

We show them how to take cover from aircraft, how to simulate a dead man when one is overrun in an attack, how to time hand-grenades so that they explode half a second before hitting the ground; we teach them to fling themselves into holes as quick as lightning before the shells with instantaneous fuses; we show them how to clean up a trench with a handful of bombs; we explain the difference between the fuse-length of the enemy bombs and our own; we put them wise to the sound of gas shells;—show them all the tricks that can save them from death.

They listen, they are docile—but when it begins again, in their excitement they do everything wrong.

▶ What happens to Haie?

Haie Westhus drags off with a great wound in his back through which the lung pulses at every breath. I can only press his hand; "It's all up, Paul," he groans and bites his arm because of the pain.

We see men living with their skulls blown open; we see soldiers run with their two feet cut off, they stagger on their splintered stumps into the next shell-hole; a lance-corporal crawls a mile and a half on his hands dragging his smashed knee after him; another goes to the dressing station and over his clasped hands bulge his intestines; we see men without mouths, without jaws, without faces; we find

---

35. **waggle-top.** Mortar shell that wobbles as it falls

| words for everyday use | ma • li • cious (mə lish′ əs) adj., spiteful; intentionally mischievous or harmful. *The beautiful building was the target of malicious vandalism.* | simulate the look of dried savannah grass so it can better sneak up on its prey. |
|---|---|---|
| | sim • u • late (sim′ yü lāt′) vt., have or take on the external appearance of; look or act like. *The lion's golden fur helps it* | doc • ile (däs′ əl) adj., easy to manage or discipline; submissive. *It was hard to believe such a big, terrifying-looking dog could be so docile.* |

one man who has held the artery of his arm in his teeth for two hours in order not to bleed to death. The sun goes down, night comes, the shells whine, life is at an end.

Still the little piece of convulsed earth in which we lie is held. We have yielded no more than a few hundred yards of it as a prize to the enemy. But on every yard there lies a dead man.

◀ How much progress has the enemy made?

\*

We have just been relieved. The wheels roll beneath us, we stand dully, and when the call "Mind—wire" comes, we bend our knees. It was summer when we came up, the trees were still green, now it is autumn and the night is grey and wet. The lorries stop, we climb out—a confused heap, a remnant of many names. On either side stand people, dark, calling out the numbers of the brigades, the battalions. And at each call a little group separates itself off, a small handful of dirty, <u>pallid</u> soldiers, a dreadfully small handful, and a dreadfully small remnant.

◀ At last, what happens to the soldiers?

Now someone is calling the number of our company, it is, yes, the Company Commander, he has come through, then; his arm is in a sling. We go over to him and I recognize Kat and Albert, we stand together, lean against each other, and look at one another.

And we hear the number of our company called again and again. He will call a long time, they do not hear him in the hospitals and shell-holes.

Once again: "Second Company, this way!" And then more softly: "Nobody else, Second Company?"

He is silent, and then huskily he says: "Is that all?" and gives the order: "Number!"

The morning is grey, it was still summer when we came up, and we were one hundred and fifty strong. Now we freeze, it is autumn, the leaves rustle, the voices flutter out wearily: "One—two—three—four—" and cease at thirty-two. And there is a long silence before the voice asks: "Anyone else?"—and waits and then says softly: "In squads—" and then breaks off and is only able to finish: "Second Company—" with difficulty: "Second Company—march easy!"

◀ How many men were in Paul's company? How many are left?

A line, a short line trudges off into the morning.

Thirty-two men.

| words for everyday use | **pal • lid** (pal' id) *adj.*, faint in color; pale; wan. *After her long illness, Betty's skin was* <u>*pallid*</u>. |
| --- | --- |

## Respond to the Selection

What experiences have you had with your friends that have brought you closer together?

## Investigate, Inquire, and Imagine

**Recall:** GATHERING FACTS

1a. What types of things do Kat, Haie, and Detering plan to do after the war? What do Paul, Kropp, and Müller plan to do after the war? What does Kropp say the war has done to him and the younger men?

2a. What happens after the soldiers are bombarded at the front for many days? What happens to the enemy's attack? Whom are the soldiers sent as reinforcements, and what happens to most of the reinforcements?

3a. What are some of the hardships and horrors that Paul and his fellow soldiers experience in battle?

**Interpret:** FINDING MEANING

1b. In what ways are Paul and his classmates different from Kat, Haie, and Detering? Why do their plans differ so greatly? When Paul says of his classmates, "We believe in the war," what does he mean? In what way do he and his classmates believe in the war?

2b. Why do you think the enemy launches a bombardment before the attack? Explain whether either side seems to be making much progress. Paul says the reinforcements "have the awful expressionlessness of dead children." In what way are they like children when compared with Paul and his classmates even though they are only a couple of years younger?

3b. Describing the soldiers' reaction to all the horrors around them, Paul says, "We are insensible, dead men, who through some trick, some dreadful magic, are still able to run and kill." In what way are Paul and his fellow soldiers like dead men?

**Analyze:** TAKING THINGS APART

4a. Paul says, "We are forlorn like children, and experienced like old men, we are crude and sorrowful and superficial—I believe we are lost." In fact, the generation of young men who fought in World War I were sometimes called the "lost generation." Using quotations from the text, explain the way in which Paul and his classmates are lost.

**Synthesize:** BRINGING THINGS TOGETHER

→ 4b. Imagine that the war ends in the next chapter of this novel. Predict what you think Paul and his classmates would do after the war. How would they be different? What things in life might they rediscover?

**Evaluate:** MAKING JUDGMENTS

5a. Using examples from the text to support your opinion, explain who is winning the war and who is losing.

**Extend:** CONNECTING IDEAS

→ 5b. What would you do if you were a soldier fighting a losing battle? What might some of your options be?

## Understanding Literature

THEME. A **theme** is a central idea in a literary work. One theme in *All Quiet on the Western Front* is comradeship or friendship. Citing passages from Chapter 5, explain who Paul considers to be his closest comrade. How does he feel about this person? Why might friendship become so important in war?

IMAGE AND IMAGERY. An **image** is language that creates a concrete representation of an object or an experience. An image is also the vivid mental picture created in the reader's mind by that language. The images in a work are referred to, collectively, as the work's **imagery.** Paul says, "Bombardment, barrage, curtain-fire, mines, gas, tanks, machine-guns, hand-grenades—words, words, but they hold the horror of the world." Indeed, *All Quiet on the Western Front* is well known for its use of vivid and horrifying war imagery. List some examples of war imagery that you found to be most vivid and horrifying. Why do you think Remarque makes use of such imagery?

PERSONIFICATION. **Personification** is a figure of speech in which an idea, animal, or thing is described as if it were a person. Explain what is personified in the following passage. "We do not fight, we defend ourselves against annihilation. It is not against men that we fling our bombs, what do we know of men in this moment when Death is hunting us down—now, for the first time in three days we can see his face, now for the first time in three days we can oppose him; we feel a mad anger."

# Chapter VII

They have taken us farther back than usual to a field depot[1] so that we can be re-organized. Our company needs more than a hundred reinforcements.

In the meantime, when we are off duty, we <u>loaf</u> around. After a couple of days Himmelstoss comes up to us. He has had the bounce knocked out of him since he has been in the trenches and wants to get on good terms with us. I am willing, because I saw how he brought Haie Westhus in when he was hit in the back. Besides he's decent enough to treat us in the canteen when we are out of funds. Only Tjaden is still reserved and suspicious.

But he is won over, too, when Himmelstoss tells us that he is taking the place of the sergeant-cook who has gone on leave. As a proof he produces on the spot two pounds of sugar for us and a half-pound of butter specially for Tjaden. He even sees to it that we are detailed the next two or three days to the cook-house for potato and turnip peeling. The grub he gives us there is real officers' fare.

Thus momentarily we have the two things a soldier needs for contentment: good food and rest. That's not much when one comes to think of it. A few years ago we would have despised ourselves terribly. But now we are almost happy. It is all a matter of habit—even the front-line.

Habit is the explanation of why we seem to forget things so quickly. Yesterday we were under fire, today we act the fool and go <u>foraging</u> through the countryside, tomorrow we go up to the trenches again. We forget nothing really. But so long as we have to stay here in the field, the front-line days, when they are past, sink down in us like a stone; they are too grievous for us to be able to reflect on them at once. If we did that, we should have been destroyed long ago. I soon found out this much:—terror can be endured so long as a man simply ducks;—but it kills, if a man thinks about it.

Just as we turn into animals when we go up to the line, because that is the only thing which brings us through

----
1. **field depot.** Station for assembling either recruits for training or combat replacements for assignment to a unit

▶ Why is Paul willing to be on good terms with Himmelstoss now?

▶ In what way does Himmelstoss win over Tjaden?

▶ What cannot the soldiers reflect on while they are still in the field?

▶ What do the soldiers turn into when at the front? What do they turn into when they are resting?

**words for everyday use**

loaf (lōf) *vi.*, spend time idly; loiter or lounge about. *On Saturday mornings, I like to <u>loaf</u> about until noon, but my sister gets up early.*

for • age (fôr′ ij) *vi.*, search for food or provisions. *People can survive in the forest by <u>foraging</u>, finding food, water, and shelter there.*

safely, so we turn into wags[2] and loafers when we are resting. We can do nothing else, it is a sheer necessity. We want to live at any price; so we cannot burden ourselves with feelings which, though they might be ornamental enough in peace-time, would be out of place here. Kemmerich is dead, Haie Westhus is dying, they will have a job with Hans Kramer's body at the Judgment Day, piecing it together after a direct hit; Martens has no legs anymore, Meyer is dead, Max is dead, Beyer is dead, Hämmerling is dead, there are a hundred and twenty wounded men lying somewhere or other; it is a damnable business, but what has it to do with us now—we live. If it were possible for us to save them, then it would be seen how much we cared—we would have a shot at it though we went under ourselves; for we can be damned <u>quixotic</u> when we like; fear we do not know much about—terror of death, yes; but that is a different matter, that is physical.

But our comrades are dead, we cannot help them, they have their rest—and who knows what is waiting for us? We will make ourselves comfortable and sleep, and eat as much as we can stuff into our bellies, and drink and smoke so that hours are not wasted. Life is short.

*

The terror of the front sinks deep down when we turn our backs upon it; we make grim, coarse jests about it, when a man dies, then we say he has nipped off his turd, and so we speak of everything; that keeps us from going mad; as long as we take it that way we maintain our own resistance.

◀ What keeps the soldiers from going mad?

But we do not forget. It's all rot that they put in the war-news about the good humour of the troops, how they are arranging dances almost before they are out of the front-line. We don't act like that because we are in a good humour: we are in a good humour because otherwise we should go to pieces. Even so we cannot hold out much longer; our humour becomes more bitter every month.

◀ Why are the soldiers in good humor? What is happening to their humor?

And this I know: all these things that now, while we are still in the war, sink down in us like a stone, after the war

---

2. **wags.** Comical or humorous people; jokers

shall waken again, and then shall begin the disentanglement of life and death.

The days, the weeks, the years out here shall come back again, and our dead comrades shall then stand up again and march with us, our heads shall be clear, we shall have a purpose, and so we shall march, our dead comrades beside us, the years at the Front behind us:—against whom, against whom?

▶ What will come back to the soldiers after the war?

*

▶ What are the soldiers amazed by?

Some time ago there was an army theatre in these parts. Coloured posters of the performances are still sticking on a hoarding.[3] With wide eyes Kropp and I stand in front of it. We can hardly credit that such things still exist. A girl in a light summer dress, with a red patent-leather belt about her hips! She is standing with one hand on a railing and with the other she holds a straw hat. She wears white stockings and white shoes, fine buckle shoes with high heels. Behind her smiles the blue sea with white-horses, at the side is a bright bay. She is a lovely girl with a delicate nose, red lips, and slender legs, wonderfully clean and well cared for, she certainly baths twice a day and never has any dirt under her nails. At most perhaps a bit of sand from the beach.

Beside her stands a man in white trousers, a blue jacket, and sailor's cap; but he interests us much less.

The girl on the poster is a wonder to us. We have quite forgotten that there are such things, and even now we hardly believe our eyes. We have seen nothing like it for years, nothing like it for happiness, beauty and joy. That is peace-time, that is as it should be; we feel excited.

▶ What is Paul's reaction to the picture of the woman?

"Just look at those thin shoes though, she couldn't march many miles in those," I say, and then begin to feel silly, for it is absurd to stand in front of a picture like this and think of nothing but marching.

"How old would she be?" Kropp asks.

"About twenty-two at the most," I hazard.

"Then she would be older than us! She is not more than seventeen, let me tell you!"

It gives us goose flesh.

"That would be good, Albert, what do you think?"

He nods. "I have some white trousers at home too."

"White trousers," say I, "but a girl like that—"

▶ Why do Paul and Kropp tear off the picture of the man?

We look <u>askance</u> at one another. There's not much to boast of here—two ragged, stained, and dirty uniforms. It is hopeless to compete.

---

3. **hoarding.** Billboard

So we proceed to tear the young man with the white trousers off the hoarding, taking care not to damage the girl. That is something toward it.

"We could go and get deloused, anyway," Kropp then suggests.

I am not very enthusiastic because it doesn't do one's clothes any good and a man is lousy again inside two hours. But when we have considered the picture once more, I declare myself willing. I go even farther.

"We might see if we could get a clean shirt as well—"

"Socks might be better," says Albert, not without reason.

"Yes, socks too perhaps. Let's go and explore a bit."

Then Leer and Tjaden stroll up; they look at the poster and immediately the conversation becomes smutty. Leer was the first of our class to have intercourse, and he gave stirring details of it. After his fashion he enjoys himself over the picture, and Tjaden supports him nobly.

It does not distress us exactly. Who isn't smutty is no soldier; it merely does not suit us at the moment, so we edge away and march off to the delousing station with the same feeling as if it were a swell gentlemen's outfitters.[4]

\* 

The houses in which we are billeted[5] lie near the canal. On the other side of the canal there are ponds flanked with poplars;—on the other side of the canal there are women too.

The houses on our side have been abandoned. On the other side though one occasionally sees inhabitants.

In the evening we go swimming. Three women come strolling along the bank. They walk slowly and don't look away, although we have no bathing suits.

◀ *Whom do the men see when they go swimming?*

Leer calls out to them. They laugh and stop to watch us. We fling remarks at them in broken French, anything that comes into our heads, hastily and all jumbled together, anything to detain them. They are not specially wonderful pieces, but then where are such to be had about here?

There is one slim little brunette, her teeth gleam when she laughs. She has quick movements, her dress swings loosely about her legs. Although the water is cold we are

---

4. **outfitters.** Clothing maker
5. **billeted.** Quartered or lodged

**words for everyday use**

a • skance (ə skans') *adv.,* with suspicion or disapproval. *Fran's mother looked <u>askance</u> at her when she came home with her jeans muddy up to her knees.*

▶ *What does Tjaden do to get the women's attention?*

very jovial and do our best to interest them so that they will stay. We try to make jokes and they answer with things we cannot understand; we laugh and beckon. Tjaden is more crafty. He runs into the house, gets a loaf of army bread and holds it up.

That's produces a great effect. They nod and beckon us to come over. But we don't dare to do that. It is forbidden to cross to the opposite bank. There are sentries on all the bridges. It's impossible without a pass. So we indicate that they should come over to us; but they shake their heads and point to the bridge. They are not allowed to pass either. They turn back and walk slowly down the canal, keeping along the tow-path[6] all the way. We accompany them swimming. After a few hundred yards they turn off and point to a house that stands a little distance away among the trees and shrubbery.

Leer asks if they live there.

They laugh—sure, that's their house.

We call out to them that we would like to come, sometime when the guards cannot see us. At night. Tonight.

They raise their hands, put them together, rest their faces on them and shut their eyes. They understand. The slim brunette does a two-step. The blonde girl twitters: "Bread—good—"

Eagerly we assure them that we will bring some with us. And other tasty bits too, we roll our eyes and try to explain with our hands. Leer nearly drowns trying to demonstrate a sausage. If it were necessary we would promise them a whole quartermaster's store. They go off and frequently turn and look back. We climb out on the bank on our side of the canal and watch to see whether they go into the house, for they might easily have been lying. Then we swim back.

No one can cross the bridge without leave, so we will simply have to swim over tonight. We are full of excitement. We cannot last out without a drink, so we go to the canteen where there is beer and a kind of punch.

We drink punch and tell one another lying tales of our experiences. Each man gladly believes the other man's

---

6. **tow-path.** Path used to move goods along a canal by tying ropes to a barge and then dragging the barge using animals or motor power

**words for everyday use**

jo • vi • al (jō′ vē əl) *adj.,* full of hearty, playful good humor. *Ahmed's jovial mood was infectious; soon we all were laughing along with him.*

story, only waiting impatiently till he can cap it with a taller one. Our hands are fidgety, we smoke countless cigarettes, until Kropp says: "We might as well take them a few cigarettes too." So we put some inside our caps to keep them.

The sky turns apple-green. There are four of us, but only three can go; we must shake off Tjaden, so ply him[7] with rum and punch until he rocks. As it turns dark we go to our billets, Tjaden in the centre. We are glowing and full of a lust for adventure.

The little brunette is mine, we have settled all that.

Tjaden drops on his sack of straw and snores. Once he wakes up and grins so craftily that we are alarmed and begin to think he is cheating, and that we have given him the punch to no purpose. Then he drops back again and sleeps on.

We each get hold of a whole army loaf and wrap it up in newspaper. The cigarettes we put in too, as well as three good rations of liver-sausage that were issued to us this evening. That makes a decent present.

◀ What do the men plan to bring to the French women? How must they carry their gift?

We stow the things carefully in our boots; we have to take them to protect our feet against treading on wire and broken glass on the other bank. As we must swim for it we can take no other clothes. But it is not far and quite dark.

We make off with our boots in our hands. Swiftly we slip into the water, lie on our backs and swim, holding the boots with their contents up over our heads.

We climb out carefully on the opposite bank, take out the packages and put on our boots. We put the things under our arms. And so, all wet and naked, clothed only in our boots, we break into a trot. We find the house at once. It lies among the trees. Leer trips over a root and skins his elbows.

"No matter," he says gaily.

The windows are shuttered. We slip round the house and try to peer through the cracks. Then we grow impatient. Suddenly Kropp hesitates:

"What if there's a Major with them?"

"Then we just clear off," grins Leer, "he can try to read our regimental numbers here," and smacks his behind.

The door of the courtyard stands open. Our boots make a great clatter. The house door opens, a chink of light shines through and a woman cries out in a scared voice.

"Ssh, ssh! camerade—bon ami—" we say, and show our packages protestingly.

---

7. **ply him.** Keep supplying him

The other two are now on the scene, the door opens and the light floods over us. They recognize us and all three burst into laughter at our appearance. They rock and sway in the doorway, they laugh so much. How supple their movements are.

"Un moment—" They disappear and throw us bits of clothing which we gladly wrap round ourselves. Then we are allowed in. A small lamp burns in their room, which is warm and smells a little of perfume. We unwrap our parcels and hand them over to the women. Their eyes shine, it is obvious that they are hungry.

▶ What can the men tell about the women?

Then we all become rather embarrassed. Leer makes the gestures of eating, and then they come to life again and bring out plates and knives and fall to on the food, and they hold up every slice of livered sausage and admire it before they eat it, and we sit proudly by.

They overwhelm us with their chatter;—we understand very little of it, but we listen and the words sound friendly. No doubt we all look very young. The little brunette strokes my hair and says what all French women say: "La guerre— grand malheur—pauvres garçons—"[8]

▶ What does the brunette call Paul?

I hold her arm tightly and press my lips into the palm of her hand. Her fingers close round my face. Close above me are her bewildering eyes, the soft brown of her skin and her red lips. Her mouth speaks words I do not understand. Nor do I fully understand her eyes; they seem to say more than we anticipated when we came here.

There are other rooms adjoining. In passing I see Leer, he has made a great hit with the blonde. He's an old hand at the game. But I—I am lost in remoteness, in weakness, and in a passion to which I yield myself trustingly. My desires are strangely compounded of yearning and misery. I feel giddy, there is nothing here that a man can hold on to. We have left our boots at the door, they have given us slippers instead, and now nothing remains to recall for me the <u>assurance</u> and self-confidence of the soldier; no rifle, no belt, no tunic, no cap. I let myself drop into the unknown, come what may—yet, in spite of all, I feel somewhat afraid.

▶ Why doesn't Paul have any self-assurance?

---

8. "**La guerre—grand malheur—pauvres garçons—**." French for "The war—great unhappiness—poor boys"

---

**words for everyday use**  as • sur • ance (ə shûr′ əns) *n.,* sureness; confidence. *Melinda had great <u>assurance</u> in her artistic abilities—she could paint almost anything vividly and realistically.*

The little brunette contracts her brows when she is thinking; but when she talks they are still. And often sound does not quite become a word but suffocates or floats away over me half finished; an arch, a pathway, a comet. What have I known of it—what do I know of it?— The words of this foreign tongue, that I hardly understand, they caress me to a quietness, in which the room grows dim, and dissolves in the half light, only the face above me lives and is clear.

How various is a face; but an hour ago it was strange and it is now touched with a tenderness that comes, not from it, but from out of the night, the world and the blood, all these things seem to shine in it together. The objects in the room are touched by it and transformed, they become isolated, and I feel almost awed at the sight of my clear skin when the light of the lamp falls upon it and the cool, brown hand passes over it.

◀ What does Paul feel toward this woman? What is this experience different from?

How different this is from the conditions in the soldiers' brothels, to which we are allowed to go, and where we have to wait in long queues. I wish I never thought of them; but desire turns my mind to them involuntarily and I am afraid for it might be impossible ever to be free of them again.

But then I feel the lips of the little brunette and press myself against them, my eyes close, I want it all to fall from me, war and terror and grossness, in order to awaken young and happy; I think of the picture of the girl on the poster and, for a moment, believe that my life depends on winning her. And if I press ever deeper into the arms that embrace me, perhaps a miracle may happen. . . .

· · · · · ·

So, after a time we find ourselves reassembled again. Leer is in high spirits. We pull on our boots and take our leave warmly. The night air cools our hot bodies. The rustling poplars loom large in the darkness. The moon floats in the heavens and in the waters of the canal. We do not run, we walk beside one another with long strides.

"That was worth a ration-loaf," says Leer.

I cannot trust myself to speak, I am not in the least happy.

Then we hear footsteps and dodge behind a shrub.

The steps come nearer, close by us. We see a naked soldier, in boots, just like ourselves; he has a package under his arm, and gallops onward. It is Tjaden in full course. He has disappeared already.

We laugh. In the morning he will curse us.

Unobserved, we arrive again at our sacks of straw.

▶ What does Paul learn in the orderly room?

I am called to the Orderly Room. The Company Commander gives me a leave-pass and a travel-pass[9] and wishes me a good journey. I look to see how much leave I have got. Seventeen days—fourteen days leave and three days for travelling. It is not enough and I ask whether I cannot have five days for travelling. Bertinck points to my pass. There I see that I am not to return to the front immediately. After my leave I have to report for a course of training to a camp on the moors.

The others envy me. Kat gives me good advice, and tells me I ought to try to get a base-job. "If you're smart, you'll hang on to it."

I would rather not have gone for another eight days; we are to stay here that much longer and it is good here.

▶ Why is Paul gloomy?

Naturally I have to stand the others drinks at the canteen. We are all a little bit drunk. I become gloomy: I will be away for six weeks—that is lucky, of course, but what may happen before I get back? Shall I meet all these fellows again? Already Haie and Kemmerich have gone—who will the next be?

As we drink, I look at each of them in turn. Albert sits beside me and smokes, he is cheerful, we have always been together;—opposite squats Kat, with his drooping shoulders, his broad thumb, and calm voice—Müller with the projecting teeth and the booming laugh; Tjaden with his mousey eyes;—Leer who has grown a full beard and looks at least forty.

Over us hangs a dense cloud of smoke. Where would a soldier be without tobacco? The canteen is his refuge, and beer is far more than a drink, it is a token that a man can move his limbs and stretch in safety. We do it ceremonially, we stretch our legs out in front of us and spit deliberately, that is the only way. How it all rises up before a man when he is going away the next morning!

▶ What is the brunette's reaction when Paul says he is going on leave? What does Paul realize?

At night we go again to the other side of the canal. I am almost afraid to tell the little brunette that I am going away, and when I return we will be far from here; we will never see one another again. But she merely nods and takes no special notice. At first I am at a loss to understand, then it suddenly dawns on me. Yes, Leer is right: if I were going up to the front, then she would have called me again "pauvre garçon"; but merely going on leave—she does not want to hear about that, that is not nearly so interesting.

---

9. **leave-pass and a travel-pass.** Official papers giving Paul permission to leave the front for a vacation

May she go to the devil with her chattering talk. A man dreams of a miracle and wakes up to loaves of bread.

Next morning, after I have been de-loused, I go to the rail head. Albert and Kat come with me. At the halt we learn that it will be a couple of hours yet before the train leaves. The other two have to go back to duty. We take leave of one another.

"Good luck, Kat: good luck, Albert."

They go off and wave once or twice. Their figures dwindle. I know their every step and movement; I would recognize them at any distance. Then they disappear. I sit down on my pack and wait.

Suddenly I become filled with a consuming impatience to be gone.

*

I lie down on many a station platform; I stand before many a soup-kitchen; I squat on many a bench;—then at last the landscape becomes disturbing, mysterious, and familiar. It glides past the western windows with its villages, their thatched roofs like caps, pulled over the whitewashed, half-timbered houses, its corn-fields, gleaming like mother-of-pearl in the slanting light, its orchards, its barns and old lime trees.

The names of the stations begin to take on meaning and my heart trembles. The train stamps and stamps onward. I stand at the window and hold on to the frame. These names mark the boundaries of my youth.

Smooth meadows, fields, farm-yards; a solitary team moves against the sky-line along the road that runs parallel to the horizon—a barrier, before which peasants stand waiting, girls waving, children playing on the embankment, roads, leading into the country, smooth roads without artillery.

It is evening, and if the train did not rattle I should cry out. The plain unfolds itself.

In the distance, the soft, blue silhouette of the mountain ranges begins to appear. I recognize the characteristic outline of the Dolbenberg, a jagged comb, springing up precipitously from the limits of the forests. Behind it should lie the town.

But now the sun streams through the world, dissolving everything in its golden-red light, the train swings round one curve and then another;—for away, in a long line one behind the other, stand the poplars, unsubstantial, swaying and dark, fashioned out of shadow, light, and desire.

The field swings round as the train encircles it, and the intervals between the trees diminish; the trees become a block and for a moment I see one only—then they reappear from behind the foremost tree and stand out a long line against the sky until they are hidden by the first houses.

A street-crossing. I stand by the window, I cannot drag myself away. The others put their baggage ready for getting out. I repeat to myself the name of the street that we cross over—Bremerstrasse—Bremerstrasse—

▶ How does Paul feel when he sees the street and subway?

Below there are cyclists, lorries, men; it is a grey street and a grey subway;—it affects me as though it were my mother.

Then the train stops, and there is the station with noise and cries and signboards. I pick up my pack and fasten the straps, I take my rifle in my hand and stumble down the steps.

On the platform I look round; I know no one among all the people hurrying to and fro. A red-cross sister offers me something to drink. I turn away, she smiles at me too foolishly, so obsessed with her own importance: "Just look, I am giving a soldier coffee!"—She calls me "Comrade," but I will have none of it.

Outside in front of the station the stream roars alongside the street, it rushes foaming from the sluices[10] of the mill bridge. There stands the old, square watchtower, in front of it the great <u>mottled</u> lime tree and behind it the evening.

Here we have often sat—how long ago it is—we have passed over this bridge and breathed the cool, acid smell of the <u>stagnant</u> water; we have leaned over the still water on this side of the lock,[11] where the green creepers and weeds hang from the piles of the bridge;—and on hot days we rejoiced in the spouting foam on the other side of the lock and told tales about our school-teachers.

I pass over the bridge, I look right and left; the water is as full of weeds as ever, and it still shoots over in gleaming arches; in the tower building laundresses still stand with bare arms as they used to over the clean linen, and the

---

10. **sluices.** Artificial channel or passage for water having a gate or valve at its head to regulate the flow
11. **lock.** Enclosed part of a canal equipped with a gate so the water level can be changed to raise or lower boats from one level to another

---

**words for everyday use**

**mot • tled** (mät' 'ld) *adj.,* marked with blotches, streaks, and spots of different colors or shades. *The trout were <u>mottled</u> brown, black, and gray, providing them with excellent camouflage in the stony river.*

**stag • nant** (stag' nənt) *adj.,* foul from lack of movement. *The small pond's water turned <u>stagnant</u> and green from algae during the hot summer months.*

heat from the ironing pours out through the open windows. Dogs trot along the narrow street, before the doors of the houses people stand and follow me with their gaze as I pass by, dirty and heavy laden.

In this confectioner's we used to eat ices, and there we learned to smoke cigarettes. Walking down the street I know every shop, the grocer's, the chemist's, the baker's. Then at last I stand before the brown door with its worn latch and my hand grows heavy. I open the door and a strange coolness comes out to meet me, my eyes are dim.

The stairs creak under my boots. Upstairs a door rattles, someone is looking over the railing. It is the kitchen door that was opened, they are cooking potato-cakes, the house reeks of it, and today of course is Saturday; that will be my sister leaning over. For a moment I am shy and lower my head, then I take off my helmet and look up. Yes, it is my eldest sister.

◀ What does Paul smell when he arrives back home? Whom does he see first?

"Paul," she cries, "Paul—"

I nod, my pack bumps against the banisters; my rifle is so heavy.

She pulls a door open and calls: "Mother, mother, Paul is here."

I can go no further—mother, mother, Paul is here.

I lean against the wall and grip my helmet and rifle. I hold them as tight as I can, but I cannot take another step, the staircase fades before my eyes, I support myself with the butt of my rifle against my feet and clench my teeth fiercely, but I cannot speak a word, my sister's call has made me powerless, I can do nothing, I struggle to make myself laugh, to speak, but no word comes, and so I stand on the steps, miserable, helpless, paralysed, and against my will the tears run down my cheeks.

My sister comes back and says: "Why, what is the matter?"

Then I pull myself together and stagger on to the landing. I lean my rifle in a corner, I set my pack against the wall, place my helmet on it and fling down my equipment and baggage. Then I say fiercely: "Bring me a handkerchief."

She gives me one from the cupboard and I dry my face. Above me on the wall hangs the glass case with the coloured butterflies that once I collected.

---

**words for everyday use**  stag • ger (stag′ ər) vi., move unsteadily, as though about to collapse. *Obviously in a great deal of pain, the injured player staggered off the field.*

▶ What does Paul learn about his mother?

Now I hear my mother's voice. It comes from the bedroom.

"Is she in bed?" I ask my sister.

"She is ill—" she replies.

I go into her, give her my hand and say as calmly as I can: "Here I am, Mother."

She lies still in the dim light. Then she asks anxiously: "Are you wounded?" and I feel her searching glance.

"No, I have got leave."

My mother is very pale. I am afraid to make a light.

"Here I lie now," says she, "and cry instead of being glad."

"Are you sick, Mother?" I ask.

"I am going to get up a little today," she says and turns to my sister, who is continually running to the kitchen to watch that the food does not burn: "And put out that jar of preserved whortleberries[12]—you like that, don't you?" she asks me.

"Yes, Mother, I haven't had any for a long time."

"We might almost have known you were coming," laughs my sister, "there is just your favourite dish, potato-cakes, and even whortleberries to go with them too."

"And it is Saturday," I add.

"Sit here beside me," says my mother.

She looks at me. Her hands are white and sickly and frail compared with mine. We say very little and I am thankful that she asks nothing. What ought I to say? Everything I could have wished for has happened. I have come out of it safely and sit here beside her. And in the kitchen stands my sister preparing supper and singing.

"Dear boy," says my mother softly.

▶ Why does Paul's mother saying "dear boy" mean so much to him? What does he know about the whortleberries?

We were never very <u>demonstrative</u> in our family; poor folk who toil and are full of cares are not so. It is not their way to protest what they already know. When my mother says to me "dear boy," it means much more than when another uses it. I know well enough that the jar of whortleberries is the only one they have had for months, and that she has kept it for me; and the somewhat stale cakes that she gives me too. She must have got them cheap some time and put them all by for me.

---

12. **whortleberries.** Type of European blueberry

**words for everyday use**
de • mon • stra • tive (di män' strə tiv) *adj.,* showing feelings openly and frankly. *While my family is very reserved, Ricky's family is very open and <u>demonstrative</u>.*

I sit by her bed, and through the window the chestnut trees in the beer garden[13] opposite glow in brown and gold. I breathe deeply and say over to myself:—"You are at home, you are at home." But a sense of strangeness will not leave me, I cannot feel at home amongst these things. There is my mother, there is my sister, there my case of butterflies, and there the mahogany piano—but I am not myself there. There is a distance, a veil between us.

◀ What won't leave Paul? What does he feel exists between him and his family?

I go and fetch my pack to the bedside and turn out the things I have brought—a whole Edamer cheese, that Kat provided me with, two loaves of army bread, three-quarters of a pound of butter, two tins of livered sausage, a pound of dripping and a little bag of rice.

"I suppose you can make some use of that—"

They nod.

"Is it pretty bad for food here?" I enquire.

"Yes, there's not much. Do you get enough out there?"

I smile and point to the things I have brought. "Not always quite as much as that, of course, but we fare reasonably well."

Erna takes away the food. Suddenly my mother seizes hold of my hand and asks <u>falteringly</u>: "Was it very bad out there, Paul?"

◀ What does Paul's mother ask him? What does he say in response?

Mother, what should I answer to that! You would not understand, you could never realize it. And you never shall realize it. Was it bad, you ask.—You, Mother,—I shake my head and say: "No, Mother, not so very. There are always a lot of us together so it isn't so bad."

"Yes, but Heinrich Bredemeyer was here just lately and said it was terrible out there now, with the gas and all the rest of it."

It is my mother who says that. She says: "With the gas and all the rest of it." She does not know what she is saying, she is merely anxious for me. Should I tell her how we once found three enemy trenches with their garrison[14] all stiff as though stricken with apoplexy?[15] against the parapet, in the dug-outs, just where they were, the men stood and lay about, with blue faces, dead.

---

13. **beer garden.** Place that serves beer, usually outdoors
14. **garrison.** Troops
15. **apoplexy.** Strokes

---

**words for everyday use**   fal • ter • ing • ly (fôl' tər iŋ lē) *adv.*, hesitantly; showing uncertainty. *"You're not going to leave me behind, are you?" he asked <u>falteringly</u>.*

"No Mother, that's only talk," I answer, "there's not very much in what Bredemeyer says. You see for instance, I'm well and fit—"

Before my mother's tremulous anxiety I recover my composure. Now I can walk about and talk and answer questions without fear of having suddenly to lean against the wall because the world turns soft as rubber and my veins become brimstone.[16]

My mother wants to get up. So I go for a while to my sister in the kitchen. "What is the matter with her?" I ask.

▶ With what is Paul's mother ill?

She shrugs her shoulders: "She has been in bed some months now, but we did not want to write and tell you. Several doctors have been to see her. One of them said it is probably cancer again."

*

I go to the district commandant to report myself. Slowly I wander through the streets. Occasionally someone speaks to me. I do not delay long for I have little <u>inclination</u> to talk.

▶ Why does the major confront Paul?

On my way back from the barracks a loud voice calls out to me. Still lost in thought I turn round and find myself confronted by a Major. "Can't you salute?" he <u>blusters</u>.

"Sorry, Major," I say in embarrassment, "I didn't notice you."

"Don't you know how to speak properly?" he roars.

I would like to hit him in the face, control myself, for my leave depends on it. I click my heels and say: "I did not see you, Herr[17] Major."

Then keep your eyes open," he snorts. "What is your name?" I give it.

His fat red face is furious. "What regiment?"

I give him full particulars. Even yet he has not had enough. "Where are you quartered?"

But I have had more than enough and say: "Between Langemark and Bixschoote."[18]

"Eh?" he asks, a bit stupefied.

---

16. **brimstone.** Sulfur, as if filled with a hot, fiery substance
17. **Herr.** German title of respect, similar to *sir*
18. **Langemark and Bixschoote.** War-torn part of Belgium during World War I

**words for everyday use**

in • cli • na • tion (in' klə nā' shən) n., particular disposition or bent of mind. *It was a beautiful spring day, so Bea had an inclination to celebrate by having an outdoor picnic.*

blus • ter (blus' tər) vi., speak or conduct oneself in a noisy, swaggering, or bullying manner. *Although Mick blusters about his tennis game, he is actually a terrible player.*

I explain to him that I arrived on leave only an hour or two since, thinking that he would then trot along. But not at all. He gets even more furious: "You think you can bring your front-line manners here, what? Well, we don't stand for that sort of thing. Thank God, we have discipline here!"

"Twenty paces backwards, double march!" he commands.

I am mad with rage. But I cannot say anything to him; he could put me under arrest if he liked. So I double back, and then march up to him. Six paces from him I spring to a stiff salute and maintain it until I am six paces beyond him.

He calls me back again and <u>affably</u> gives me to understand that for once he is pleased to put mercy before justice. I pretend to be duly grateful. "Now, dismiss!" he says. I turn about smartly and march off.

That ruins the evening for me. I go back home and throw my uniform into a corner; I had intended to change it in any case. Then I take out my civilian clothes from the wardrobe and put them on.

◀ How does Paul feel about his encounter with the major?

I feel awkward. The suit is rather tight and short, I have grown in the army. Collar and tie give me some trouble. In the end my sister ties the bow for me. But how light the suit is, it feels as though I had nothing on but a shirt and underpants.

I look at myself in the glass. It is a strange sight. A sunburnt, overgrown candidate for confirmation gazes at me in astonishment.

My mother is pleased to see me wearing civilian clothes; it makes me less strange to her. But my father would rather I kept my uniform on so that he could take me to visit his acquaintances.

◀ Why does Paul's father want him to wear his uniform?

But I refuse.

*

It is pleasant to sit quietly somewhere, in the beer garden for example, under the chestnuts by the skittle-alley.[19] The leaves fall down on the table and on the ground, only a few, the first. A glass of beer stands in front of me, I've learned to drink in the army. The glass is half empty, but there are a few good swigs ahead of me, and besides I can always order a second and a third if I wish to. There are no

---

19. **skittle-alley.** Type of bowling alley

---

**words for everyday use**

af • fa • bly (af' ə blē) *adj.,* in a pleasant and friendly manner. *The small town was filled with friendly people who <u>affably</u> greeted newcomers.*

bugles and no bombardments, the children of the house play in the skittle-alley, and the dog rests his head against my knee. The sky is blue, between the leaves of the chestnuts rises the green spire of St. Margaret's Church.

▶ What does Paul's father want to hear about? How does Paul feel about his father's curiosity? What is he unable to do?

This is good, I like it. But I cannot get on with the people. My mother is the only one who asks no questions. Not so my father. He wants me to tell him about the front; he is curious in a way that I find stupid and distressing; I no longer have any real contact with him. There is nothing he likes more than just hearing about it. I realize he does not know that a man cannot talk of such things; I would do it willingly, but it is too dangerous for me to put these things into words. I am afraid they might then become gigantic and I be no longer able to master them. What would become of us if everything that happens out there were quite clear to us?

So I confine myself to telling him a few amusing things. But he wants to know whether I have ever had a hand-to-hand fight. I say "No," and get up and go out.

▶ What do the tram cars sound like to Paul?

But that does not mend matters. After I have been startled a couple of times in the street by the screaming of the tramcars,[20] which resembles the shriek of a shell coming straight for one, somebody taps me on the shoulder. It is my German-master, and he fastens on me with the usual question: "Well, how are things out there? Terrible, terrible, eh? Yes, it is dreadful, but we must carry on. And after all, you do at least get decent food out there, so I hear. You look well, Paul, and fit. Naturally it's worse here. Naturally. The best for our soldiers every time, that goes without saying."

▶ What does Paul's former teacher say about conditions at home compared with at the front?

He drags me along to a table with a lot of others. They welcome me, a head-master shakes hands with me and says: "So you come from the front? What is the spirit like out there? Excellent, eh? Excellent?"

I explain that no one would be sorry to be back home.

He laughs uproariously. "I can well believe it! But first you have to give the Froggies[21] a good hiding. Do you smoke? Here, try one. Waiter, bring a beer as well for our young warrior."

---

20. **tramcars.** Railway cars
21. **Froggies.** Derogatory term for French people

---

**words for everyday use**

up • roar • i • ous • ly (up rôr′ ē əs lē) *adv.*, in a loud and boisterous manner. *Victor laughed uproariously at his own joke, even though nobody else thought it was funny.*

Unfortunately I have accepted the cigar, so I have to remain. And they are all so dripping with good will that it is impossible to object. All the same I feel annoyed and smoke like a chimney as hard as I can. In order to make at least some show of appreciation I toss off the beer in one gulp. Immediately a second is ordered; people know how much they are indebted to the soldiers. They argue about what we ought to annex.[22] The head-master with the steel watch-chain wants to have at least the whole of Belgium, the coal-areas of France, and a slice of Russia. He produces reasons why we must have them and is quite inflexible until at last the others give in to him. Then he begins to expound just whereabouts in France the break-through must come, and turns to me: "Now, shove ahead a bit out there with your everlasting trench warfare—Smash through the johnnies[23] and then there will be peace."

◄ *What does the headmaster tell Paul to do? What is Paul's response?*

I reply that in our opinion a break-through may not be possible. The enemy may have too many reserves. Besides, the war may be rather different from what people think.

He dismisses the idea <u>loftily</u> and informs me I know nothing about it. "The details, yes," says he, "but this relates to the whole. And of that you are not able to judge. You see only your little sector and so cannot have any general survey. You do your duty, you risk your lives, that deserves the highest honour—every man of you ought to have the Iron Cross[24]—but first of all the enemy line must be broken through in Flanders and then rolled up from the top."

He blows his nose and wipes his beard. "Completely rolled up they must be, from the top to the bottom. And then to Paris."

I would like to know just how he pictures it to himself, and pour the third glass of beer into me. Immediately he orders another.

But I break away. He stuffs a few more cigars into my pocket and sends me off with a friendly slap. "All of the best! I hope we will soon hear something worth while from you."

---

22. **annex.** Incorporate as your own territory
23. **johnnies.** English soldiers
24. **Iron Cross.** Distinguished German military honor

---

**words for everyday use**    loft • i • ly (lôf′ tə lē) *adv.,* in a haughty, arrogant manner. *"Oh, making that basket should be no trouble for me," said Fran <u>loftily</u> as she dribbled the ball.*

▶ What does Paul realize has happened to him?

▶ What two ways does Paul feel about the people who are not involved in the fighting?

*

I imagined leave would be different from this. Indeed, it was different a year ago. It is I of course that have changed in the interval. There lies a gulf between that time and today. At that time I still knew nothing about the war, we had only been in quiet sectors. But now I see that I have been crushed without knowing it. I find I do not belong here any more, it is a foreign world. Some of these people ask questions, some ask no questions, but one can see that the latter are proud of themselves for their silence; they often say with a wise air that these things cannot be talked about. They plume[25] themselves on it.

I prefer to be alone, so that no one troubles me. For they all come back to the same thing, how badly it goes and how well it goes; one thinks it is this way, another that; and yet they are always absorbed in the things that go to make up their existence. Formerly I lived in just the same way myself, but now I feel no contact here.

They talk too much for me. They have worries, aims, desires, that I cannot comprehend. I often sit with one of them in the little beer garden and try to explain to him that this is really the only thing: just to sit quietly, like this. They understand of course, they agree, they may feel it so too, but only with words, only with words, yes, that is it— they feel it, but always with only half of themselves, the rest of their being is taken up with other things, they are so divided in themselves that none feels it with his whole essence; I cannot even say myself exactly what I mean.

When I see them here, in their rooms, in their offices, about their occupations, I feel an irresistible attraction in it, I would like to be here too and forget the war; but also it repels me, it is so narrow, how can that fill a man's life, he ought to smash it to bits; how can they do it, while out at the front the splinters are whining over the shell-holes and the star-shells go up, the wounded are carried back on waterproof sheets and comrades crouch in the trenches.— They are different men here, men I cannot properly understand, whom I envy and despise. I must think of Kat and Albert and Müller and Tjaden, what will they be doing? No doubt they are sitting in the canteen, or perhaps swimming—soon they will have to go up to the front-line again.

*

In my room behind the table stands a brown leather sofa. I sit down on it.

---

25. **plume.** Pride

On the walls are pinned countless pictures that I once used to cut out of the newspapers. In between are drawings and postcards that have pleased me. In the corner is a small iron stove. Against the wall opposite stand the bookshelves with my books.

◀ What did Paul used to collect?

I used to live in this room before I was a soldier. The books I bought gradually with the money I earned by coaching. Many of them are secondhand, all the classics for example, one volume in blue cloth boards cost one mark twenty pfennig. I bought them complete because it was thorough-going, I did not trust the editors of selections to choose all the best. So I purchased only "collected works." I read most of them with laudible zeal, but few of them really appealed to me. I preferred the other books, the moderns, which were of course much dearer. A few I came by not quite honestly, I borrowed and did not return them because I did not want to part with them.

One shelf is filled with school books. They are not so well cared for, they are badly thumbed, and pages have been torn out for certain purposes. Then below are periodicals, papers, and letters all jammed in together with drawings and rough sketches.

I want to think myself back into that time. It is still in the room, I feel it at once, the walls have preserved it. My hands rest on the arms of the sofa; now I make myself at home and draw up my legs so that I sit comfortably in the corner, in the arms of the sofa. The little window is open, through it I see the familiar picture of the street with the rising spire of the church at the end. There are a couple of flowers on the table. Pen-holders, a shell as a paper-weight, the ink-well—here nothing is changed.

It will be like this too. If I am lucky, when the war is over and I come back here for good. I will sit here just like this and look at my room and wait.

I feel excited; but I do not want to be, for that is not right. I want that quiet <u>rapture</u> again. I want to feel the same powerful, nameless urge that I used to feel when I turned to my books. The breath of desire that then arose from the coloured backs of the books, shall fill me again, melt the heavy, dead lump of lead that lies somewhere in me and waken again the impatience of the future, the

◀ What does Paul want to feel again?

---

**words for everyday use**    rap • ture (rap′ chər) *n.*, state of being carried away with joy or love. *People who believe in love at first sight claim that you are filled with rapture when you meet the person you are destined to be with.*

quick joy in the world of thought, it shall bring back again the lost eagerness of my youth. I sit and wait.

▶ Whom must Paul see?

It occurs to me that I must go and see Kemmerich's mother;—I might visit Mittelstaedt too, he should be at the barracks. I look out of the window;—beyond the picture of the sunlit street appears a range of hills, distant and light; it changes to a clear day in autumn, and I sit by the fire with Kat and Albert and eat potatoes baked in their skins.

▶ For what does Paul wish?

But I do not want to think of that, I sweep it away. The room shall speak, it must catch me up and hold me, I want to feel that I belong here, I want to hearken and know when I go back to the front that the war will sink down, be drowned utterly in the great homecoming tide, know that it will then be past forever, and not gnaw us continually, that it will have none but an outward power over us.

The backs of the books stand in rows. I know them all still, I remember arranging them in order. I implore them with my eyes: Speak to me—take me up—take me, Life of my Youth—you who are care-free, beautiful—receive me again—

I wait, I wait.

Images float through my mind, but they do not grip me, they are mere shadows and memories.

Nothing—nothing—

My <u>disquietude</u> grows.

A terrible feeling of foreignness suddenly rises up in me. I cannot find my way back, I am shut out though I entreat earnestly and put forth all my strength.

Nothing stirs; listless and wretched, like a condemned man, I sit there and the past withdraws itself. And at the same time I fear to <u>importune</u> it too much, because I do not know what might happen then. I am a soldier, I must cling to that.

Wearily I stand up and look out of the window. Then I take one of the books, intending to read, and turn over the leaves. But I put it away and take out another. There are passages in it that have been marked. I look, turn over the pages, take up fresh books. Already they are piled up beside me. Speedily more join the heap, papers, magazines, letters.

I stand there dumb. As before a judge.

Dejected.

---

**words for everyday use**

**dis • qui • e • tude** (dis kwī ə tüd′) *n.*, disturbed or uneasy condition; restlessness; anxiety. *Looking at the narrow suspension bridge he would have to cross, Bill was filled with <u>disquietude</u>.*

**im • por • tune** (im′ pòr tün′) *vt.*, trouble with requests or demands; urge or entreat persistently or repeatedly. *The child continued to <u>importune</u> his mother for a cookie.*

Words, Words, Words—they do not reach me.
Slowly I place the books back in the shelves.
Nevermore.
Quietly, I go out of the room.

*

Still I do not give up hope. I do not indeed go to my room any more, but comfort myself with the thought that a few days are not enough to judge by. Afterwards—later on—there is plenty of time for that.

So I go over to see Mittelstaedt in the barracks, and we sit in his room; there is an atmosphere about it that I do not like but with which I am quite familiar.

Mittelstaedt has some news ready for me that electrifies me on the spot. He tells me Kantorek has been called up as a territorial.[26]

"Just think of it," says he, and takes out a couple of good cigars, "I come back here from the hospital and bump right into him. He stretches out his paw to me and bleats: 'Hullo Mittelstaedt, how are you?'—I look at him and say: 'Territorial Kantorek, business is business and schnapps is schnapps,[27] you ought to know that well enough. Stand to attention when you speak to a superior officer.' You should have seen his face! A cross between a dud and a pickled cucumber. He tried once again to chum up. So I snubbed him a bit harder. Then he brought up his biggest guns and asked confidentially: 'Would you like me to use my influence so that you can take an emergency-exam?' He was trying to remind me of those things, you know. Then I got mad, and I reminded him of something instead. 'Territorial Kantorek, two years ago you preached us into enlisting; and among us there was one, Joseph Behm, who didn't want to enlist. He was killed three months before he would have been called up in the ordinary way. If it had not been for you he would have lived just that much longer. And now: Dismiss. You will hear from me later.' It was easy to get put in charge of his company. First thing I did was to take him to the stores and fit him out with suitable equipment. You will see in a minute."

We go to the parade ground. The company has fallen in, Mittelstaedt stands them at ease and inspects.

Then I see Kantorek and am scarcely able to stifle my laughter. He is wearing a faded blue tunic. On the back and in the sleeves there are big dark patches. The tunic must have belonged to a giant. The black, worn breeches are just

---

◀ What no longer reaches Paul?

◀ What news does Mittelstaedt have for Paul?

◀ Of what does Mittelstaedt remind Kantorek?

◀ With what type of uniform has Mittelstaedt outfitted Kantorek?

---

26. **territorial.** Home guard
27. **schnapps.** Type of strong alcoholic beverage

as much too short; they reach barely halfway down his calf. The boots, tough old clod-hoppers, with turned-up toes and laces at the side are much too big for him. But as a compensation the cap is too small, a terribly dirty, mean little pill-box. The whole rig-out[28] is just pitiful.

▶ Why does Mittelstaedt chastise Kantorek by calling him inadequate?

Mittelstaedt stops in front of him: "Territorial Kantorek, do you call those buttons polished? You seem as though you can never learn. Inadequate, Kantorek, quite inadequate—"

It makes me bubble with glee. In school Kantorek used to chasten Mittelstaedt with exactly the same expression—"Inadequate, Mittelstaedt, quite inadequate."

Mittelstaedt continues to upbraid him: "Look at Boettcher now, there's a model for you to learn from."

I can hardly believe my eyes. Boettcher is there too, Boettcher, our school porter. And he is a model! Kantorek shoots a glance at me as if he would like to eat me. But I grin at him innocently, as though I do not recognize him any more.

Nothing could look more ludicrous than his forage-cap and his uniform. And this is the object before whom we used to stand in anguish as he sat up there enthroned at his desk, spearing at us with his pencil for our mistakes in those irregular French verbs with which afterwards we made so little headway in France. That is barely two years ago—and now here stands Territorial Kantorek, the spell quite broken, with bent knees, arms like pothooks, unpolished buttons and that ludicrous rig-out—an impossible soldier. I cannot reconcile this with the menacing figure at the schoolmaster's desk. I wonder what I, the old soldier, would do if this skinful of woe ever dared to say to me again: "Bäumer, give the imperfect of 'aller.'"

Then Mittelstaedt makes them practise skirmishing,[29] and as a favour appoints Kantorek squad leader.

Now, in skirmishing the squad leader has always to keep twenty paces in front of his squad; if the order comes "On the march, about turn," the line of skirmishers simply turns about, but the squad leader, who now finds himself suddenly twenty paces in the rear of the line, has to rush up at the double and take his position again twenty paces in front of the squad. That makes altogether forty paces double march. But no sooner has he arrived than the order "On the march, about turn," comes again and he once more has to race at top speed another forty paces to the other side. In this way the squad has merely made the turn-about and a

---

28. **rig-out.** Outfit
29. **skirmishing.** Fighting in small groups

couple of paces, while the squad-leader dashes backwards and forwards like a fart on a curtain-pole. That is one of Himmelstoss' well-worn recipes.

Kantorek can hardly expect anything else from Mittelstaedt, for he once messed up the latter's chance of promotion, and Mittelstaedt would be a big fool not to make the best of such a good opportunity as this before he goes back to the front again. A man might well die easier after the army has given him just one such stroke of luck.

In the meantime Kantorek is dashing up and down like a wild boar. After a while Mittelstaedt stops the skirmish and begins the very important exercise of creeping.

On hands and knees, carrying his gun in regulation fashion, Kantorek shoves his absurd figure over the sand immediately in front of us. He is breathing hard, and his panting is music.

Mittelstaedt encourages Kantorek the territorial with quotations from Kantorek the schoolmaster. "Territorial Kantorek, we have the good fortune to live in a great age, we must brace ourselves and triumph over hardship."

Kantorek sweats and spits out a dirty piece of wood that has lodged in his teeth.

Mittelstaedt stoops down and says <u>reproachfully</u>: "And in the trifles never lose sight of the great adventure, Territorial Kantorek!"

It amazes me that Kantorek does not explode with a bang, especially when, during physical exercises, Mittelstaedt copies him to perfection, seizing him by the seat of his trousers as he is pulling himself up on the horizontal bar so that he can just raise his chin above the beam, and then starts to give him good advice. That is exactly what Kantorek used to do to him at school.

◀ *Why is Paul amazed that Kantorek doesn't explode?*

The extra fatigues[30] are next detailed off. "Kantorek and Boettcher, bread fatigue! Take the handcart with you."

A few minutes later the two set off together pushing the barrow. Kantorek in a fury walks with his head down. But the porter is delighted to have scored light duty.

---

30. **fatigues.** Duties

**words for everyday use**    re • proach • ful • ly (ri prōch′ fəl lē) *adv.*, in a manner that expresses blame or criticism. *"You didn't invite me to your party,"* said Brian *reproachfully*.

The bakehouse is away at the other end of the town, and the two must go there and back through the whole length of it.

"They've done that a couple of times already," grins Mittelstaedt. "People have begun to watch for them coming."

"Excellent," I say, "but hasn't he reported you yet?"

"He did try. Our C.O.[31] laughed like the deuce[32] when he heard the story. He hasn't any time for schoolmasters. Besides, I'm sweet with his daughter."

"He'll mess up the examination for you."

"I don't care," says Mittelstaedt calmly. "Besides, his complaint came to nothing because I could show that he had had hardly anything but light duty."

"Couldn't you polish him up a bit?" I ask.

"He's too stupid, I couldn't be bothered," answers Mittelstaedt contemptuously.

\*

▶ What is leave?

What is leave?—A pause that only makes everything after it so much worse. Already the sense of parting begins to intrude itself. My mother watches me silently; I know she counts the days; every morning she is sad. It is one day less. She has put away my pack, she does not want to be reminded by it.

▶ For what do people line up and wait?

The hours pass quickly if a man <u>broods</u>. I pull myself together, and go with my sister to the slaughterhouse to get a pound or two of bones. That is a great favour and people line up early in the morning and stand waiting. Many of them faint.

We have no luck. After waiting by turns for three hours the queue disperses. The bones have not lasted out.

It is a good thing that I get my rations. I bring them to my mother and in that way we all get something decent to eat.

The days grow ever more strained and my mother's eyes more sorrowful. Four days left now. I must go and see Kemmerich's mother.

---

31. **C.O.** Commanding officer
32. **deuce.** The devil, used here as a mild oath

---

**words for everyday use**

**brood** (brüd) *vi.*, keep thinking about something in a distressed or troubled way. *Simone did not know how to forgive people and <u>brooded</u> over every wrong done her and every harsh word said.*

I cannot write that down. This quaking, sobbing woman who shakes me and cries out on me: "Why are you living then, when he is dead?"—who drowns me in tears and calls out: "What are you there for at all, child, when you—" —who drops into a chair and wails: "Did you see him? Did you see him then? How did he die?"

I tell her he was shot through the heart and died instantaneously. She looks at me, she doubts me: "You lie. I know better. I have felt how terribly he died. I have heard his voice at night, I have felt his anguish—tell the truth, I want to know it, I must know it."

"No," I say, "I was beside him. He died at once."

She pleads with me gently: "Tell me. You must tell me. I know you want to comfort me, but don't you see, you torment me far more than if you told me the truth? I cannot bear the uncertainty. Tell me how it was and even though it will be terrible, it will be far better than what I have to think if you don't."

I will never tell her, she can make mincemeat out of me first. I pity her, but she strikes me as rather stupid all the same. Why doesn't she stop worrying? Kemmerich will stay dead whether she knows about it or not. When a man has seen so many dead he cannot understand any longer why there should be so much anguish over a single individual. So I say rather impatiently: "He died immediately. He felt absolutely nothing at all. His face was quite calm."

She is silent. Then she says slowly: "Will you swear it?"

"Yes."

"By everything that is sacred to you?"

Good God, what is there that is sacred to me?—such things change pretty quickly with us.

"Yes, he died at once."

"Are you willing never to come back yourself, if it isn't true?"

"May I never come back if he wasn't killed instantaneously."

I would swear to anything. But she seems to believe me. She moans and weeps steadily. I have to tell how it happened, so I invent a story and I almost believe it myself.

As I leave she kisses me and gives me a picture of him. In his recruit's uniform he leans on a round rustic table with legs made of birch branches. Behind him a wood is painted on a curtain, and on the table stands a mug of beer.

◄ What does Kemmerich's mother ask Paul?

◄ What lie does Paul tell her?

◄ Why does Kemmerich's mother seem stupid to Paul?

◄ What does Kemmerich's mother ask Paul to swear?

It is the last evening at home. Everyone is silent. I go to bed early, I seize the pillow, press it against myself and bury my head in it. Who knows if I will ever lie in a feather bed again?

Late in the night my mother comes into my room. She thinks I am asleep, and I pretend to be so. To talk, to stay awake with one another, it is too hard.

She sits long into the night although she is in pain and often writhes. At last I can bear it no longer, and pretend I have just wakened up.

"Go and sleep, Mother, you will catch cold here."

"I can sleep enough later," she says.

I sit up. "I don't go straight back to the front, mother. I have to do four weeks at the training camp. I may come over from there one Sunday, perhaps."

She is silent. Then she asks gently: "Are you very much afraid?"

"No Mother."

"I would like to tell you to be on your guard against the women out in France. They are no good."

▶ What does Paul wish to do?

Ah! Mother, Mother! You still think I am a child—why can I not put my head in your lap and weep? Why have I always to be strong and self-controlled? I would like to weep and be comforted too, indeed I am little more than a child; in the wardrobe[33] still hang short, boy's trousers—it is such a little time ago, why is it over?

"Where we are there aren't any women, Mother," I say as calmly as I can.

"And be very careful at the front, Paul."

Ah, Mother, Mother! Why do I not take you in my arms and die with you. What poor wretches we are!

"Yes Mother, I will."

"I will pray for you every day, Paul."

Ah! Mother, Mother! Let us rise up and go out, back through the years, where the burden of all this misery lies on us no more, back to you and me alone, Mother!

"Perhaps you can get a job that is not so dangerous."

"Yes, Mother, perhaps I can get into the cookhouse, that can easily be done."

"You do it then, and if the others say anything—"

"That won't worry me, Mother—"

She sighs. Her face is a white gleam in the darkness.

"Now you must go to sleep, Mother."

---

33. **wardrobe.** Closet

She does not reply. I get up and wrap my cover round her shoulders.

She supports herself on my arm, she is in pain. And so I take her to her room. I stay with her a little while.

"And you must get well again, Mother, before I come back."

"Yes, yes, my child."

"You ought not to send your things to me, Mother. We have plenty to eat out there. You can make much better use of them here."

How <u>destitute</u> she lies there in her bed, she that loves me more than all the world. As I am about to leave, she says hastily: "I have two pairs of underpants for you. They are all wool. They will keep you warm. You must not forget to put them in your pack."

◀ What does Paul know about the underpants his mother gives him?

Ah! Mother! I know what these underpants have cost you in waiting, and walking, and begging! Ah! Mother, Mother! how can it be that I must part from you? Who else is there that has any claim on me but you? Here I sit and there you are lying; we have so much to say, and we shall never say it.

"Good-night, Mother."

"Good-night, my child."

The room is dark. I hear my mother's breathing, and the ticking of the clock. Outside the window the wind blows and the chestnut trees rustle.

On the landing I stumble over my pack, which lies there already made up because I have to leave early in the morning.

I bite into my pillow. I grasp the iron rods of my bed with my fists. I ought never to have come here. Out there I was indifferent and often hopeless—I will never be able to be so again. I was a soldier, and now I am nothing but an agony for myself, for my mother, for everything that is so comfortless and without end.

I ought never to have come on leave.

words for everyday use

des • ti • tute (des' tə tüt') adj., lacking the necessities of life; living in complete poverty. During the Great Depression, the numbers of poor and <u>destitute</u> people in the United States swelled.

# Chapter VIII

▶ In what way is the training camp on the moor different now?

I already know the camp on the moors. It was here that Himmelstoss gave Tjaden his education. But now I know hardly anyone here; as ever, all is altered. There are only a few people that I have occasionally met before.

I go through the routine mechanically. In the evenings I generally go to the Soldiers' Home,[1] where the newspapers are laid out, but I do not read them; still there is a piano there that I am glad enough to play on. Two girls are in attendance, one of them is young.

The camp is surrounded with high barbed-wire fences. If we come back late from the Soldiers' Home we have to show passes. But those who are on good terms with the guard can get through, of course.

Among the junipers and the birch trees on the moor we practise company drill each day. It is bearable if one expects nothing better. We advance at a run, fling ourselves down, and our panting breath moves the stalks of the grasses and the flowers of the heather to and fro. Looked at so closely one sees the fine sand is composed of millions of the tiniest pebbles, as clear as if they had been made in a laboratory. It is strangely inviting to dig one's hands into it.

But most beautiful are the woods with their line of birch trees. Their colour changes with every minute. Now the stems gleam purest white, and between them airy and silken, hangs the pastel-green of the leaves; the next moment all changes to an opalescent[2] blue, as the shivering breezes pass down from the heights and touch the green lightly away; and again in one place it deepens almost to black as a cloud passes over the sun. And this shadow moves like a ghost through the dim trunks and rides far out over the moor to the sky—then the birches stand out again like gay banners on white poles, with their red and gold patches of autumn-tinted leaves.

▶ When does one begin to love nature?

I often become so lost in the play of soft light and transparent shadow, that I almost fail to hear the commands. It is when one is alone that one begins to observe Nature and to love her. And here I have not much companionship, and do not even desire it. We are too little acquainted with one another to do more than joke a bit and play poker or nap in the evenings.

---

1. **Soldiers' Home.** Recreation place for soldiers
2. **opalescent.** Colored like an opal, which is mostly white but reflects light in a play of colors

Alongside our camp is the big Russian prison camp.[3] It is separated from us by a wire fence, but in spite of this the prisoners come across to us. They seem nervous and fearful, though most of them are big fellows with beards—they look like <u>meek</u>, scolded, St. Bernard dogs.

They <u>slink</u> about our camp and pick over the garbage tins. One can imagine what they find there. With us food is pretty scarce and none too good at that—turnips cut into six pieces and boiled in water, and unwashed carrot tops—mouldy potatoes are tit-bits,[4] and the chief luxury is a thin rice soup in which float little bits of beef-sinew, but these are cut up so small that they take a lot of finding.

Everything gets eaten, notwithstanding, and if ever anyone is so well off as not to want all his share, there are a dozen others standing by ready to relieve him of it. Only the <u>dregs</u> that the ladle cannot reach are tipped out and thrown into the garbage tins. Along with that there sometimes go a few turnip peelings, mouldy bread crusts and all kinds of muck.

This thin, miserable, dirty garbage is the objective of the prisoners. They pick it out of the stinking tins greedily and go off with it under their blouses.

It is strange to see these enemies of ours so close up. They have faces that make one think—honest peasant faces, broad foreheads, broad noses, broad mouths, broad hands, and thick hair.

They ought to be put to threshing, reaping,[5] and apple picking. They look just as kindly as our own peasants in Friesland.

It is distressing to watch their movements, to see them begging for something to eat. They are all rather feeble, for they only get enough nourishment to keep them from starving. Ourselves we have not had sufficient to eat for long enough. They have dysentery;[6] <u>furtively</u> many of

◀ What is near the German soldiers' camp?

◀ On what do the Russian prisoners survive?

◀ What is it strange for Paul to see? What does he think the Russian prisoners ought to be doing?

◀ What disease do many of the prisoners have?

---

3. **Russian prison camp.** Where Russian prisoners of war are kept
4. **tit-bits.** Tidbits, choice bits of food
5. **threshing, reaping.** Harvesting grain
6. **dysentery.** Often fatal illness that strikes people kept close together in unsanitary conditions. The illness is marked by extreme intestinal pain and bloody diarrhea.

---

**words for everyday use**

**meek** (mēk) *adj.,* too submissive; easily imposed on; spineless; spiritless. *After his mother scolded him, Julio acted very <u>meek</u>.*

**slink** (sliŋk) *vi.,* move in a quiet, furtive, or sneaking manner, as from fear or guilt. *The cat began to <u>slink</u> through the grassy field, stalking the mouse.*

**dregs** (dregz) *n. pl.,* particles of solid matter that settle at the bottom in a liquid.

*The bottle of juice sat so long on the shelf that we could clearly see the <u>dregs</u>—bits of fruit particles—at the bottom.*

**fur • tive • ly** (fʉr′ tiv lē) *adv.,* in a stealthy or sneaky manner. *When Ramon asked us what we were doing Saturday, we all behaved rather <u>furtively</u> because we were planning a surprise party for him.*

them display the blood-stained tails of their shirts. Their backs, their necks are bent, their knees sag, their heads droop as they stretch out their hands and beg in the few words of German that they know—beg with those soft, deep, musical voices, that are like warm stoves and cosy rooms at home.

Some men there are who give them a kick, so that they fall over;—but those are not many. The majority do nothing to them, just ignore them. Occasionally, when they are too <u>grovelling</u>, it makes a man mad and then he kicks them. If only they would not look at one so—What great misery can be in two such small spots, no bigger than a man's thumb—in their eyes!

They come over to the camp in the evenings and trade. They exchange whatever they possess for bread. Often they have fair success, because they have very good boots and ours are bad. The leather of their knee boots is wonderfully soft, like suede. The peasants among us who get tit-bits sent from home can afford to trade. The price of a pair of boots is about two or three loaves of army bread, or a loaf of bread and a small, tough ham sausage.

But most of the Russians have long since parted with whatever things they had. Now they wear only the most pitiful clothing, and try to exchange little carvings and objects that they have made out of shell fragments and copper driving bands. Of course, they don't get much for such things, though they may have taken <u>immense</u> pains with them—they go for a slice or two of bread. Our peasants are hard and cunning when they bargain. They hold the piece of bread or sausage right under the nose of the Russian till he grows pale with greed and his eyes bulge and then he will give anything for it. The peasants wrap up their booty with the utmost solemnity, and then get out their big pocket knives, and slowly and deliberately cut off a slice of bread for themselves from their supply and with every mouthful take a piece of the good tough sausage and so reward themselves with a good feed. It is distressing to watch them take their afternoon meal thus; one would like to crack them over their thick pates.[7]

▶ What annoys the soldiers about the prisoners?

---

7. **pates.** Heads

---

**words for everyday use**

grov • el (gruv′ əl) vi., behave humbly; debase oneself in a servile fashion. *The queen's subjects were <u>groveling</u> before her, afraid of making her angry.*

im • mense (im mens′) adj., very large; vast; huge. *When we first saw the desert, we were amazed by the <u>immense</u> expanse of sand.*

They rarely give anything away. How little we understand one another.

◀ According to the narrator, what don't we understand?

*

I am often on guard over the Russians. In the darkness one sees their forms move like sick storks,[8] like great birds. They come close up to the wire fence and lean their faces against it; their fingers hook round the mesh. Often many stand side by side, and breathe the wind that comes down from the moors and the forest.

They rarely speak and then only a few words. They are more human and more brotherly towards one another, it seems to me, than we are. But perhaps that is merely because they feel themselves to be more unfortunate than us. Anyway the war is over so far as they are concerned. But to wait for dysentery is not much of a life either.

The territorials who are in charge of them say that they were much more lively at first. They used to have intrigues among themselves, as always happens, and it would often come to blows and knives. But now they are quite <u>apathetic</u> and <u>listless</u>; most of them do not masturbate any more, they are so feeble, though otherwise things come to such a pass that whole huts full of them do it.

They stand at the wire fence; sometimes one goes away and then another at once takes his place in the line. Most them are silent; occasionally one begs a cigarette butt.

I see their dark forms, their beards move in the wind. I know nothing of them except that they are prisoners; and that is exactly what troubles me. Their life is obscure and guiltless;—if I could know more of them, what their names are, how they live, what they are waiting for, what their burdens are, then my emotion would have an object and might become sympathy. But as it is I perceive behind them only the suffering of the creature, the awful melancholy of life and the pitilessness of men.

◀ What would cause Paul to feel sympathy for the prisoners?

A word of command has made these silent figures our enemies; a word of command might transform them into our friends. At some table a document is signed by some persons whom none of us knows, and then for years together that very crime on which formerly the world's

◀ What has the word of command done? What could it do?

---

8. **storks.** Type of long-legged, long-necked bird

**words for everyday use**

ap • a • thet • ic (ap' ə thet' ik) *adj.,* feeling little or no emotion; indifferent. *Because the movie did not fully develop its characters, we were <u>apathetic</u> to their fates.*

list • less (list' lis) *adj.,* having no interest in what is going on about one, as a result of illness, weariness, or dejection. *During her illness, Una lay <u>listless</u>, never seeming to notice her visitors.*

▶ According to Paul, who is more an enemy to the recruit than the Russians?

<u>condemnation</u> and severest penalty fall, becomes our highest aim. But who can draw such a distinction when he looks at these quiet men with their childlike faces and apostles'[9] beards. Any non-commissioned officer is more of an enemy to a recruit, any schoolmaster to a pupil, than they are to us. And yet we would shoot at them again and they at us if they were free.

I am frightened: I dare think this way no more. This way lies the <u>abyss</u>. It is not now the time but I will not lose these thoughts, I will keep them, shut them away until the war is ended. My heart beats fast: this is the aim, the great, the sole aim, that I have thought of in the trenches; that I have looked for as the only possibility of existence after this annihilation of all human feeling; this is a task that will make life afterward worthy of these hideous years.

▶ What comforts Paul?

I take out my cigarettes, break each one in half and give them to the Russians. They bow to me and then light the cigarettes. Now red points glow in every face. They comfort me; it looks as though there were little windows in dark village cottages saying that behind them are rooms full of peace.

\*

The days go by. On a foggy morning another of the Russians is buried; almost every day one of them dies. I am on guard during the burial. The prisoners sing a chorale,[10] they sing in parts, and it sounds almost as if there were no voices, but an organ far away on the moor.

The burial is quickly over.

In the evening they stand again at the wire fence and the wind comes down to them from the beech woods. The stars are cold.

I now know a few of those who speak a little German. There is a musician amongst them, he says he used to be a violinist in Berlin. When he hears that I can play the piano he fetches his violin and plays. The others sit down and lean their backs against the fence. He stands up and plays, sometimes he has that absent expression which violinists

---

9. **apostles'.** Like one of the twelve disciples sent by Jesus to teach the gospel; they are typically depicted with heavy beards.
10. **chorale.** Hymn with a simple melody and rhythm

---

**words for everyday use**

con • dem • na • tion (kän′ dem nā′ shən) n., adverse judgment; disapproval. *Suki had impeccable manners, so she looked at me with* condemnation *as I chose the wrong fork at dinner.*

a • byss (ə bis′) n., deep fissure in the earth; bottomless gulf. *When we visited the Grand Canyon, it seemed to us like a bottomless* abyss *into the earth.*

get when they close their eyes; or again he sways the instrument to the rhythm and smiles across to me.

He plays mostly folk songs and the others hum with him. They are like a country of dark hills that sing far down under the ground. The sound of the violin stands like a slender girl above it and is clear and alone. The voices cease and the violin continues alone. In the night it is so thin it sounds frozen; one must stand close up; it would be much better in a room—out here it makes a man grow sad.

*

Because I have already had a long leave I get none on Sundays. So the last Sunday before I go back to the front my father and eldest sister came over to see me. All day we sit in the Soldiers' Home. Where else could we go? We don't want to stay in the camp. About midday we go for a stroll on the moors.

The hours are a torture; we do not know what to talk about, so we speak of my mother's illness. It is now definitely cancer, she is already in the hospital and will be operated on shortly. The doctors hope she will recover, but we have never heard of cancer being cured.

"Where is she then?" I ask.

"In the Luisa Hospital," says my father.

"In which class?"

"Third. We must wait till we know what the operation costs. She wanted to be in the third herself. She said that then she would have some company. And besides it is cheaper."

"So she is lying there with all those people. If only she could sleep properly."

My father nods. His face is broken and full of furrows. My mother has always been sickly; and though she has only gone to the hospital when she has been compelled to, it has cost a great deal of money, and my father's life has been practically given up to it.

"If only I knew how much the operation costs," says he.

"Have you not asked?"

"Not directly, I cannot do that—the surgeon might take it <u>amiss</u> and that would not do; he must operate on Mother."

◀ *What has been a great expense to Paul's family?*

**words for everyday use**    a • miss (ə mis') *adv.*, in a wrong way. *Sarah said she was busy, but Lucy took her words* <u>*amiss*</u> *and assumed Sarah meant she didn't want to spend time with her.*

Yes, I think bitterly, that's how it is with us, and with all poor people. They don't dare ask the price, but worry themselves dreadfully beforehand about it; but the others, for whom it is not important, they settle the price first as a matter of course. And the doctor does not take it amiss from them.

"The dressings afterwards are so expensive," says my father.

"Doesn't the Invalid's Fund[11] pay anything toward it, then?" I ask.

"Mother has been ill too long."

"Have you any money at all?"

He shakes his head: "No, but I can do some overtime."

I know. He will stand at his desk folding and pasting and cutting until twelve o'clock at night. At eight o'clock in the evening he will eat some miserable rubbish they get in exchange for their food tickets, then he will take a powder for his headache and work on.

In order to cheer him up a bit I tell him a few stories, soldiers' jokes and the like, about generals and sergeant-majors.

Afterwards I accompany them both to the railway station. They give me a pot of jam and a bag of potato-cakes that my mother has made for me.

Then they go off and I return to the camp.

In the evening I spread the jam on the cakes and eat some. But I have no taste for them. So I go out to give them to the Russians. Then it occurs to me that my mother cooked them herself and that she was probably in pain as she stood before the hot stove. I put the bag back in my pack and take only two cakes to the Russians.

▶ What will Paul's father do to earn money to pay for Paul's mother's illness?

▶ What does Paul want to give to the Russians? Why does he bring them only two?

---

11. **Invalid's Fund.** Type of charity for sick people

## Respond to the Selection

Write a journal entry about a time you returned home or to another place that is special to you after a long absence. How did you feel? Explain whether the place seemed different to you in any way after your absence.

## Investigate, Inquire, and Imagine

**Recall:** GATHERING FACTS

**Interpret:** FINDING MEANING

1a. How do Paul and his friends meet the three women? What nationality are the women? What do they bring the women later that night when they visit them? What does the woman that Paul likes call him? What is the brunette's reaction when Paul tells her he is going on leave?

➤ 1b. Why don't the women view Paul and his friends as enemies? Compare and contrast the reasons Paul and his friends have for being interested in the women with the women's reasons for being interested in the men. What does Paul realize about the brunette when he tells her he is going on leave? How do you think he feels about this?

2a. When Paul returns home, what lies does he tell his mother and father? What lies does he tell Kemmerich's mother? What does his former headmaster tell him he must do in the war?

➤ 2b. In Chapter 7, Paul says he feels as if there is a veil between him and his family. Explain what he means by this remark. Why is Paul unwilling to talk honestly about his experiences at the front? What is he afraid of? Why might Paul be annoyed by his former headmaster's remarks? Why does Paul wish he never went on leave?

3a. What are conditions like for the Russians in the prison camp? What does Paul give to the prisoners? According to Paul, what has made the Russians his enemy?

➤ 3b. How does Paul feel about the Russians? Explain whether Paul views the Russians as his enemy. Why doesn't he want to think about whether or not the Russians are his enemy?

**Analyze:** Taking Things Apart

4a. Explain whether Paul classifies his enemies following the politics of the war. Whom does he see as enemies? Whom doesn't he believe are enemies?

**Synthesize:** Bringing Things Together

→ 4b. Summarize the statement Remarque is making against nationalism in chapters 7 and 8.

**Evaluate:** Making Judgments

5a. In Chapter 7, Paul says that when his memories of the front come back to him after the war, he and his dead comrades will stand up again and march with a purpose, but he doesn't know whom they should march against. In your opinion, whom should they march against? Who is to blame for what happened to this lost generation of young men?

**Extend:** Connecting Ideas

→ 5b. What do you want to march against? What experiences in your own life have led you to wish to march against, or protest, this thing?

# Understanding Literature

CARPE DIEM. *Carpe diem* is a Latin term meaning "seize the day." The *carpe diem* theme, telling people not to waste time but rather to enjoy themselves while they have a chance, was common in Renaissance English poetry. What examples of the *carpe diem* theme can you find in Chapter 7? Why might this theme have emerged in Remarque's writing?

SETTING, DESCRIPTION, AND SENSORY DETAILS. The setting of a literary work is the time and place in which it occurs, together with all the details used to create a sense of a particular time and place. **Description** is a type of writing that portrays a character, an object, or a scene. Descriptions make use of **sensory details**— words and phrases that describe how things look, sound, feel, taste, or smell. In Chapter 7, the author shifts the setting of the story from the battlefront to Paul's home town. In writing about Paul's homecoming, Remarque makes use of descriptive writing full of sensory details. Make a chart like the one below. In it, list the sensory details Paul notes and remembers as the train pulls into his home town and as he walks into his home.

| Sight | Sound | Touch | Taste | Smell |
|-------|-------|-------|-------|-------|
|       |       |       |       |       |

ALLUSION. An **allusion** is a rhetorical technique in which reference is made to a person, event, object, or work from history or literature. In Chapter 7, Paul is looking at his old books and is dejected because he doesn't feel the joy in them that he did before the war. He says, "Words, Words, Words—they do not reach me." This line can be read as an allusion to a line from William Shakespeare's play *Hamlet, Prince of Denmark*. In this play, when Hamlet is asked what he is reading, he responds, "Words, words, words." Hamlet is a young man who has discovered that his uncle killed his father to claim the throne of Denmark and marry Hamlet's mother. Hamlet feigns madness and spends much of the play thinking about what has happened and trying to goad himself into action. Compare Paul's situation to Hamlet's. Why might Remarque have included this allusion?

# Chapter IX

We travel for several days. The first aeroplanes appear in the sky. We roll on past transport lines. Guns, guns. The light railway picks us up. I search for my regiment. No one knows exactly where it lies. Somewhere or other I put up for the night, somewhere or other I receive provisions and a few vague instructions. And so with my pack and my rifle I set out again on the way.

▶ What has Paul's division become? How does he feel about this?

By the time I come up they are no longer in the devastated place. I hear we have become one of the flying divisions[1] that are pushed in wherever it is hottest.[2] That does not sound cheerful to me. They tell me of heavy losses that we have been having. I inquire after Kat and Albert. No one knows anything of them.

I search farther and wander about here and there; it is a strange feeling. One night more and then another I camp out like a Red Indian. Then at last I get some definite information, and by the afternoon I am able to report to the Orderly Room.

The sergeant-major detains me there. The company comes back in two days' time. There is no object in sending me up now.

"What was it like on leave?" he asks, "pretty good, eh?"

"In parts," I say.

▶ According to the sergeant-major, what messes up the second part of a soldier's leave?

"Yes," he sighs, "yes, if a man didn't have to come away again. The second half is always rather messed up by that."

I loaf around until the company comes back in the early morning, grey, dirty, soured, and gloomy. Then I jump up, push in amongst them, my eyes searching. There is Tjaden, there is Müller blowing his nose, and there are Kat and Kropp. We arrange our sacks of straw side by side. I have an uneasy conscience when I look at them, and yet without any good reason. Before we turn in I bring out the rest of the potato-cakes and jam so that they can have some too.

▶ What does Paul do with the cakes his mother gave him?

The outer cakes are mouldy, still it is possible to eat them. I keep those for myself and give the fresh ones to Kat and Kropp.

Kat chews and says: "These are from your mother?"

I nod.

"Good," says he, "I can tell by the taste."

I could almost weep. I can hardly control myself any longer. But it will soon be all right again back here with Kat and Albert. This is where I belong.

---

1. **flying divisions.** Mobile military units that are sent wherever they are most needed
2. **hottest.** Most violent and dangerous

"You've been lucky," whispers Kropp to me before we drop off to sleep, "they say we are going to Russia."

To Russia? It's not much of a war over there.

In the distance the front thunders. The walls of the hut rattle.

\*

There's a great deal of polishing being done. We are inspected at every turn. Everything that is torn is exchanged for new. I score a spotless new tunic out of it and Kat, of course, an entire outfit. A rumour is going round that there may be peace, but the other story is more likely—that we are bound for Russia. Still, what do we need new things for in Russia? At last it leaks out—the Kaiser[3] is coming to review us. Hence all the inspections.

◀ What are the soldiers given? What rumors circulate? Who is coming to visit?

For eight whole days one would suppose we were in a base-camp, there is so much drill and fuss. Everyone is <u>peevish</u> and touchy, we do not take kindly to all this polishing, much less to the full-dress parades. Such things <u>exasperate</u> a soldier more than the front-line.

At last the moment arrives. We stand to attention and the Kaiser appears. We are curious to see what he looks like. He stalks along the line, and I am really rather disappointed; judging from his pictures I imagined him to be bigger and more powerfully built, and above all to have a thundering voice.

◀ Why is Paul disappointed when he sees the Kaiser?

He distributes Iron Crosses, speaks to this man and that. Then we march off.

Afterwards we discuss it. Tjaden says with astonishment:

"So that is the All-Highest! And everyone, bar nobody,[4] has to stand up stiff in front of him!" He meditates: "Hindenburg[5] too, he has to stand up stiff to him, eh?"

"Sure," says Kat.

Tjaden hasn't finished yet. He thinks for a while and then asks: "And would a king have to stand up stiff to an emperor?"

---

3. **Kaiser.** Kaiser Wilhelm II (1859–1941), emperor of Germany and king of Prussia

4. **bar nobody.** Nobody excepted

5. **Hindenburg.** Paul von Hindenburg (1847–1934), German field marshal, an officer of the highest rank

**words for everyday use**

pee • vish (pēv′ ish) adj., showing ill humor or impatience. *After staying up all night, Sasha was peevish, taking offense at almost every remark.*

ex • as • per • ate (eg zas′ pər āt′) vt., irritate or annoy very much; make angry. *Nick's two-year-old brother's constant question, "Why?", served tp exasperate him after it was asked the first dozen times.*

None of us is quite sure about it, but we don't suppose so. They are both so <u>exalted</u> that standing strictly to attention is probably not insisted on.

"What rot you do hatch out," says Kat. "The main point is that you have to stand stiff yourself."

But Tjaden is quite fascinated. His otherwise prosy[6] fancy is blowing bubbles. "But look," he announces, "I simply can't believe that an emperor has to go to the latrine the same as I have."

"You can bet your boots on it."

"Four and a half-wit make seven," says Kat. "You've got a maggot in your brain, Tjaden, just you run along to the latrine quick, and get your head clear, so that you don't talk like a two-year-old."

Tjaden disappears.

▶ What does Albert Kropp want to know?

"But what I would like to know," says Albert, "is whether there would not have been a war if the Kaiser had said No."

"I'm sure there would," I interject, "he was against it from the first."

"Well, if not him alone, then perhaps if twenty or thirty people in the world had said No."

"That's probable," I agree, "but they damned well said Yes."

▶ What does Kropp find queer?

"It's queer, when one thinks about it," goes on Kropp, "we are here to protect our fatherland. And the French are over there to protect their fatherland. Now who's in the right?"

"Perhaps both," say I without believing it.

"Yes, well now," pursues Albert, and I see that he means to drive me into a corner, "but our professors and parsons[7] and newspapers say that we are the only ones that are right, and let's hope so;—but the French professors and parsons and newspapers say that the right is on their side, now what about that?"

"That I don't know," I say, "but whichever way it is there's war all the same and every month more countries coming in."

---

6. **prosy.** Commonplace, dull
7. **parsons.** Ministers; religious leaders

---

**words for everyday use**

ex • alt (eg zôlt') *vt.*, raise on high; elevate; lift up; specifically, raise in status, dignity, power, honor, or wealth. *The peasant was afraid to address the king because of the difference between his humble station and the king's <u>exalted</u> one.*

Tjaden reappears. He is still quite excited and again joins the conversation, wondering just how a war gets started.

"Mostly by one country badly offending another," answers Albert with a slight air of superiority.

◄ What starts wars, according to Albert? What does Tjaden point out?

Then Tjaden pretends to be <u>obtuse</u>. "A country? I don't follow. A mountain in Germany cannot offend a mountain in France. Or a river, or a wood, or a field of wheat."

"Are you really as stupid as that, or are you just pulling my leg?" growls Kropp, "I don't mean that at all. One people offends the other—"

◄ How does Albert Kropp clarify his last remark? What is Tjaden's response?

"Then I haven't any business here at all," replies Tjaden, "I don't feel myself offended."

"Well, let me tell you," says Albert sourly, "it doesn't apply to tramps like you."

"Then I can be going home right away," retorts Tjaden, and we all laugh.

"Ach, man! he means the people as a whole, the State—" exclaims Müller.

"State, State"—Tjaden snaps his fingers contemptuously, "Gendarmes,[8] police, taxes, that's your State;—if that's what you are talking about, no, thank you."

◄ According to Tjaden, what is a state? From what is it different?

"That's right," says Kat, "you've said something for once, Tjaden. State and home-country, there's a big difference."

"But they go together," insists Kropp, "without the State there wouldn't be any home-country."

"True, but just you consider, almost all of us are simple folk. And in France, too, the majority of men are labourers, workmen, or poor clerks. Now just why would a French blacksmith or a French shoemaker want to attack us? No, it is merely the rulers. I had never seen a Frenchman before I came here, and it will be just the same with the majority of Frenchmen as regards us. They weren't asked about it any more than we were."

"Then what exactly is the war for?" asks Tjaden.

Kat shrugs his shoulders. "There must be some people to whom the war is useful."

"Well, I'm not one of them," grins Tjaden.

"Not you, nor anybody else here."

---

8. **Gendarmes.** Soldiers serving as armed police

**words for everyday use**
ob • tuse (äb tüs') *adj.*, slow to understand or perceive. *Although Marisa is very quick with math, she is somewhat more *obtuse* when it comes to history.*

▶ According to Kat, why might the Kaiser want a war?

"Who are they then?" persists Tjaden. "Isn't any use to the Kaiser either. He has everything he can want already."

"I'm not so sure about that," contradicts Kat, "he has not had a war up till now. And every full-grown emperor requires at least one war, otherwise he would not become famous. You look in your school books."

"And generals too," adds Detering, "they become famous through war."

"Even more famous than emperors," adds Kat.

▶ According to Detering, what do some people do during the war? To what does Albert compare war?

"There are other people back behind there who profit by the war, that's certain," growls Detering.

"I think it is more of a kind of fever," says Albert. "No one in particular wants it, and then all at once there it is. We didn't want the war, the others say the same thing— and yet half the world is in it all the same."

"But there are more lies told by the other side than by us," say I; "just think of those pamphlets the prisoners have on them, where it says that we eat Belgian children. The fellows who write those lies ought to go and hang themselves. They are the real <u>culprits</u>."

Müller gets up. "Anyway, it is better that the war is here instead of in Germany. Just you look at the shell-holes."

"True," assents Tjaden, "but no war at all would be better still."

He is quite proud of himself because he has scored for once over us volunteers. And his opinion is quite typical, here one meets it time and again, and there is nothing with which one can properly counter it, because that is the limit of their comprehension of the factors involved. The national feeling of the tommy[9] resolves itself into this— here he is. But that is the end of it; everything else he criticizes from his own practical point of view.

▶ Why don't the soldiers want to talk about the causes of war anymore?

▶ What happens to the soldiers' new clothes?

Albert lies down on the grass and growls angrily: "The best thing is not to talk about the rotten business."

"It won't make any difference, that's sure," agrees Kat.

To make matters worse, we have to return almost all the new things and take back our old rags again. The good ones were merely for the inspection.

---

9. **tommy.** Private in the British army

**words for everyday use**

cul • prit (kul' prit) *n.*, person guilty of a crime or offense; offender. *After the <u>culprit</u> was featured on the FBI's ten most wanted list, the police caught him.*

*

Instead of going to Russia, we go up the line again. On the way we pass through a devastated wood with the tree trunks shattered and the ground ploughed up.

At several places there are tremendous craters. "Great guns, something's hit that," I say to Kat.

"Trench mortars,"[10] he replies, and then points up at one of the trees.

In the branches dead men are hanging. A naked soldier is squatting in the fork of a tree, he still has his helmet on, otherwise he is entirely unclad. There is only half of him sitting up there, the top half, the legs are missing.

◀ What are in the trees?

"What can that mean?" I ask.

"He's been blown out of his clothes," mutters Tjaden.

"It's funny," says Kat, "we have seen that several times now. If a mortar gets you it blows you clean out of your clothes. It's the concussion[11] that does it."

I search around. And so it is. Here hang bits of uniform, and somewhere else is plastered a bloody mess that was once a human limb. Over there lies a body with nothing but a piece of the underpants on one leg and the collar of the tunic around its neck. Otherwise it is naked and the clothes are hanging up in the tree. Both arms are missing as though they had been pulled out. I discover one of them twenty yards off in a shrub.

◀ What else do the soldiers find?

The dead man lies on his face. There, where the arm wounds are, the earth is black with blood. Underfoot the leaves are scratched up as though the man had been kicking.

"That's no joke, Kat," say I.

"No more is a shell splinter in the belly," he replies, shrugging his shoulders.

"But don't get tender-hearted," says Tjaden.

All this can only have happened a little while ago, the blood is still fresh. As everybody we see there is dead we do not waste any more time, but report the affair at the next stretcher-bearers' post.[12] After all it is not our business to take these stretcher-bearers' jobs away from them.

*

A patrol has to be sent out to discover just how strongly the enemy position is manned. Since my leave I feel a certain strange attachment to the other fellows, and so I

◀ Why does Paul volunteer for patrol?

---

10. **Trench mortars.** Portable canon used to shoot shells at short range and in a high trajectory
11. **concussion.** Shock from the impact
12. **stretcher-bearers' post.** Place where people who carry away the dead and wounded on stretchers are stationed

volunteer to go with them. We agree on a plan, slip out through the wire and then divide and creep forward separately. After a while I find a shallow shell-hole and crawl into it. From here I peer forward.

There is moderate machine-gun fire. It sweeps across from all directions, not very heavy, but always sufficient to make one keep down.

A parachute star-shell[13] opens out. The ground lies <u>stark</u> in the pale light, and then the darkness shuts down again blacker than ever. In the trenches we were told there were black troops[14] in front of us. That is nasty, it is hard to see them; they are very good at patrolling, too. And oddly enough they are often quite stupid; for instance, both Kat and Kropp were once able to shoot down a black enemy patrol because the fellows in their enthusiasm for cigarettes smoked while they were creeping about. Kat and Albert had simply to aim at the glowing ends of the cigarettes.

▶ What happens to Paul when he hears the first bomb land?

A bomb or something lands close beside me. I have not heard it coming and am terrified. At the same moment a senseless fear takes hold on me. Here I am alone and almost helpless in the dark—perhaps two other eyes have been watching me for a long while from another shell-hole in front of me, and a bomb lies ready to blow me to pieces. I try to pull myself together. It is not my first patrol and not a particularly risky one. But it is the first since my leave, and besides, the lie[15] of the land is still rather strange to me.

I tell myself that my alarm is absurd, that there is probably nothing at all there in the darkness watching me, otherwise they would not be firing so low.

It is in vain. In whirling confusion my thoughts hum in my brain—I hear the warning voice of my mother, I see the Russians with the flowing beards leaning against the wire fence, I have a bright picture of a canteen with stools, of a cinema in Valenciennes;[16] tormented, terrified, in my imagination I see the grey, <u>implacable</u> muzzle of a rifle

---

13. **parachute star-shell.** Parachute with a light for illuminating the movements of enemy troops
14. **black troops.** Paul displays prejudice against people of African descent; such bigotry was widespread in Germany during this period in history.
15. **lie.** The way something is situated or arranged
16. **Valenciennes.** City in northern France near the Belgium border

---

**words for everyday use**

**stark** (stärk) *adj.,* sharply outlined or prominent. *In the <u>stark</u> light of morning, all the leafless trees looked gray and dead.*

**im • pla • ca • ble** (im plā′ kə bəl) *adj.,* that cannot be appeased or pacified; relentless. *From Mark's <u>implacable</u> face, I knew he was not ready to forgive me.*

which moves noiselessly before me whichever way I try to turn my head. The sweat breaks out from every pore.

I still continue to lie in the shallow bowl. I look at the time; only a few minutes have passed. My forehead is wet, the sockets of my eyes are damp, my hands tremble, and I am panting softly. It is nothing but an awful spasm of fear, a simple animal fear of poking out my head and crawling on farther.

All my efforts <u>subside</u> like froth into the one desire to be able just to stay lying there. My limbs are glued to the earth. I make a vain attempt;—they refuse to come away. I press myself down on the earth, I cannot go forward, I make up my mind to stay lying there.

But immediately the wave floods over me anew, a mingled sense of shame, of remorse, and yet at the same time of security. I raise myself up a little to take a look round.

My eyes burn with staring into the dark. A star-shell goes up;—I duck down again.

I <u>wage</u> a wild and senseless fight, I want to get out of the hollow and yet slide back into it again; I say "You must, it is your comrades, it is not an idiotic command," and again: "What does it matter to me, I have only one life to lose—"

That is the result of all this leave, I plead in <u>extenuation</u>. But I cannot reassure myself; I become terribly faint. I raise myself slowly and reach forward with my arms, dragging my body after me and then lie on the edge of the shell-hole, half in and half out.

There I hear sounds and drop back. Suspicious sounds can be detected clearly despite the noise of the artillery-fire. I listen; the sound is behind me. They are our people moving along the trench. Now I hear muffled voices. To judge by the tone that might be Kat talking.

At once a new warmth flows through me. These voices, these quiet words, these footsteps in the trench behind me recall me at a bound from the terrible loneliness and fear of death by which I had been almost destroyed. They are more to me than life, these voices, they are more than

◀ What does Paul believe is the cause of his fear?

◀ What does Paul find to be the most comforting thing there is?

---

**words for everyday use**

sub • side (səb sīd') vi., become less active or intense. As the wind <u>subsided</u>, the waves became smaller until eventually the bay was calm.

wage (wāj) vt., engage in or carry on (a war, struggle, campaign, etc.). To become independent, American colonists had to <u>wage</u> war against Great Britain.

ex • ten • u • a • tion (ek sten' yü ā' shən) n., lessening or seeming to lessen the seriousness of (an offense, guilt, etc.) by giving excuses. The defense attorney said her client had a mental illness, hoping that the judge might take this in account as an <u>extenuation</u> when its was time for sentencing.

motherliness and more than fear; they are the strongest, most comforting thing there is anywhere: they are the voices of my comrades.

I am no longer a shuddering speck of existence, alone in the darkness;—I belong to them and they to me; we all share the same fear and the same life, we are nearer than lovers, in a simpler, a harder way; I could bury my face in them, in these voices, these words that have saved me and will stand by me.

*

Cautiously I glide out over the edge and snake my way forward. I shuffle along on all fours a bit farther, I keep track of my bearings, look around me and observe the distribution of the gunfire so as to be able to find my way back. Then I try to get in touch with the others.

I am still afraid, but it is an intelligent fear, an extraordinarily heightened caution. The night is windy and shadows <u>flit</u> hither and thither in the flicker of the gunfire. It reveals too little and too much. Often I pause, stock still, motionless, and always for nothing. Thus I advance a long way and then turn back in a wide curve. I have not established touch with the others. Every yard nearer our trench fills me with confidence—and with haste, too. It would be bad to get hit now.

▶ *What new fear strikes Paul?*

Then a new fear lays hold of me. I can no longer remember the direction. Quiet, I squat in a shell-hole and try to locate myself. More than once it has happened that some fellow has jumped joyfully into a trench, only then to discover that it was the wrong one.

After a little time I listen again, but still I am not sure. The confusion of shell-holes now seems so bewildering that I can no longer tell in my agitation which way I should go. Perhaps I am crawling parallel to the lines, and that might go on forever. So I crawl round once again in a wide curve.

These damned rockets! They seem to burn for an hour, and a man cannot make the least movement without bringing the bullets whistling round.

But there is nothing for it, I must get out. Falteringly I work my way farther, I move off over the ground like a crab and rip my hands sorely on the jagged splinters, as

---

**words for everyday use**

**flit** (flit) *vi.*, pass lightly and rapidly. *Sherry <u>flitted</u> from one activity to the next, trying everything from basketball to French club, in a whirlwind of activity.*

sharp as razor blades. Often I think that the sky is becoming lighter on the horizon, but it may be merely my imagination. Then gradually I realize that to crawl in the right direction is a matter of life or death.

A shell crashes. Almost immediately two others. And then it begins in earnest. A bombardment. Machine-guns rattle. Now there is nothing for it but to stay lying low. Apparently an attack is coming. Everywhere the rockets shoot up. Unceasing.

◀ What happens while Paul is lost?

I lie huddled in a large shell-hole, my legs in the water up to the belly. When the attack starts I will let myself fall into the water, with my face as deep in the mud as I can keep it without suffocating. I must pretend to be dead.

Suddenly I hear the barrage lift. At once I slip down into the water, my helmet on the nape[17] of my neck and my mouth just clear so that I can get a breath of air.

I lie motionless;—somewhere something clanks, it stamps and stumbles nearer—all my nerves become taut and icy. It clatters over me and away, the first wave has passed. I have but this one shattering thought: What will you do if someone jumps into your shell-hole?—Swiftly I pull out my little dagger, grasp it fast and bury it in my hand once again under the mud. If anyone jumps in here I will go for him. It hammers in my forehead; at once, stab him clean through the throat, so that he cannot call out; that's the only way; he will be just as frightened as I am; when in terror we fall upon one another, then I must be first.

◀ What does Paul decide to do if someone jumps in his shell hole?

Now our batteries are firing. A shell lands near me. That makes me savage with fury, all it needs now is to be killed by our own shells; I curse and grind my teeth in the mud; it is a raving frenzy; in the end all I can do is groan and pray.

The crash of the shells bursts in my ears. If our fellows make a counter-raid I will be saved. I press my head against the earth and listen to the muffled thunder, like the explosions of quarrying—and raise it again to listen for the sounds on top.

The machine-guns rattle. I know our barbed wire entanglements are strong and almost undamaged;—parts of them are charged with a powerful electric current. The rifle fire increases. They have not broken through; they have to retreat.

I sink down again, huddled, strained to the uttermost. The banging, the creeping, the clanging becomes audible. One single cry yelling amongst it all. They are raked with fire, the attack is repulsed.

---

17. **nape.** Back of the neck

*

▶ What happens to
Paul? How does he
react?

Already it has become somewhat lighter. Steps hasten over me. The first. Gone. Again, another. The rattle of machine-guns becomes an unbroken chain. Just as I am about to turn round a little, something heavy stumbles, and with a crash a body falls over me into the shell-hole, slips down, and lies across me—

I do not think at all, I make no decision—I strike madly home,[18] and feel only how the body suddenly convulses, then becomes limp, and collapses. When I recover myself, my hand is sticky and wet.

The man gurgles. It sounds to me as though he bellows, every gasping breath is like a cry, a thunder—but it is only my heart pounding. I want to stop his mouth, stuff it with earth, stab him again, he must be quiet, he is betraying me; now at last I regain control of myself, but have suddenly become so feeble that I cannot any more lift my hand against him.

So I crawl away to the farthest corner and stay there, my eyes glued on him, my hand grasping the knife—ready, if he stirs, to spring at him again. But he won't do so any more, I can hear that already in his gurgling.

▶ What does Paul
want to do? Why
can't he do this
thing?

I can see him indistinctly. I have but one desire, to get away. If it is not soon it will be too light; it will be difficult enough now. Then as I try to raise up my head I see it is impossible already. The machine-gunfire so sweeps the ground that I should be shot through and through before I could make one jump.

I test it once with my helmet, which I take off and hold up to find out the level of the shots. The next moment it is knocked out of my hand by a bullet. The fire is sweeping very low to the ground. I am not far enough from the enemy line to escape being picked off by one of the snipers if I attempt to get away.

The light increases. Burning I wait for our attack. My hands are white at the knuckles, I clench them so tightly in my longing for the fire to cease so that my comrades may come.

Minute after minute trickles away. I dare not look again at the dark figure in the shell-hole. With an effort I look past it and wait, wait. The bullets hiss, they make a steel net, never ceasing, never ceasing.

▶ Why does Paul rub
his hand with mud?

Then I notice my bloody hand and suddenly feel nauseated. I take some earth and rub the skin with it; now my hand is muddy and the blood cannot be seen any more.

---

18. **home.** Reaching its goal or target

The fire does not diminish. It is equally heavy from both sides. Our fellows have probably given me up for lost long ago.

*

It is early morning, clear and grey. The gurgling continues, I stop my ears, but soon take my fingers away again, because then I cannot hear the other sound.

The figure opposite me moves. I shrink together and involuntarily look at it. Then my eyes remain glued to it. A man with a small pointed beard lies there; his head is fallen to one side, one arm is halfbent, his head rests helplessly upon it. The other hand lies on his chest, it is bloody.

He is dead, I say to myself, he must be dead, he doesn't feel anything any more; it is only the body that is gurgling there. Then the head tries to raise itself, for a moment the groaning becomes louder, his forehead sinks back upon his arm. The man is not dead, he is dying, but he is not dead. I drag myself toward him, hesitate, support myself on my hands, creep a bit farther, wait, again a terrible journey. At last I am beside him.

Then he opens his eyes. He must have heard me, for he gazes at me with a look of utter terror. The body lies still, but in the eyes there is such an extraordinary expression of fright that for a moment I think they have power enough to carry the body off with them. Hundreds of miles away with one bound. The body is still perfectly still, without a sound, the gurgle has ceased, but the eyes cry out, yell, all the life is gathered together in them for one tremendous effort to flee, gathered together there in a dreadful terror of death, of me.

My legs give way and I drop on my elbows. "No, no," I whisper.

The eyes follow me. I am powerless to move so long as they are there.

Then his hand slips slowly from his breast, only a little bit, it sinks just a few inches, but this movement breaks the power of the eyes. I bend forward, shake my head and whisper: "No, no, no," I raise one hand, I must show him that I want to help him, I stroke his forehead.

The eyes shrink back as the hand comes, then they lose their stare, the eyelids droop lower, the tension is past. I open his collar and place his head more comfortably.

His mouth stands half open, it tries to form words. The lips are dry. My water bottle is not there. I have not brought it with me. But there is water in the mud, down at the bottom of the crater. I climb down, take out my handkerchief, spread it out, push it under and scoop up the yellow water that strains through into the hollow of my hand.

◀ How does the dying man react when Paul crawls closer?

◀ Why does Paul whisper, "No, no"?

◀ What does Paul do for the enemy soldier? Why must he try to bandage the enemy soldier?

He gulps it down. I fetch some more. Then I unbutton his tunic in order to bandage him if it is possible. In any case I must do it, so that if the fellows over there capture me they will see that I wanted to help him, and so will not shoot me. He tries to resist, but his hand is too feeble. The shirt is stuck and will not come away, it is buttoned at the back. So there is nothing for it but to cut it open.

I look for the knife and find it again. But when I begin to cut the shirt the eyes open once more and the cry is in them again and the demented expression, so that I must close them, press them shut and whisper: "I want to help you, Comrade, camerade, camerade, camerade—" eagerly repeating the word, to make him understand.

▶ What does Paul call the soldier?

There are three stabs. My field dressing covers them, the blood runs out under it, I press it tighter; there; he groans.

That is all I can do. Now we must wait, wait.

\*

These hours. . . . The gurgling starts again—but how slowly a man dies! For this I know—he cannot be saved, I have, indeed, tried to tell myself that he will be, but at noon this <u>pretense</u> breaks down and melts before his groans. If only I had not lost my revolver crawling about, I would shoot him. Stab him I cannot.

By noon I am groping on the outer limits of reason. Hunger devours me, I could almost weep for something to eat, I cannot struggle against it. Again and again I fetch water for the dying man and drink some myself.

▶ What has Paul done for the first time?

This is the first time I have killed with my hands, whom I can see close at hand, whose death is my doing. Kat and Kropp and Müller have experienced it already, when they have hit someone; it happens to many, in hand-to-hand fighting especially—

But every gasp lays my heart bare. This dying man has time with him, he has an invisible dagger with which he stabs me: Time and my thoughts.

I would give much if he would but stay alive. It is hard to lie here and to have to see and hear him.

▶ What finally happens?

In the afternoon, about three, he is dead.

I breathe freely again. But only for a short time. Soon the silence is more unbearable than the groans. I wish the

---

**words for everyday use**   pre • tense (prē tens') *n.*, false show of something. *For the school play, we had to talk in British accents, and the director suggested we keep up the* <u>pretense</u> *even at home.*

---

gurgling were there again, gasping, hoarse, now whistling softly and again hoarse and loud.

It is mad, what I do. But I must do something. I prop the dead man up again so that he lies comfortably, although he feels nothing any more. I close his eyes. They are brown, his hair is black and a bit curly at the sides.

◀ What does Paul do for the dead soldier?

The mouth is full and soft beneath his moustache; the nose is slightly arched, the skin brownish; it is now not so pale as it was before, when he was still alive. For a moment the face seems almost healthy;—then it collapses suddenly into the strange face of the dead that I have so often seen, strange faces, all alike.

No doubt his wife still thinks of him; she does not know what has happened. He looks as if he would have often written to her;—she will still be getting mail from him—Tomorrow, in a week's time—perhaps even a stray letter a month hence. She will read it, and in it he will be speaking to her.

My state is getting worse, I can no longer control my thoughts. What would his wife look like? Like the little brunette on the other side of the canal? Does she belong to me now? Perhaps by this act she becomes mine. I wish Kantorek were sitting here beside me. If my mother could see me—. The dead man might have had thirty more years of life if only I had impressed the way back to our trench more sharply on my memory. If only he had run two yards farther to the left, he might now be sitting in the trench over there and writing a fresh letter to his wife.

But I will get no further that way; for that is the fate of all of us: if Kemmerich's leg had been six inches to the right: if Haie Westhus had bent his back three inches further forward—

*

The silence spreads. I talk and must talk. So I speak to him and say to him: "Comrade, I did not want to kill you. If you jumped in here again, I would not do it, if you would be sensible too. But you were only an idea to me before, an <u>abstraction</u> that lived in my mind and called forth its appropriate response. It was that abstraction I stabbed. But now, for the first time, I see you are a man like

◀ What does Paul tell the dead man?

◀ What does Paul now see about the soldier? According to Paul, what do they never tell us?

---

**words for everyday use**   ab • strac • tion (ab strak' shən) *n.,* formation of an idea, as of the qualities or properties of a thing, by mental separation from particular instances. *Rommie liked French food only as an <u>abstraction</u>; when she was actually faced with a plate of escargots—snails, a French delicacy—she nearly fainted.*

me. I thought of your hand-grenades, of your bayonet, of your rifle; now I see your wife and your face and our fellowship. Forgive me, comrade. We always see it too late. Why do they never tell us that you are poor devils[19] like us, that your mothers are just as anxious as ours, and that we have the same fear of death, and the same dying and the same agony—Forgive me, comrade; how could you be my enemy? If we threw away these rifles and this uniform you could be my brother just like Kat and Albert. Take twenty years of my life, comrade, and stand up—take more, for I do not know what I can even attempt to do with it now."

It is quiet, the front is still except for the crackle of rifle fire. The bullets rain over, they are not fired <u>haphazard</u>, but shrewdly aimed from all sides. I cannot get out.

"I will write to your wife," I say hastily to the dead man, "I will write to her, she must hear it from me, I will tell her everything I have told you, she shall not suffer, I will help her, and your parents too, and your child—"

His tunic is half open. The pocket-book is easy to find. But I hesitate to open it. In it is the book with his name. So long as I do not know his name perhaps I may still forget him, time will obliterate it, this picture. But his name, it is a nail that will be hammered into me and never come out again. It has the power to recall this forever, it will always come back and stand before me.

<u>Irresolutely</u> I take the wallet in my hand. It slips out of my hand and falls open. Some pictures and letters drop out. I gather them up and want to put them back again, but the strain I am under, the uncertainty, the hunger, the danger, these hours with the dead man have made me desperate, I want to hasten the relief, to intensify and to end the torture, as one strikes an unendurably painful hand against the trunk of a tree, regardless of everything.

There are portraits of a woman and a little girl, small amateur photographs taken against an ivy-clad wall. Along with them are letters. I take them out and try to read them. Most of it I do not understand, it is so hard to decipher and I scarcely know any French. But each word I translate pierces me like a shot in the chest;—like a stab in the chest.

▶ *Why does Paul hesitate in opening the dead man's wallet?*

▶ *Of whom does Paul find photos?*

---

19. **devils.** Unlucky, unhappy people

**words for everyday use**

hap • haz • ard (hap′ haz′ ərd) *adv.,* by chance; casually. *Will pitched the ball* <u>haphazard</u>, *missing the catcher's glove and nearly hitting the batter.*

ir • res • o • lute • ly (ir rez′ ə lüt′ lē) *adv.,* indecisively. *Stan stared at the multiple choice question <u>irresolutely</u>, not sure whether to pick B or C.*

My brain is <u>taxed</u> beyond endurance. But I realize this much, that I will never dare to write to these people as I intended. Impossible. I look at the portraits once more; they are clearly not rich people. I might send them money anonymously if I earn anything later on. I seize upon that, it is at least something to hold on to. This dead man is bound up with my life, therefore I must do everything, promise everything in order to save myself; I swear blindly that I mean to live only for his sake and his family, with wet lips I try to <u>placate</u> him—and deep down in me lies the hope that I may buy myself off in this way and perhaps even get out of this; it is a little <u>stratagem</u>: if only I am allowed to escape, then I will see to it. So I open the book and read slowly:—Gérard Duval, compositor.[20]

◀ What does Paul swear to the dead man? What is Paul's stratagem?

With the dead man's pencil I write the address on an envelope, then swiftly thrust everything back into his tunic.

◀ What was the dead man's name and profession?

I have killed the printer, Gérard Duval. I must be a printer, I think confusedly, be a printer, printer—

*

By afternoon I am calmer. My fear was <u>groundless</u>. The name troubles me no more. The madness passes. "Comrade," I say to the dead man, but I say it calmly, "today you, tomorrow me. But if I come out of it, comrade, I will fight against this, that has struck us both down; from you, taken life—and from me—? Life also. I promise you, comrade. It shall never happen again."

◀ What does Paul tell the dead man when he is calmer? What promise does he make? What does he say they have both lost?

The sun strikes low, I am stupefied with exhaustion and hunger. Yesterday is like a fog to me, there is no hope of ever getting out of this. I fall into a doze and do not at first realize that evening is approaching. The twilight comes. It seems to me to come quickly now. One hour more. If it were summer, it would be three hours more. One hour more.

---

20. **compositor.** Person who sets matter for printing; typesetter

---

**words for everyday use**

tax (taks) *vt.*, impose a burden on; put a strain on. *Doing that last pushup* <u>taxed</u> *Judy's strength, but she completed it.*

pla • cate (plā′ kāt′) *vt.*, stop from being angry; appease. *Jenna* <u>placated</u> *the sobbing baby by giving him a pacifier.*

strat • a • gem (strat′ ə jəm) *n.*, any trick or scheme for achieving some purpose.

*We needed to come up with a* <u>stratagem</u> *to keep Louisa away so we could set up for her surprise party.*

ground • less (ground′ lis) *adj.*, without reason or cause; unjustified. *Cecile's fears about the piano competition proved* <u>groundless</u> *because she easily won it.*

▶ *Why does Paul think no more about the dead man?*

Now suddenly I begin to tremble; something might happen in the interval. I think no more of the dead man, he is of no consequence to me now. With one bound the lust to live flares up again and everything that has filled my thoughts goes down before it. Now, merely to avert any ill-luck, I babble mechanically: "I will fulfil everything, fulfil everything I have promised you—" but already I know that I shall not do so.

Suddenly it occurs to me that my own comrades may fire on me as I creep up; they do not know I am coming. I will call out as soon as I can so that they will recognize me. I will stay lying in front of the trench until they answer me.

The first star. The front remains quiet. I breathe deeply and talk to myself in my excitement: "No foolishness now, Paul—Quiet, Paul, quiet—then you will be saved, Paul." When I use my Christian name it works as though someone else spoke to me, it has more power.

The darkness grows. My excitement subsides, I wait cautiously until the first rocket goes up. Then I crawl out of the shell-hole. I have forgotten the dead man. Before me lies the oncoming night and the pale gleaming field. I fix my eyes on a shell-hole; the moment the light dies I scurry over into it, grope farther, spring into the next, duck down, scramble onward.

I come nearer. There, by the light of a rocket I see something move in the wire, then it stiffens and I lie still. Next time I see it again, yes, they are men from our trench. But I am suspicious until I recognize our helmets. Then I call. And immediately an answer rings out my name: "Paul—Paul—"

I call again in answer. It is Kat and Albert who have come out with a stretcher to look for me.

▶ *Who finds Paul?*

"Are you wounded?"

"No, no—"

We drop into the trench. I ask for something to eat and wolf it down. Müller gives me a cigarette. In a few words I tell what happened. There is nothing new about it; it happens quite often. The night attack is the only unusual feature of the business. In Russia Kat once lay for two days behind the enemy lines before he could make his way back.

I do not mention the dead printer.

But by next morning I can keep it to myself no longer. I must tell Kat and Albert. They both try to calm me. "You can't do anything about it. What else could you have done? That is what you are here for."

I listen to them and feel comforted, reassured by their presence. It was mere <u>driveling</u> nonsense that I talked out there in the shell-hole.

"Look there for instance," points Kat.

◀ What does Paul now think about his words to the dead man?

On the fire-step stand some snipers. They rest their rifles with telescopic sights[21] on the parapet and watch the enemy front. Once and again a shot cracks out.

Then we hear the cry: "That's found a billet!"[22] "Did you see how he leapt in the air?" Sergeant Oellrich turns round proudly and scores his point. He heads the shooting list for today with three unquestionable hits.

◀ What do Albert and Kat say it is good for Paul to see?

"What do you say to that?" asks Kat.

I nod.

"If he keeps that up he will get a little coloured bird for his buttonhole by this evening," says Albert.

"Or rather he will soon be made acting sergeant-major," says Kat.

We look at one another. "I would not do it," I say.

"All the same," says Kat, "it's very good for you to see it just now."

Sergeant Oellrich returns to the fire-step. The muzzle of his rifle searches to and fro.

"You don't need to lose any sleep over your affair," nods Albert.

And now I hardly understand it myself any more.

"It was only because I had to lie there with him so long," I say. "After all, war is war."

Oellrich's rifle cracks out sharply and dry.

---

21. **telescopic sights.** Device used to aid the eyes in lining up a gun with its target
22. **billet.** Quarters or place where military personnel sleep; here, used in place of the word *target*

| words for everyday use | driv • el (driv' əl) *vt.,* say in a silly or stupid manner. *We laughed at the soap opera characters' <u>driveling</u> and overly dramatic manner of speech.* |
|---|---|

# Chapter X

▶ *What makes this job a good one?*

We have dropped in for a good job. Eight of us have to guard a village that has been abandoned because it is being shelled too heavily. In particular we have to watch the supply dump[1] as that is not empty yet. We are supposed to provision ourselves from the same store. We are just the right people for that;—Kat, Albert, Müller, Tjaden, Detering, our whole gang is there. Haie is dead, though. But we are mighty lucky all the same, all the other squads have had more casualties than we have.

We select, as a dug-out, a reinforced concrete cellar into which steps lead down from above. The entrance is protected by a separate concrete wall.

Now we develop an immense industry. This is an opportunity not only to stretch one's legs, but to stretch one's soul also. We make the best use of such opportunities. The war is too desperate to allow us to be sentimental for long. That is only possible so long as things are not going too badly. After all, we cannot afford to be anything but matter-of-fact. So matter-of-fact, indeed, that I often shudder when a thought from the days before the war comes momentarily into my head. But it does not stay long.

We have to take things as lightly as we can, so we make the most of every opportunity, and nonsense stands stark and immediate beside horror. It cannot be otherwise, ▶ *What do the soldiers decide to create?* that is how we <u>hearten</u> ourselves. So we <u>zealously</u> set to work to create an <u>idyll</u>—an idyll of eating and sleeping of course.

The floor is first covered with mattresses which we haul in from the houses. Even a soldier's behind likes to sit soft. Only in the middle of the floor is there any clear space. Then we furnish ourselves with blankets, and eiderdowns,[2] luxurious soft affairs.[3] There is plenty of everything to be ▶ *What do Albert and Paul find?* had in the village. Albert and I find a mahogany bed which can be taken to pieces with a sky of blue silk and a lace coverlet. We sweat like monkeys moving it in, but a man

---

1. **supply dump.** Temporary storage center for food and other supplies
2. **eiderdowns.** Quilts stuffed with soft duck feathers
3. **affairs.** Things

---

**words for everyday use**

**heart • en** (härt' 'n) *vt.,* cheer up; encourage. *On snowy February days, Josh would* <u>hearten</u> *himself by thinking that spring and baseball season would arrive soon.*

**zeal • ous • ly** (zel' əs lē) *adv.,* in an intensely enthusiastic manner. *We* <u>zealously</u> *cheered as our hometown team won the state championship.*

**i • dyll** (īd' 'l) *n.,* simple, peaceful scene of rural or pastoral life. *We enjoyed our* <u>idyll</u> *in the park in which we picnicked in a shady grove.*

cannot let a thing like that slip, and it would certainly be shot to pieces in a day or two.

Kat and I do a little patrolling through the houses. In very short time we have collected a dozen eggs and two pounds of fairly fresh butter. Suddenly there is a crash in the drawing-room, and an iron stove hurtles through the wall past us and on, a yard from us out through the wall behind. Two holes. It comes from the house opposite where a shell has just landed. "The swine," grimaces Kat, and we continue our search. All at once we prick up our ears, hurry across, and suddenly stand petrified—there running up and down in a little sty are two live sucking pigs.[4] We rub our eyes and look once again to make certain. Yes, they are still there. We seize hold of them—no doubt about it, two real young pigs.

◀ What petrifies Paul and Kat?

This will make a grand feed. About twenty yards from our dug-out there is a small house that was used as an officers' billet. In the kitchen is an immense fireplace with two ranges, pots, pans, and kettles—everything, even to a stack of small chopped wood in an outhouse—a regular cook's paradise.

Two of our fellows have been out in the fields all the morning hunting for potatoes, carrots and green peas. We are quite uppish and sniff at the tinned stuff[5] in the supply dump, we want fresh vegetables. In the dining-room there are already two heads of cauliflower.

The sucking pigs are slaughtered. Kat sees to them. We want to make potato-cakes to go with the roast. But we cannot find a grater for the potatoes. However, that difficulty is soon got over. With a nail we punch a lot of holes in a pot lid and there we have a grater. Three fellows put on thick gloves to protect their fingers against the grater, two others peel the potatoes, and the business gets going.

Kat takes charge of the sucking pigs, the carrots, the peas, and the cauliflower. He even mixes a white sauce for the cauliflower. I fry the pancakes, four at a time. After ten minutes I get the knack of tossing the pan so that the pancakes which are done on one side sail up, turn in the air and are caught again as they come down. The sucking pigs are roasted whole. We all stand round them as before an altar.

In the meantime we receive visitors, a couple of wireless-men,[6] who are generously invited to the feed.

---

4. **sucking pigs.** Suckling pigs, baby pigs that still live on their mother's milk
5. **uppish . . . tinned stuff.** They scornfully turn up their noses at the canned goods
6. **wireless-men.** Radio operators, who keep lines of communication open in war

They sit in the living-room where there is a piano. One of them plays, the other sings "An der Weser." He sings feelingly, but with a rather Saxon accent.[7] All the same it moves us as we stand at the fireplace preparing the good things.

▶ What trouble are Paul and his friends in?

Then we begin to realize we are in for trouble. The observation balloons have spotted the smoke from our chimney, and the shells start to drop on us. They are those damned spraying little daisy-cutters that make only a small hole and scatter widely close to the ground. They keep dropping closer and closer all round us; still we cannot leave the grub in the lurch.[8] A couple of splinters whizz through the top of the kitchen window. The roast is ready. But frying the pancakes is getting difficult. The explosions come so fast that the splinters strike again and again against the wall of the house and sweep in through the window. Whenever I hear a shell coming I drop down on one knee with the pan and the pancakes, and duck behind the wall of the window. Immediately afterwards I am up again and going on with the frying.

▶ What does Paul do as the shells fly?

The Saxon stops singing—a fragment has smashed the piano. At last everything is ready and we organize the transport of it back to the dug-out. After the next explosion two men dash across the fifty yards to the dug-out with the pots of vegetables. We see them disappear.

The next shot. Everyone ducks and then two more trot off, each with a big can of finest grade coffee, and reach the dug-out before the next explosion.

Then Kat and Kropp seize the masterpiece—the big dish with the brown, roasted sucking pigs. A screech, a knee bend, and away they race over the fifty yards of open country.

I stay to finish my last four pancakes; twice I have to drop on the floor;—after all, it means four pancakes more, and they are my favourite dish.

Then I grab the plate with the great pile of cakes and squeeze myself behind the house door. A hiss, a crash, and I gallop off with the plate clamped against my chest with both hands. I am almost in, there is a rising screech, I bound, I run like a deer, sweep round the wall, fragments clatter against the concrete, I tumble down the cellar steps, my elbows are skinned, but I have not lost a single pancake, nor even upset the plate.

---

7. **"An der Weser" . . . accent.** He sings a German song about a river in an accent that marks him as coming from Saxony, a region in eastern Germany.
8. **grub in the lurch.** Food in danger

At two o'clock we start the meal. It lasts till six. We drink coffee until half-past six—officer's coffee from the supply dump—and smoke officer's cigars and cigarettes—also from the supply dump. Punctually at half-past six we begin supper. At ten o'clock we throw the bones of the sucking pigs outside the door. Then there is cognac and rum—also from the blessed supply dump—and once again long, fat cigars with belly-bands. Tjaden says that it lacks only one thing: Girls from an officer's brothel.

◄ What do Paul and his friends do from two o'clock on?

Late in the evening we hear mewing. A little grey cat sits in the entrance. We <u>entice</u> it in and give it something to eat. And that wakes up our own appetites once more. Still chewing, we lie down to sleep.

But the night is bad. We have eaten too much fat. Fresh baby pig is very griping[9] to the bowels. There is an ever-lasting coming and going in the dug-out. Two, three men with their pants down are always sitting about outside and cursing. I have been out nine times myself. About four o'clock in the morning we reach a record: all eleven men, guards and visitors, are squatting outside.

Burning houses stand out like torches against the night. Shells lumber across and crash down. Munition columns tear along the street. On one side the supply dump has been ripped open. In spite of all the flying fragments the drivers of the munition columns pour in like a swarm of bees and pounce on the bread. We let them have their own way. If we said anything it would only mean a good hiding for us. So we go differently about it. We explain that we are the guard and so know our way about, we get hold of the tinned stuff and exchange it for things we are short of. What does it matter anyhow—in a while it will all be blown to pieces. For ourselves we take some chocolate from the depot and eat it in slabs. Kat says it is good for loose bowels.

Almost a fortnight passes thus in eating, drinking and roaming about. No one disturbs us. The village gradually vanishes under the shells and we lead a charmed life. So long as any part of the supply dump still stands we don't worry, we desire nothing better than to stay here till the end of the war.

---

9. **griping.** Irritating

**words for everyday use**  en • tice (en tīs') vt., attract by offering hope of reward or pleasure. *I put up a bird feeder to <u>entice</u> the birds to my window.*

Tjaden has become so <u>fastidious</u> that he only half smokes his cigars. With his nose in the air he explains to us that he was brought up that way. And Kat is most cheerful. In the morning his first call is: "Emil, bring in the caviare and coffee." We put on extraordinary airs, every man treats the other as his valet,[10] bounces him and gives him orders. "There is something itching under my foot; Kropp my man, catch that louse at once," says Leer, poking out his leg at him like a ballet girl, and Albert drags him up the stairs by the foot. "Tjaden!"—"What?"—"Stand at ease, Tjaden; and what's more, don't say 'What,' say 'Yes, Sir,'—now: Tjaden!" Tjaden retorts in the well-known phrase from Goethe's "Götz von Berlichingen,"[11] with which he is always free.

► What orders do the soldiers receive? What do they take with them?

After eight more days we receive orders to go back. The palmy[12] days are over. Two big motor lorries take us away. They are stacked high with planks. Nevertheless, Albert and I erect on top our four-poster bed complete with blue silk canopy, mattress, and two lace coverlets. And behind it at the head is stowed a bag full of choicest edibles. We often dip into it, and the tough ham sausages, the tins of liver sausages, the conserves,[13] the boxes of cigarettes rejoice our hearts. Each man has a bag to himself.

Kropp and I have rescued two big red armchairs as well. They stand inside the bed, and we sprawl back in them as in a theatre box. Above us swells the silken cover like a baldaquin.[14] Each man has a long cigar in his mouth. And thus from aloft we survey the scene.

Between us stands a parrot cage that we found for the cat. She is coming with us, and lies in the cage before her saucer of meat, and purrs.

Slowly the lorries roll down the road. We sing. Behind us shells are sending up fountains from the now utterly abandoned village.

*

A few days later we are sent to evacuate a village. On the way we meet the fleeing inhabitants <u>trundling</u> their goods

---

10. **valet.** Personal servant
11. **phrase . . . "Gotz von Berlichingen."** Vulgar curse
12. **palmy.** Prosperous
13. **conserves.** Kind of jam
14. **baldaquin.** Rich fabric made of silk and gold often placed over an altar or throne

---

**words for everyday use**

fas • tid • i • ous (fas tid′ ē əs) *adj.*, refined in a too dainty or oversensitive way, so as to be easily disgusted. *Olivia is a <u>fastidious</u> eater who won't eat her bread if its has touched her meat or vegetables.*

trun • dle (trun′ dəl) *vt.*, move along in a wheeled vehicle. *My little brother seems to enjoy <u>trundling</u> our intended purchases around the grocery store in the shopping cart.*

and chattels[15] along with them in wheelbarrows, in perambulators,[16] and on their backs. Their figures are bent, their faces full of grief, despair, haste, and resignation. The children hold on to their mothers' hands, and often an older girl leads the little ones who stumble onward and are for ever looking back. A few carry miserable-looking dolls. All are silent as they pass us by.

We are marching in column; the French certainly will not fire on a town in which there are still inhabitants. But a few minutes later the air screams, the earth heaves, cries ring out; a shell has landed among our rear squad. We scatter and fling ourselves down on the ground, but at that moment I feel the instinctive alertness leave me which hitherto has always made me do unconsciously the right thing under fire; the thought leaps up with a terrible throttling fear: "You are lost"—and the next moment a blow sweeps like a whip over my left leg. I hear Albert cry out; he is beside me.

"Quick, up, Albert!" I yell, for we are lying unsheltered in the open field.

He staggers up and runs. I keep beside him. We have to get over a hedge; it is higher than we are. Kropp seizes a branch, I heave him up by the leg, he cries out, I give him a swing and he flies over. With one bound I follow him and fall into a ditch that lies behind the hedge.

Our faces are smothered with duck-weed and mud, but the cover is good. So we wade in up to our necks. Whenever a shell whistles we duck our heads under the water. After we have done this a dozen times, I am exhausted.

"Let's get away, or I'll fall in and drown," groans Albert.

"Where has it got you?" I ask him.

"In the knee I think."

"Can you run?"

"I think—"

"Then out!"

We make for the ditch beside the road, and stooping, run along it. The shelling follows us. The road leads towards the munition dump.[17] If that goes up there won't be so much as a boot-lace left of us. So we change our plan and run diagonally across country.

Albert begins to drag. "You go, I'll come on after," he says, and throws himself down.

◀ What does Paul believe the French will not do? What happens to dispel this belief?

◀ What does Paul feel leave him? What happens to Paul and Albert?

---

15. **chattels.** Movable items of personal property
16. **perambulators.** Baby carriages
17. **munition dump.** Temporary military site for weapons and ammunition, highly explosive

▶ Why does Paul make Albert get up?

▶ Where have Paul and Albert been injured?

I seize him by the arm and shake him. "Up, Albert, if once you lie down you'll never get any farther. Quick, I'll hold you up."

At last we reach a small dug-out. Kropp pitches in and I bandage him up. The shot is just a little above his knee. Then I take a look at myself. My trousers are bloody and my arm, too. Albert binds up my wounds with his field dressing. Already he is no longer able to move his leg, and we both wonder how we managed to get this far. Fear alone made it possible; we should have run even if our feet had been shot off;—we would have run on the stumps.

I can still crawl a little. I call out to a passing ambulance wagon which picks us up. It is full of wounded. There is an army medical lance-corporal with it who sticks an anti-tetanus needle[18] into our chests.

At the dressing station we arrange matters so that we lie side by side. They give us a thin soup which we spoon down greedily and scornfully, because we are accustomed to better times but are hungry all the same.

"Now for home, Albert," I say.

"Let's hope so," he replies, "I only wish I knew what I've got."

The pain increases. The bandages burn like fire. We drink and drink, one glass of water after another.

"How far above the knee am I hit?" asks Kropp.

▶ What lie does Paul tell Albert?

"At least four inches, Albert," I answer. Actually it is perhaps one.

"I've made up my mind," he says after a while, "if they take off my leg, I'll put an end to it. I won't go through life as a cripple."

So we lie there with our thoughts and wait.

*

▶ Why doesn't Paul want to let the surgeons chloroform him?

In the evening we are hauled on to the chopping-block.[19] I am frightened and think quickly what I ought to do; for everyone knows that the surgeons in the dressing stations amputate on the slightest provocation. Under the

---

18. **anti-tetanus.** Immunization to protect against tetanus, a highly infectious disease sometimes called lockjaw that people can get when they are wounded by a wood or metal object

19. **chopping-block.** Paul is referring to the operating table, implying that the surgeons only use it for amputating.

---

**words for everyday use**  prov • o • ca • tion (präv′ ə kā′ shən) *n.*, something that angers, irritates, or annoys. *The other team's bragging cheers were a provocation that led us to play harder.*

great business that is much simpler than complicated patching. I think of Kemmerich. Whatever happens I will not let them chloroform[20] me, even if I have to crack a couple of their skulls.

It is all right. The surgeon pokes around in the wound and a blackness comes before my eyes. "Don't carry on so," he says gruffly, and hacks away. The instruments gleam in the bright light like <u>malevolent</u> animals. The pain is <u>insufferable</u>. Two orderlies hold my arms fast, but I break loose with one of them and try to crash into the surgeon's spectacles just as he notices and springs back. "Chloroform the scoundrel," he roars madly.

Then I become quiet. "Pardon me, Herr Doctor, I will keep still but do not chloroform me."

"Well now," he cackles and takes up his instrument again. He is a fair fellow, not more than thirty years old, with scars and disgusting gold spectacles. Now I see that he is tormenting me, he is merely raking about in the wound and looking up <u>surreptitiously</u> at me over his glasses. My hands squeeze around the grips, I'll kick the bucket before he will get a squeak out of me.

◀ What does Paul believe the surgeon is doing?

He has fished out a piece of shell and tosses it to me. Apparently he is pleased at my self-control, for he now sets my leg carefully in splints and says: "Tomorrow you'll be off home." Then I am put in plaster.[21] When I am back again with Kropp I tell him that apparently a hospital train comes in tomorrow morning.

"We must work the army medical sergeant-major so that we can keep together, Albert."

◀ What do Paul and Albert do to keep from being separated?

I manage to slip the sergeant-major two of my cigars with belly-bands, and then tip the word to him. He smells the cigars and says: "Have you got any more of them?"

"Another good handful," I say, "and my comrade," I point to Kropp, "he has some as well. We might possibly be glad to hand them to you out of the window of the hospital train in the morning."

---

20. **chloroform.** Knock out with anesthesia
21. **plaster.** Plaster cast

---

**words for everyday use**

ma • lev • o • lent (mə lev′ ə lənt) adj., wishing evil or harm to others; having or showing ill will. *Casey carved a happy-looking jack-o-lantern, but I carved a frightening one with a <u>malevolent</u> look.*

in • suf • fer • a • ble (in suf′ ər ə bəl) adj., intolerable; unbearable. *When the music teacher passes out musical instruments to the kindergartners, the noise is <u>insufferable</u>.*

sur • rep • ti • tious • ly (sɘr′ əp tish′ əs lē) adv., in a secret, stealthy way. *Lola has such a love for sweets, she <u>surreptitiously</u> grabbed more than her fair share of dessert.*

He understands, of course, smells them once again and says: "Done."

We cannot get a minute's sleep all night. Seven fellows died in our ward. One of them sings hymns in a high cracked tenor[22] before he begins to gurgle. Another has crept out of his bed to the window. He lies in front of it as though he wants to look out for the last time.

*

Our stretchers stand on the platform. We wait for the train. It rains and the station has no roof. Our blankets are thin. We have waited already two hours.

The sergeant-major looks after us like a mother. Although I feel pretty bad I do not let our scheme out of my mind. Casually I let him see the packet and give him one cigar in advance. In exchange the sergeant-major covers us over with a waterproof sheet.

▶ Why are Paul and Albert melancholy?

"Albert, old man," I suddenly bethink myself, "our four-poster and the cat—"

"And the club chairs," he adds.

Yes, the club chairs with red plush. In the evening we used to sit in them like lords, and intended later on to let them out by the hour. One cigarette per hour. It might have turned into a regular business, a real good living.

"And our bags of grub, too, Albert."

We grow melancholy. We might have made some use of the things. If only the train left one day later Kat would be sure to find us and bring us the stuff.

What damned hard luck! In our bellies there is gruel, mean hospital stuff, and in our bags roast pork. But we are so weak that we cannot work up any more excitement about it.

The stretchers are sopping wet by the time the train arrives in the morning. The sergeant-major sees to it that we are put in the same car. There is a crowd of red-cross nurses. Kropp is stowed in below.[23] I am lifted up and told to get into the bed above him.

▶ What surprises Paul about the bed on the train? What does Paul ask the sister to do?

"Good God!" I exclaim suddenly.

"What is it?" asks the sister.

I cast a glance at the bed. It is covered with clean snow-white linen, that even has got the marks of the iron still on it. And my shirt has gone six weeks without being washed and is terribly muddy.

"Can't you get in by yourself?" asks the sister gently.

---

22. **tenor.** High singing voice
23. **stowed in below.** Put in the bottom bunk

"Why yes," I say in a sweat, "but take off the bed cover first."

"What for?"

I feel like a pig. Must I get in there?—"It will get—" I hesitate.

"A little bit dirty?" she suggests helpfully. "That doesn't matter, we will wash it again afterwards."

"No, no, not that—" I say excitedly. I am not equal to such overwhelming refinement.

"When you have been lying out there in the trenches, surely we can wash a sheet," she goes on.

I look at her, she is young and crisp, spotless and neat, like everything here; a man cannot realize that it isn't for officers only, and feels himself strange and in some way even alarmed.

All the same the woman is a tormentor, she is going to force me to say it. "It is only—" I try again, surely she must know what I mean.

"What is it then?"

"Because of the lice," I bawl out at last.

She laughs. "Well, they must have a good day for once, too."

◀ Why doesn't Paul want to get into the bed? What does the sister say to set his mind at ease?

Now I don't care any more. I scramble into bed and pull up the covers.

A hand gropes over the bed-cover. The sergeant-major. He goes off with the cigars.

An hour later we notice we are moving.

*

I wake up during the night. Kropp is restless too. The train rides easily over the rails. I cannot realize it all yet; a bed, a train, home. "Albert!" I whisper.

"Yes—"

"Do you know where the latrine is?"

"The door is on the right, I think."

"I'm going to have a look." It is dark, I grope for the edge of the bed and cautiously try to slide down. But my foot finds no support, I begin to slip, the plaster leg is no help, and with a crash I lie on the floor.

"Damn!" I say.

"Have you bumped yourself?" asks Kropp.

"You could hear that well enough for yourself," I growl, "my head—"

◀ Where is Paul trying to go?

A door opens at the rear of the car. The sister comes with a light and looks at me.

"He has fallen out of bed—"

She feels my pulse and smooths my forehead. "You haven't any fever, though."

"No," I agree.

"Have you been dreaming then?" she asks.

"Perhaps—" I evade. The interrogation starts again. She looks at me with her clear eyes, and the more wonderful and sweet she is the less am I able to tell her what I want.

▶ Why can't Paul tell the sister he is trying to go to the latrine?

I am lifted up into bed again. That will be all right. As soon as she goes I must try to climb down again. If she were an old woman, it might be easier to say what a man wants, but she is so very young, at the most twenty-five, it can't be done, I cannot possibly tell her.

Then Albert comes to my rescue, he is not bashful, it makes no difference to him who is upset. He calls to the sister. She turns round. "Sister, he wants—" but no more does Albert know how to express it modestly and decently. Out there we say it in a single word, but here, to such a lady—All at once he remembers his school days and finishes hastily: "He wants to leave the room, sister."

"Ah!" says the sister, "but he shouldn't climb out of his bed with plaster bandage. What do you want then?" she says turning to me.

I am in mortal terror at this turn, for I haven't any idea what the things are called professionally. She comes to my help.

"Little or big?"

Shocking business! I sweat like a pig and say shyly: "Well, only quite a little one—"

At any rate it produces the effect.

▶ How do Paul and the others no longer act after a few hours?

I get a bottle. After a few hours I am no longer the only one, and by morning we are quite accustomed to it and ask for what we want without any false modesty.

The train travels slowly. Sometimes it halts and the dead are unloaded. It halts often.

Albert is feverish. I don't feel too bad; I have some pain, but the worst of it is that apparently there are still lice under the plaster bandage. They itch terribly, and I cannot scratch myself.

▶ Why will Albert be put off the train at the next station?

We sleep through the days. The country glides quietly past the window. The third night we reach Herbesthal. I hear from the sister that Albert is to be put off at the next station because of his fever. "How far does the train go?" I ask.

"To Cologne."

"Albert," I say "we stick together; you see."

▶ What does Paul do so he can stay with Albert?

On the sister's next round I hold my breath and press it up into my head. My face swells and turns red. She stops. "Are you in pain?"

"Yes," I groan, "all of a sudden."

She gives me a thermometer and goes on. I would not have been under Kat's tuition if I did not know what to do now. These army thermometers are not made for old soldiers. All one has to do is to drive the quicksilver up and then it stays without falling again.

I stick the thermometer under my arm at a slant, and flip it steadily with my forefinger. Then I give it a shake. I send it up to 100.2°. But that is not enough. A match held cautiously near to it brings it up to 101.6°.

As the sister comes back, I blow myself out, breathe in short gasps, goggle at her with vacant eyes, toss about restlessly, and mutter in a whisper: "I can't bear it any longer—"

She notes me down on a slip of paper. I know perfectly well my plaster bandage will not be reopened if it can be avoided.

Albert and I are put off together.

*

We are in the same room in a Catholic Hospital. That is a piece of luck, the Catholic infirmaries are noted for their good treatment and good food. The hospital has been filled up from our train, there are a great many bed cases[24] amongst them. We do not get examined today because there are too few surgeons. The flat trolleys with the rubber wheels pass continually along the corridor, and always with someone stretched at full length upon them. A damnable position, stretched out full length like that;—the only time it is good is when one is asleep.

The night is very disturbed. No one can sleep. Toward morning we doze a little. I wake up just as it grows light. The doors stand open and I hear voices from the corridor. The others wake up too. One fellow who has been there a couple of days already explains it to us: "Up here in the corridor every morning the sisters say prayers. They call it Morning Devotion.[25] And so that you can get your share, they leave the door open."

*◄ What wakes up the injured soldiers?*

No doubt it is well meant, but it gives us aches in our heads and bones.

"Such an absurdity!" I say, "just when a man dropped off to sleep."

"All the light cases are up here, that's why they do it here," he replies.

Albert groans. I get furious and call out: "Be quiet out there!"

---

24. **bed cases.** People who are too injured or sick to get out of bed
25. **Morning Devotion.** Morning prayers

A minute later a sister appears. In her black and white dress she looks like a beautiful tea-cosy.[26] "Shut the door, will you, sister?" says someone.

▶ What is the nun's response when the soldiers ask her to shut the door?

"We are saying prayers, that is why the door is open," she responds.

"But we want to go on sleeping—"

"Prayer is better than sleeping," she stands there and smiles innocently. "And it is seven o'clock already."

Albert groans again. "Shut the door," I snort.

She is quite <u>disconcerted</u>. Apparently she cannot understand. "But we are saying prayers for you too."

"Shut the door, anyway."

She disappears, leaving the door open. The intoning of the litany[27] proceeds.

▶ What does Paul do to make the prayers stop?

I feel savage, and say: "I'm going to count up to three. If it doesn't stop before then I'll let something fly."

"Me too," says another.

I count up to five. Then I take hold of a bottle, aim, and heave it through the door into the corridor. It smashes into a thousand pieces. The praying stops. A swarm of sisters appear and reproach us in concert.

"Shut the door!" we yell.

They withdraw. The little one who came first is the last to go. "Heathen,"[28] she chirps but shuts the door all the same. We have won.

* 

At noon the hospital inspector arrives and abuses us. He threatens us with clink and all the rest of it. But a hospital inspector is just the same as a commissariat[29] inspector, or any one else who wears a long sword and shoulder straps, but is really a clerk, and is never considered even by a recruit as a real officer. So we let him talk. What can they do to us, anyway—

"Who threw the bottle?" he asks.

Before I can think whether I should report myself, someone says: "I did."

---

26. **tea-cosy.** Padded cover placed over a teapot to keep the tea warm
27. **litany.** Series of fixed invocations and responses in a prayer
28. **Heathen.** Derogatory term for an irreligious person
29. **commissariat.** Food supplies

---

**words for everyday use**
dis • con • cert (dis' kən surt') vt., upset the composure of; embarrass; confuse. *Because he is shy and modest, Jeremy was <u>disconcerted</u> when the principal announced he had the highest grade point average.*

A man with a bristling beard sits up. Everyone is excited; why should he report himself?

"You?"

"Yes. I was annoyed because we were waked up unnecessarily and lost my senses so that I did not know what I was doing."

He talks like a book.

"What is your name?"

"Reinforcement-Reservist Josef Hamacher."

The inspector departs.

We are all curious. "But why did you say you did it? It wasn't you at all!"

He grins. "That doesn't matter. I have a shooting license."

Then of course, we all understand. Whoever has a shooting license can do just whatever he pleases.

"Yes," he explains, "I got a crack in the head and they presented me with a certificate to say that I was periodically not responsible for my actions. Ever since then I've had a grand time. No one dares to annoy me. And nobody does anything to me."

◀ Why did Josef Hamacher take the blame for Paul's actions?

"I reported myself because the shot amused me. If they open the door again tomorrow we will pitch another."

We are overjoyed. With Josef Hamacher in our midst we can now risk anything.

Then come the soundless, flat trollies to take us away. The bandages are stuck fast. We bellow like steers.

*

There are eight men in our room. Peter, a curly black-haired fellow, has the worst injury;—a severe lung wound. Franz Wächter, alongside him, has a shot in the arm which didn't look too bad at first. But the third night he calls out to us, telling us to ring, he thinks he has a haemorrhage.

◀ What happens to Franz Wächter's wound one night?

I ring loudly. The night sister does not come. We have been making rather heavy demands on her during the night, because we have all been freshly bandaged, and so have a good deal of pain. One wants his leg placed so, another so, a third wants water, a fourth wants her to shake up his pillow;—in the end the buxom[30] old body grumbled bad-temperedly and slammed the doors. Now no doubt she thinks it is something of the same sort and so she is not coming.

We wait. Then Franz says: "Ring again."

I do so. Still she does not put in an appearance. In our wing there is only one night sister, perhaps she has

---

30. **buxom.** Full-figured

something to do in one of the other rooms. "Franz, are you quite sure you are bleeding?" I ask. "Otherwise we shall be getting cursed again."

"The bandage is wet. Can't anybody make a light?"

That cannot be done either. The switch is by the door and none of us can stand up. I hold my thumb against the button of the bell till it becomes numb. Perhaps the sister has fallen asleep. They certainly have a great deal to do and are all overworked day after day. And added to that is the everlasting praying.

"Should we smash a bottle?" asks Josef Hamacher of the shooting license.

"She wouldn't hear that any more than the bell."

At last the door opens. The old lady appears, mumbling. When she perceives Franz's trouble she begins to <u>bustle</u>, and says: "Why did not someone say I was wanted?"

"We did ring. And none of us here can walk."

He has been bleeding badly and she binds him up. In the morning we look at his face, it has become sharp and yellow, whereas the evening before he looked almost healthy. Now a sister comes oftener.

*

Sometimes there are red-cross voluntary aid sisters. They are pleasant, but often rather unskilled. They frequently give us pain when re-making our beds, and then are so frightened that they hurt us still more.

The nuns are more reliable. They know how they must take hold of us, but we would be better pleased if they were somewhat more cheerful. A few of them have real spirit, they are superb. There is no one but would do anything for Sister Libertine, this marvelous sister, who spreads good cheer through the whole wing even when she can only be seen in the distance. And there are others like her. We would go through fire for her. A man cannot really complain, here he is treated by the nuns exactly like a civilian. And just to think of a garrison hospital[31] gives one the creeps.

Franz Wächter does not regain his strength. One day he is taken away and does not come back. Josef Hamacher

▶ How does Paul feel about nuns like Sister Libertine?

▶ Whom does Josef Hamacher say they won't see again? Where have they put this person?

---

31. **garrison hospital.** Military hospital

---

**words for everyday use**

**bus • tle** (bus′ əl) *vi.*, hurry busily or with much fuss and bother. *We excitedly started to* <u>bustle</u> *about, packing everything we would need for vacation.*

knows all about it: "We shan't see him again. They have put him in the Dead Room."

"What do you mean, Dead Room?" asks Kropp.

"Well, Dying Room—"

"What is that, then?"

"A little room at the corner of the building. Whoever is about to kick the bucket is put in there. There are two beds in it. It is generally called the Dying Room."

"But what do they do that for?"

"They don't have so much work to do afterwards. It is more convenient, too, because it lies right beside the lift to the mortuary.[32] Perhaps they do it for the sake of the others also, so that no one in the ward dies in sympathy. And they can look after him better, too, if he is by himself."

"But what about him?"

Josef shrugs his shoulders. "Usually he doesn't take much notice any more."

"Does everybody know about it then?"

"Anyone who has been here long enough knows, of course."

*Why do they put dying men in this room?*

\*

In the afternoon Franz Wächter's bed has a fresh occupant. A couple of days later they take the new man away, too. Josef makes a significant gesture. We see many come and go.

Often relatives sit by the beds and weep or talk softly and awkwardly. One old woman will not go away, but she cannot stay there the whole night through. The next morning she comes very early, but not early enough; for when she goes up to the bed, someone else is in it already. She has to go to the mortuary. The apples that she has brought with her she gives to us.

And then little Peter begins to get worse. His temperature chart looks bad, and one day the flat trolley stands beside his bed. "Where to?" he asks.

"To the bandaging ward."

He is lifted out. But the sister makes the mistake of removing his tunic from the hook and putting it on the trolley too, so that she should not have to make two journeys. Peter understands immediately and tries to roll off the trolley. "I'm stopping here!"

*Why doesn't Peter want the sister to take him away?*

They push him back. He cries out feebly with his shattered lung: "I won't go to the Dying Room."

"But we are going to the bandaging ward."

---

32. **mortuary.** Place where dead bodies are kept before burial or cremation

"Then what do you want my tunic for?" He can speak no more. Hoarse, agitated, he whispers: "Stopping here!"

They do not answer but wheel him out. At the door he tries to raise himself up. His black curly head sways, his eyes are full of tears. "I will come back again! I will come back again!" he cries.

▶ What does Peter cry as he is wheeled away?

The door shuts. We are all excited; but we say nothing. At last Josef says: "Many a man has said that. Once a man is in there, he never comes through."

\*

I am operated on and vomit for two days. My bones will not grow together, so the surgeons' secretary says. Another fellow's have grown crooked; his are broken again. It is damnable.

Among our new arrivals there are two young soldiers with flat feet. The chief surgeon discovers them on his rounds, and is overjoyed. "We'll soon put that right," he tells them, "we will just do a small operation, and then you will have perfectly sound feet. Enter them down, sister."

▶ According to Josef, what does the doctor do to patients who have flat feet?

As soon as he is gone, Josef, who knows everything, warns them: "Don't you let him operate on you! That is a special scientific stunt of the old boy's. He goes absolutely crazy whenever he can get hold of anyone to do it on. He operates on you for flat feet, and there's no mistake, you don't have them anymore; you have club feet instead, and have to walk all the rest of your life on sticks."

"What should a man do, then?" asks one of them.

"Say No. You are here to be cured of your wound, not your flat feet. Did you have any trouble with them in the field? No, well, there you are! At present you can still walk, but if once the old boy gets you under the knife you'll be cripples. What he wants is little dogs to experiment with,

▶ Why is the war a "glorious time" for surgeons?

so the war is a glorious time for him, as it is for all the surgeons. You take a look down below at the staff; there are a dozen fellows hobbling around that he has operated on. A lot of them have been here all the time since 'fourteen and 'fifteen. Not a single one of them can walk better than he could before, almost all of them worse, and most only with plaster legs. Every six months he catches them again and breaks their bones afresh, and every time is going to be the successful one. You take my word, he won't dare to do it if you say No."

"Ach, man," says one of the two wearily, "better your feet than your brain-box. There's no telling what you'll get if you go back out there again. They can do with me just as they please, so long as I get back home. Better to have a club foot than be dead."

The other, a young fellow like ourselves, won't have it done. The next morning the old man has the two hauled up and lectures and jaws at them so long that in the end they consent. What else could they do?—They are mere privates, and he is a big bug. They are brought back chloroformed and plastered.

*

It is going badly with Albert. They have taken him and amputated his leg. The whole leg has been taken off from the thigh. Now he will hardly speak any more. Once he says he will shoot himself the first time he can get hold of his revolver again.

◀ What has happened to Albert? What does Albert say he plans to do?

A new convoy[33] arrives. Our room gets two blind men. One of them is a very youthful musician. The sisters never have a knife with them when they feed him; he has already snatched one from a sister. But in spite of this caution there is an incident. In the evening, while he is being fed, the sister is called away, and leaves the plate with the fork on his table. He gropes for the fork, seizes it and drives it with all his force against his heart, then he snatches up a shoe and strikes with it against the handle as hard as he can. We call for help and three men are necessary to take the fork away from him. The blunt prongs had already penetrated deep. He abuses us all night so that no one can go to sleep. In the morning he has lock-jaw.[34]

◀ What does the blind musician do to himself?

Again beds are empty. Day after day goes by with pain and fear, groans and death gurgles. Even the Death Room is no use any more, it is too small; fellows die during the night in our room. They go even faster than the sisters can cope with them.

But one day the door flies open, the flat trolley rolls in, and there on the stretcher, pale, thin, upright and triumphant with his shaggy head of curls sits Peter. Sister Libertine with beaming looks pushes him over to his former bed. He is back from the Dying Room. We have long supposed him dead.

◀ Who returns from the Dying Room?

He looks round: "What do you say now?"

And Josef has to admit that it is the first time he has ever known of such a thing.

*

Gradually a few of us are allowed to get up. And I am given crutches to hobble around on. But I do not make much use of them; I cannot bear Albert's gaze as I move about the room. His eyes always follow me with such a

---

33. **convoy.** Group of injured men
34. **lock-jaw.** Tetanus, see footnote 18

strange look. So I sometimes escape to the corridor;—there I can move about more freely.

On the next floor below are the abdominal and spine cases, head wounds and double amputations. On the right side of the wing are the jaw wounds, wounds in the joints, wounds in the kidneys, wounds in the testicles, wounds in the intestines. Here a man realizes for the first time in how many places a man can get hit.

▶ What does one realize in the hospital?

Two fellows die of tetanus. Their skin turns pale, their limbs stiffen, at last only their eyes live—stubbornly. Many of the wounded have their shattered limbs hanging free in the air from a gallows;[35] underneath the wound a basin is placed into which drips the pus. Every two or three hours the vessel is emptied. Other men lie in stretching bandages with heavy weights hanging from the end of the bed. I see intestine wounds that are constantly full of excreta.[36] The surgeon's clerk shows me X-ray photographs of completely smashed hipbones, knees, and shoulders.

A man cannot realize that above such shattered bodies there are still human faces in which life goes its daily round. And this is only one hospital, one single station; there are hundreds of thousands in Germany, hundreds of thousands in France, hundreds of thousands in Russia. How senseless is everything that can ever be written, done, or thought, when such things are possible. It must be all lies and of no account when the culture of a thousand years could not prevent this stream of blood being poured out, these torture-chambers in their hundreds of thousands. A hospital alone shows what war is.

▶ According to Paul, this is only one hospital out of how many?

▶ What shows what war is?

I am young, I am twenty years old; yet I know nothing of life but despair, death, fear, and <u>fatuous</u> superficiality cast over an abyss of sorrow. I see how peoples are set against one another, and in silence, unknowingly, foolishly, obediently, innocently slay one another. I see that the keenest brains of the world invent weapons and words to make it yet more refined and enduring. And all men of my age, here and over there, throughout the whole world see these things; all my generation is experiencing these

---

35. **gallows.** Upright frame
36. **excreta.** Matter excreted from the body

---

**words for everyday use**

fat • u • ous (fach' ü əs) *adj.*, complacently stupid or inane; silly; foolish. *It is <u>fatuous</u> to believe that war and poverty affect only people in other countries.*

things with me. What would our fathers do if we suddenly stood up and came before them and <u>proffered</u> our account? What do they expect of us if a time ever comes when the war is over? Through the years our business has been killing;—it was our first calling in life. Our knowledge of life is limited to death. What will happen afterwards? And what shall come out of us?

◀ According to Paul. what has his life's business been? To what is his knowledge of life limited?

\*

The oldest man in our room is Lewandowski. He is forty, and has already lain ten months in the hospital with a severe abdominal wound. Just in the last few weeks he has improved sufficiently to be able to hobble about doubled up.

For some days past he has been in great excitement. His wife has written to him from the little home in Poland where she lives, telling him that she has saved up enough money to pay for the fare, and is coming to see him.

◀ Why is Lewandowski excited?

She is already on the way and may arrive any day. Lewandowski has lost his appetite, he even gives away red cabbage and sausage after he has had a couple of mouthfuls. He goes round the room perpetually with the letter. Everyone has already read it a dozen times, the post-marks have been examined heaven knows how often, the address is hardly legible any longer for spots of grease and thumb-marks, and in the end what is sure to happen, happens. Lewandowski develops a fever, and has to go back to bed.

◀ What happens to Lewandowski before his wife arrives?

He has not seen his wife for two years. In the meantime she has given birth to a child, whom she is bringing with her. But something else occupies Lewandowski's thoughts. He had hoped to get permission to go out when his old woman came; for obviously seeing is all very well, but when a man gets his wife again after such a long time, if at all possible, a man wants something else besides.

Lewandowski has discussed it all with us at great length; in the army there are no secrets about such things. And what's more, nobody finds anything objectionable in it. Those of us who are already able to go out have told him of a couple of very good spots in the town, parks and squares, where he would not be disturbed; one of us even knows of a little room.

words
for
everyday
use

prof • fer (präf' ər) vt., offer (usually something intangible). *Simon instantly <u>proffered</u> his friendship to the new student.*

But what is the use, there Lewandowski lies in bed with his troubles. Life holds no more joy for him if he has to forgo this affair. We console him and promise to get over the difficulty somehow or other.

The next afternoon his wife appears, a tousled little woman with anxious, quick eyes like a bird, in a sort of black crinkly mantilla[37] with ribbons; heaven knows where she inherited the thing.

She murmurs something softly and stands shyly in the doorway. It terrifies her that there are six of us men present.

"Well, Marja," says Lewandowski, and gulps dangerously with his Adam's apple "you can come in all right, they won't hurt you."

She goes round and proffers each of us her hand. Then she produces the child, which in the intervals has done something in its napkin. From a large handbag embroidered with beads she takes out a clean one and makes the child fresh and presentable. This dispels her first embarrassment, and the two begin to talk.

Lewandowski is very fidgety, every now and then he squints across at us most unhappily with his round goggle eyes.

The time is favourable, the doctor's visit is over, at the most one of the sisters might come in. So one of us goes out to prospect. He comes back and nods. "Not a soul to be seen. Now's your chance, Johann, set to."

The two speak together in an undertone. The woman turns a little red and looks embarrassed. We grin good-naturedly and make pooh-poohing gestures, what does it matter! The devil take all conventions, they were made for other times; here lies the carpenter Johann Lewandowski, a soldier shot to a cripple, and there is his wife; who knows when he will see her again? He wants to have her, and he should have her, good.

Two men stand at the door to forestall the sisters and keep them occupied if they chance to come along. They agree to stand guard for a quarter of an hour or thereabouts.

Lewandowski can only lie on his side, so one of us props a couple of pillows against his side, Albert gets the child to hold, we all turn round a bit, the black mantilla disappears under the bed-clothes, we make a great clatter and play skat noisily.

All goes well. I hold a club solo with four jacks which nearly goes the round. In the process we almost forget

---

37. **mantilla.** Woman's scarf worn over the hair and shoulders

Lewandowski. After a while the child begins to squall, although Albert, in desperation, rocks it to and fro. There is a bit of creaking and rustling, and as we look up casually we see that the child has the bottle in its mouth and is back again with its mother. The business is over.

We now feel ourselves like one big family, the woman is happy, and Lewandowski lies there sweating and beaming.

◀ What does Paul say he and the others feel like? What do they call Lewandowski's wife?

He unpacks the embroidered handbag, and some good sausages come to light; Lewandowski takes up the knife with a flourish and saws the meat into slices.

With a handsome gesture he waves toward us—and the little woman goes from one to another and smiles at us and hands round the sausage; she now looks quite handsome. We call her Mother, she is pleased and shakes up our pillows for us.

*

After a few weeks I have to go each morning to the massage department. There my leg is harnessed up and made to move. The arm has healed long since.

New convoys arrive from the line. The bandages are no longer made of cloth, but of white crêpe paper. Rag bandages have become scarce at the front.

◀ Why are the bandages now made of paper?

Albert's stump heals well. The wound is almost closed. In a few weeks he should go off to an institute for artificial limbs. He continues not to talk much, and is much more solemn than formerly. He often breaks off in his speech and stares in front of him. If he were not here with us he would have shot himself long ago. But now he is over the worst of it, and he often looks on while we play skat.

◀ Where will Albert go? How has he changed?

I get convalescent leave.[38]

My mother does not want to let me go away. She is feeble. It is all much worse than it was last time.

Then I am recalled to my regiment and return once more to the line.

Parting from my friend Albert Kropp was very hard. But a man gets used to that sort of thing in the army.

---

38. **convalescent leave.** Time off from battle to heal

## Respond to the Selection

What is the worst thing you have ever done to another person? How do you feel about your actions now? In what way did this experience change you?

## Investigate, Inquire, and Imagine

### Recall: GATHERING FACTS

1a. What does Paul do to an enemy soldier for the first time when he is hiding in a shell hole unable to find his way back to his trench? What does Paul do for the soldier as he is dying? What does Paul do after he dies? What do Kat and Albert show Paul when he is reunited with his fellow soldiers?

### Interpret: FINDING MEANING

1b. In what way does the dying solider "stab" Paul? Explain whether Paul's actions to help the soldier are entirely unselfish. Why is this one death so different for Paul than the many deaths he has witnessed? What promises does Paul make to the enemy soldier? Explain whether in the end Paul intends to keep his promises to the dead man. What does this reveal about war and its effect on Paul character? Why do Kat and Albert believe it is good for Paul to witness this thing once he is reunited with his fellow soldiers?

2a. What "good job" do Paul and his friends get in Chapter 10? What happens to Paul and Albert when their job is over and they are sent to evacuate a French village?

2b. Why is this job good? What made it possible for Paul and Albert to run away despite their condition? Why does Paul lie to Albert about where he has been hit?

3a. When the surgeon is removing shrapnel from Paul's wounds, what threat makes Paul stop squirming? What does Paul believe the surgeon is deliberately doing? What is the Dying Room? According to one of the patients at the hospital, why is the chief surgeon excited to discover patients with flat feet? What happens to Albert's leg at the hospital? What happens to separate Paul from Albert?

3b. Why is the doctor's threat so effective? How would you characterize the treatment Paul and Albert receive in the hospital? What does Paul mean when he says, "A hospital alone shows what war is"?

## Analyze: TAKING THINGS APART

4a. Compare and contrast the dead soldiers Paul and his friends see before battle to the soldier Paul kills with his own hands. How did the soldiers die? How did those who witnessed their deaths react to them? In what way does Paul treat the dead French soldier differently than the dead bodies and body parts he sees scattered in the trees and field?

## Synthesize: BRINGING THINGS TOGETHER

→ 4b. Elaborate on your responses to question 4a to explain how the author presents war as both impersonal and personal.

## Evaluate: MAKING JUDGMENTS

5a. Analyze the discussion the soldiers have about the causes of war in Chapter 9. What did twenty or thirty people throughout the world have the power to do? What causes a war and what doesn't? Whom does war benefit and whom does it hurt? What role do the common people who must fight a war really have in it?

## Extend: CONNECTING IDEAS

→ 5b. What are your own thoughts and feelings about war? Is war always wrong, or is it sometimes necessary?

## Understanding Literature

IRONY. **Irony** is a difference between appearance and reality. In *irony of situation,* an event occurs that violates the expectations of the characters, the reader, or the audience. Explain why it is ironic when the commanding officers give the soldiers new uniforms when the Kaiser is coming and then take the uniforms away.

CRISIS AND CENTRAL CONFLICT. In the plot of a story or drama, the **crisis** is that point in the development of the conflict at which a decisive event occurs that causes the main character's situation to become better or worse. The **central conflict** is the primary struggle dealt with in the plot of a story or novel. Identify the crisis that occurs in Chapter 7. What is the novel's central conflict? How do you believe that this crisis will affect the central conflict in the novel?

SYMBOL. A **symbol** is a thing that stands for or represents both itself and something else. What might it symbolize when Paul calls the soldier he kills "comrade"? What does this word mean to Paul?

COMIC RELIEF. Writers sometimes insert into a serious work of fiction or drama a humorous scene that is said to provide **comic relief**, because it relieves the seriousness or emotional intensity felt by the audience. Paradoxically, a scene introduced for comic relief can sometimes, because of the contrast it provides, increase the perceived intensity or seriousness of the action around it. What scenes in Chapter 10 are examples of comic relief? Why might the author have felt the need to insert some comic relief in this particular chapter? What serious or intense things occur in Chapter 10 that stand in contrast to this comic relief?

# Chapter XI

We count the weeks no more. It was winter when I came up, and when the shells exploded the frozen clods of earth were just as dangerous as the fragments. Now the trees are green again. Our life alternates between billets and the front. We have almost grown accustomed to it; war is a cause of death like cancer and tuberculosis,[1] like influenza[2] and dysentery. The deaths are merely more frequent, more varied and terrible.

◀ What do Paul and the other soldiers no longer do?

◀ What is war like? How is it different from the diseases mentioned?

Our thoughts are clay, they are moulded with the changes of the days;—when we are resting they are good; under fire, they are dead. Fields of craters within and without.

Everyone is so, not only ourselves here—the things that existed before are no longer valid, and one practically knows them no more. Distinctions, breeding, education are changed, are almost blotted out and hardly recognizable any longer. Sometimes they give an advantage for profiting by a situation;—but they also bring consequences along with them, in that they arouse prejudices which have to be overcome. It is as though formerly we were coins of different provinces; and now we are melted down, and all bear the same stamp. To rediscover the old distinctions, the metal itself must be tested. First we are soldiers and afterwards, in a strange and shamefaced fashion, individual men as well.

It is a great brotherhood, which adds something of the good-fellowship of the folk-song, of the feeling of solidarity of convicts, and of the desperate loyalty to one another of men condemned to death, to a condition of life arising out of the midst of danger, out of the tension and forlornness of death—seeking in a wholly unpathetic way a fleeting enjoyment of the hours as they come. If one wants to appraise it, it is at once heroic and <u>banal</u>—but who wants to do that?

It is this, for example, that makes Tjaden spoon down his ham-and-pea soup in such tearing haste when an

◀ Why does Tjaden spoon down his soup in haste when an enemy attack is reported? Why does Kat condemn his actions?

---

1. **tuberculosis.** Infectious disease of the lungs
2. **influenza.** The flu, an infectious disease that affects the lungs and causes muscle pains and fever

**words for everyday use**    ba • nal (bā′ nəl) *adj.,* dull or stale because of overuse; commonplace. *Pat was beginning to find formulaic action films, with their repeated chase scenes and explosions, <u>banal</u>.*

enemy attack is reported, simply because he cannot be sure that in an hour's time he will be alive. We have discussed it at length, whether it is right or not to do so. Kat condemns it, because, he says, a man has to reckon with the possibility of an abdominal wound,[3] and that is more dangerous on a full stomach than on an empty one.

Such things are real problems, they are serious matters to us, they cannot be otherwise. Here, on the borders of death, life follows an amazingly simple course, it is limited to what is most necessary, all else lies buried in gloomy sleep;—in that besides our primitiveness and our survival. Were we more subtly differentiated we must long since have gone mad, have deserted, or have fallen. As in a polar expedition, every expression of life must serve only the preservation of existence, and is absolutely focused on that. All else is banished because it would consume energies unnecessarily. That is the only way to save ourselves. In the quiet hours when the puzzling reflection of former days like a blurred mirror, projects beyond me the figure of my present existence, I often sit over against myself, as before a stranger, and wonder how the unnameable active principle that calls itself to life has adapted itself even to this form. All other

▶ Why are the soldiers dull?

expressions lie in a winter sleep, life is simply one continual watch against the <u>menace</u> of death;—it has transformed us into unthinking animals in order to give us the weapon of instinct—it has reinforced us with dullness, so that we do not go to pieces before the horror, which would overwhelm us if we had clear, conscious thought—it has awakened in us the sense of comradeship, so that we escape the abyss of solitude—it has lent us the indifference of wild creatures, so that in spite of all, we perceive the positive in every moment, and store it up as a reserve against the onslaught

▶ What are dangerous moments for the soldiers?

of nothingness. Thus we live a closed, hard existence of the utmost <u>superficiality</u>, and rarely does an incident strike out a spark. But then unexpectedly a flame of grievous and terrible yearning flares up.

Those are the dangerous moments. They show us that the adjustment is only artificial, that it is not simple rest, but sharpest struggle for rest. In the outward form of our life we

---

3. **abdominal wound.** Wound to the abdomen, or belly

**words for everyday use**

**men • ace** (men' əs) *n.*, threat or the act of threatening. *That open manhole cover is certainly a <u>menace</u> to pedestrians.*

**su • per • fi • ci • al • i • ty** (sü' pər fish' ē al' ə tē) *adj.*, something that is only on the surface or that is shallow and not profound. *Luke was more interested in what people really thought rather than in <u>superficialities</u> such as their clothes and the cars they drove.*

are hardly distinguishable from Bushmen;[4] but whereas the latter can be so always, because they are so truly, and at best may develop further by exertion of their spiritual forces, with us it is the reverse;—our inner forces are not exerted toward <u>regeneration</u>, but toward <u>degeneration</u>. The Bushmen are primitive and naturally so, but we are primitive in an artificial sense, and by virtue of the utmost effort.

And at night, waking out of a dream, overwhelmed and bewitched by the crowding apparitions, a man perceives with alarm how slight is the support, how thin the boundary that divides him from the darkness. We are little flames poorly sheltered by frail walls against the storm of <u>dissolution</u> and madness, in which we flicker and sometimes almost go out. Then the muffled roar of the battle becomes a ring that encircles us, we creep in upon ourselves, and with big eyes stare into the night. Our only comfort is the steady breathing of our comrades asleep, and thus we wait for the morning.

*

Every day and every hour, every shell and every death cuts into this thin support, and the years waste it rapidly. I see how it is already gradually breaking down around me.

◀ What is happening to the soldier's thin emotional support?

There is the mad story of Detering.

He was one of those who kept himself to himself. His misfortune was that he saw a cherry tree in a garden. We were just coming back from the front line, and at a turning of the road near our billets, marvellous in the morning twilight, stood this cherry tree before us. It had no leaves, but was one white mass of blossom.

◀ According to Paul, what was Detering's misfortune?

In the evening Detering was not to be seen. Then at last he came back and had a couple of branches of cherry blossom in his hand. We made fun of him, and asked whether he was going to a wedding. He made no answer, but lay down on his bed. During the night I heard him making a noise, he seemed to be packing. I sensed something amiss and went over to him. He made out it was nothing, and I said to him: "Don't do anything silly, Detering."

---

4. **Bushmen.** Persons who live in the Australian bush

**words for everyday use**

re • gen • er • a • tion (ri jen′ ə rā shən) n., being renewed, reformed, or reconstituted. *It us amazing to see the <u>regeneration</u> of life in the spring, as buds form and the first flowers bloom.*

de • gen • er • a • tion (dē jen′ ər ā′ shən) n., sinking below a former condition; deterioration; corruption. *The novel* Lord of the Flies *is about the <u>degeneration</u> of society among a group of shipwrecked schoolchildren.*

dis • so • lu • tion (dis′ ə lü′ shən) n., dissolving or being dissolved. *<u>Dissolution</u> of sugar is aided by moisture and heat.*

"Ach, why—it's merely that I can't sleep—"

"What did you pick the cherry branches for?"

"Surely I can pick cherry blossom if I want to!" he replied evasively—and after a while: "I have a big orchard with cherry trees at home. When they are in blossom, from the hay loft they look like one single sheet, so white. It is just the time."

"Perhaps you will get leave soon. You may even be sent back as a farmer."

He nodded but he was far away. When these peasants are excited they have a curious expression, a mixture of cow and yearning god, half stupid and half <u>rapt</u>. In order to turn him away from this thoughts I asked him for a piece of bread. He gave it to me without a murmur. That was suspicious, for he is usually tight-fisted. So I stayed awake. Nothing happened; in the morning he was as usual.

Apparently he had noticed that I had been watching him;—but the second morning he was gone. I noticed it, but said nothing, in order to give him time; he might perhaps get through. Various fellows have already got into Holland.

But at roll call[5] he was missed. A week after we heard that he had been caught by the field gendarmes, those despicable military police. He had headed toward Germany, that was hopeless, of course—and, of course, he did everything else just as idiotically. Anyone might have known that his flight was only homesickness and a momentary <u>aberration</u>. But what does a court-martial a hundred miles behind the front-line know about it? We have heard nothing more of Detering.

*

But sometimes it broke out in other ways, this danger, these pent-up things, as from an overheated boiler. It will be enough to tell how Berger met his end.

Our trenches have now for some time been shot to pieces, and we have an elastic line, so that there is practically no longer any proper trench warfare. When attack and counter-attack have waged backwards and forwards

▶ Why did Detering pick the cherry blossoms?

▶ What does Paul find suspicious? What does Paul notice the second morning?

▶ What does Paul learn about what happened to Detering once he deserted?

▶ What has happened to the German line at the front?

---

5. **roll call.** Reading aloud a list of names to check attendance

**words for everyday use**  **rapt** (rapt) *adj.*, completely absorbed or engrossed. *Because she loves ancient history, Dominique was <u>rapt</u> as the teacher told us about the ancient Mayans.*

**ab • er • ra • tion** (ab' ər ā' shən) *n.*, deviation from the normal or the typical. *We looked forward to the field trip as a welcome <u>aberration</u> from our typical school day.*

there remains a broken line and a bitter struggle from crater to crater. The front-line has been penetrated, and everywhere small groups have established themselves, the fight is carried on from clusters of shell-holes.

We are in a crater, the English are coming down obliquely,[6] they are turning our flank and working in behind us. We are surrounded. It is not easy to surrender, fog and smoke hang over us, no one would recognize that we wanted to give ourselves up, and perhaps we don't want to, a man doesn't even know himself at such moments. We hear the explosions of the hand-grenades coming towards us. Our machine-gun sweeps over the semicircle in front of us. The cooling-water evaporates, we hastily pass round the case, every man pisses in it, and thus we again have water, and are able to continue firing. But behind us the attack crashes ever nearer.

A few minutes and we are lost.

Then, at closest range, a second machine-gun bursts out. It is set up in a crater alongside us; Berger has fetched it, and now the counter-attack comes over from behind; we are set free and make contact with the rear.

Afterwards, as we lie in comparatively good cover, one of the food-carriers reports that a couple of hundred yards distant there lies a wounded messenger-dog.

◀ What does the food-carrier report?

"Where?" asks Berger.

The other describes the place to him. Berger goes off either to fetch the beast in or to shoot it. Six months ago he would not have cared, he would have been reasonable. We try to prevent him. Then, as he goes off grimly, all we can say is: "You're mad," and let him go. For these cases of front-line madness become dangerous if one is not able to fling the man to the ground and hold him fast. And Berger is six feet and the most powerful man in the company.

◀ What does Berger set off to do? What do the others think of his actions?

He is absolutely mad for he has to pass through the barrage; but this lightning that lowers somewhere above us all has struck him and made him demented. It affects others so that they begin to rave, to run away—there was one man who even tried to dig himself into the ground with hands, feet, and teeth.

It is true, such things are often simulated, but the pretence itself is a symptom. Berger, who means to finish off the dog, is carried away with a wound in the pelvis, and one of the fellows who carry him gets a bullet in the leg while doing it.

◀ What happens to Berger?

---

6. **obliquely.** At an angle, or in an indirect manner

*

▶ What happens to Müller? What does he bequeath to Paul? What has Paul promised Tjaden?

Müller is dead. Someone shot him point-blank in the stomach with a Verey light.[7] He lived for half an hour, quite conscious, and in terrible pain.

Before he died he handed over his pocket-book to me, and <u>bequeathed</u> me his boots—the same that he once inherited from Kemmerich. I wear them, for they fit me quite well. After me Tjaden will get them, I have promised them to him.

▶ Why are the German lines falling back?

We have been able to bury Müller, but he is not likely to remain long undisturbed. Our lines are falling back. There are too many fresh English and American regiments over there. There's too much corned beef and white wheaten bread. Too many new guns. Too many aeroplanes.

▶ What has happened to the German factory owners? What has happened to the German soldiers?

But we are <u>emaciated</u> and starved. Our food is bad and mixed up with so much substitute stuff that it makes us ill. The factory owners in Germany have grown wealthy;— dysentery dissolves our bowels. The latrine poles[8] are always densely crowded; the people at home ought to be shown these grey, yellow, miserable, wasted faces here, these bent figures from whose bodies the colic[9] wrings out the blood, and who with lips trembling and distorted with pain, grin at one another and say:

"It is not much sense pulling up one's trousers again—"

▶ What has happened to the German weapons? What is the only thing the fresh troops know how to do?

Our artillery is fired out, it has too few shells and the barrels are so worn that they shoot uncertainly, and scatter so widely as even to fall on ourselves. We have too few horses. Our fresh troops are anaemic[10] boys in need of rest, who cannot carry a pack, but merely know how to die. By thousands. They understand nothing about warfare, they simply go on and let themselves be shot down. A single flyer routed two companies of them for a joke, just as they came fresh from the train—before they had ever heard of such a thing as cover.

---

7. **Verey light.** Type of flare gun
8. **latrine poles.** Poles laid horizontally above holes in the ground and used as a toilet seat
9. **colic.** Sharp abdominal pain
10. **anaemic.** Condition in which there is a reduction in the number of red blood cells, causing paleness and weakness

**words for everyday use**

**be • queath** (bē kwēth′) *vt.,* leave (property) to another by last will and testament. *Frieda's most treasured possession was a bracelet <u>bequeathed</u> to her by her grandmother.*

**e • ma • ci • ate** (ē mā′ shē āt′) *vt.,* cause to become abnormally lean; cause to lose much flesh or weight, as by starvation or disease. *When she saw pictures of the <u>emaciated</u> children, Greer decided to devote time each week to organizations that fight against hunger.*

"Germany ought to be empty soon," says Kat.

We have given up hope that some day an end may come. We never think so far. A man can stop a bullet and be killed; he can get wounded, and then the hospital is his next stop. There, if they do not amputate him, he sooner or later falls into the hands of one of those staff surgeons who, with the War Service Cross in his button-hole, says to him: "What, one leg a bit short? If you have any pluck you don't need to run at the front. The man is A1.[11] Dismiss!"

◀ What have the soldiers given up?

Kat tells a story that has travelled the whole length of the front from the Vosges to Flanders;—of the staff surgeon who reads the names on the list, and when a man comes before him, without looking up, says: "A1. We need soldiers up there." A fellow with a wooden leg comes up before him, the staff surgeon again says A1— "And then," Kat raises his voice, "the fellow says to him: 'I already have a wooden leg, but when I go back again and they shoot off my head, then I will get a wooden head made and become a staff surgeon.'" This answer tickles us all immensely.

◀ What type of men are the surgeons declaring fit for battle?

There may be good doctors, and there are, lots of them; all the same, every soldier some time during his hundreds of inspections falls into the clutches of one of these countless hero-grabbers who pride themselves on changing as many C3's and B3's[12] as possible into A1's.

There are many such stories, they are mostly far more bitter. All the same, they have nothing to do with mutiny or lead-swinging. They are merely honest and call a thing by its name; for there is a very great deal of fraud, injustice, and baseness in the army. It is nothing that regiment after regiment returns again and again to the ever more hopeless struggle, that attack follows attack along the weakening, retreating, crumbling line.

From a mockery the tanks have become a terrible weapon. Armoured they come rolling on in long lines, more than anything else embody for us the horror of war.

◀ What horrifies the soldiers?

We do not see the guns that bombard us; the attacking lines of the enemy infantry are men like ourselves; but these tanks are machines, their caterpillars[13] run on as endless as the war, they are annihilation, they roll without feeling into the craters, and climb up again without stopping, a fleeting of raring, smoke-belching armour-clads, invulnerable steel beasts squashing the dead and the

---

11. **A1.** Fit for military service
12. **C3's and B3's.** People who have been declared unfit for military service for various reasons
13. **caterpillars.** Continuous roller belt over cogged wheels on which the tank runs

wounded—we shrivel up in our thin skin before them, against their colossal weight our arms are sticks of straw, and our hand-grenades matches.

Shells, gas clouds, and flotillas[14] of tanks—shattering, corroding, death.

Dysentery, influenza, typhus[15]—scalding, choking, death.

Trenches, hospitals, the common grave—there are no other possibilities.

▶ What are the soldiers' possibilities?

*

In one attack our Company Commander, Bertinck, falls. He was one of those superb front-line officers who are foremost in every hot place. He was with us for two years without being wounded, so that something had to happen in the end.

▶ What danger did the soldiers face with Bertinck?

We occupy a crater and get surrounded. The stink of petroleum or oil blows across with the fumes of powder. Two fellows with a flame-thrower are seen, one carries the tin on his back, the other has the hose in his hands from which the fire spouts. If they get so near that they can reach us we are done for, we cannot retreat yet.

▶ What does Bertinck do to protect the men he leads? What happens to him?

We open fire on them. But they work nearer and things begin to look bad. Bertinck is lying in the hole with us. When he sees that we cannot hit them because under the sharp fire we have to think too much about keeping under cover, he takes a rifle, crawls out of the hole, and lying down propped on his elbows, he takes aim. He fires—the same moment a bullet smacks into him, they have got him. Still he lies and aims again;—once he shifts and again takes aim; at last the rifle cracks. Bertinck lets the gun drop and says: "Good," and slips back into the hole. The hindermost[16] of the two flame-throwers is hit, he falls, the hose slips away from the other fellow, the fire squirts on all sides and the man burns.

Bertinck has a chest wound. After a while a fragment smashes away his chin, and the same fragment has sufficient force to tear open Leer's hip. Leer groans as he supports himself on his arm, he bleeds quickly, no one can help him. Like an emptying tube, after a couple of minutes he collapses.

▶ What is of no use to Bertinck?

What use is it to him now that he was such a good mathematician at school.

---

14. **flotillas.** Small fleets
15. **typhus.** Infectious disease transmitted by lice that causes fever, headache, and an eruption of red spots all over the body
16. **hindermost.** The one in the back, carrying the tin

*

The months pass by. The summer of 1918 is the most bloody and the most terrible. The days stand like angels in blue and gold, incomprehensible, above the ring of annihilation. Every man here knows that we are losing the war. Not much is said about it, we are falling back, we will not be able to attack again after this big offensive, we have no more men and no more ammunition.

Still the campaign goes on—the dying goes on—

Summer of 1918—Never has life in its niggardliness[17] seemed to us so desirable as now;—the red poppies in the meadows round our billets, the smooth beetles on the blades of grass, the warm evenings in the cool, dim rooms, the black, mysterious trees of the twilight, the stars and the flowing waters, dreams and long sleep—O Life, life, life!

◄ *What seems desirable now to the soldiers?*

Summer of 1918—Never was so much silently suffered as in the moment when we depart once again for the front-line. Wild, tormenting rumours of an armistice[18] and peace are in the air, they lay hold on our hearts and make the return to the front harder than ever.

Summer of 1918—Never was life in the line more bitter and more full of horror than in the hours of the bombardment, when the blanched faces lie in the dirt and the hands clutch at the one thought: No! No! Not now! Not now at the last moment!

Summer of 1918—Breath of hope that sweeps over the scorched fields, raging fever of impatience, of disappointment, of the most agonizing terror of death, <u>insensate</u> question: Why? Why do they make an end? And why do these rumours of an end fly about?

*

There are so many airmen here, and they are so sure of themselves that they give chase to single individuals, just as though they were hares. For every one German plane there come at least five English and American. For one hungry, wretched German soldier come five of the enemy, fresh and fit. For one German army loaf there are fifty tins of canned beef over there. We are not beaten, for as

◄ *In what way are the German soldiers superior? Why are they losing?*

---

17. **niggardliness.** Stinginess
18. **armistice.** Truce, stopping of warfare by mutual agreement

**words for everyday use**   in • sen • sate (in sen′ sāt′) *adj.,* without sense or reason; foolish; stupid. *Whereas dolphins are very smart creatures, jellyfish are <u>insensate</u>.*

soldiers we are better and more experienced; we are simply crushed and driven back by overwhelming superior forces.

Behind us lay rainy weeks—grey sky, grey fluid earth, grey dying. If we go out, the rain at once soaks through our overcoat and clothing;—and we remain wet all the time we are in the line. We never get dry. Those who will wear high boots tie sand bags round the tops so that the mud does not pour in so fast. The rifles are caked, the uniforms caked, everything is fluid and dissolved, the earth one dripping, soaked, oily mass in which lie yellow pools with red spiral streams of blood and into which the dead, wounded, and survivors slowly sink down.

The storm lashes us, out of the confusion of grey and yellow the hail of splinters whips forth the child-like cries of the wounded, and in the night shattered life groans painfully into silence.

Our hands are earth, our bodies clay and our eyes pools of rain. We do not know whether we still live.

▶ What happens to Kat?

Then the heat sinks heavily into our shell-holes like a jelly fish, moist and oppressive, and on one of these late summer days, while bringing food, Kat falls. We two are alone. I bind up his wound; his shin seems to be smashed. It has got the bone, and Kat groans desperately: "At last—just at the last—"

I comfort him. "Who knows how long this mess will go on yet! Now you are saved—"

▶ What does Paul do to help Kat?

The wound begins to bleed fast. Kat cannot be left by himself while I try to find a stretcher. Anyway, I don't know of a stretcher-bearer's post in the neighbourhood.

Kat is not very heavy; so I take him up on my back and start off to the dressing station with him.

Twice we rest. He suffers acutely on the way. We do not speak much. I have opened the collar of my tunic and breathe heavily, I sweat and my face is swollen with the strain of carrying. All the same I urge him to let us go on, for the place is dangerous.

"Shall we go on again Kat?"

"Must, Paul."

"Then come."

I raise him up, he stands on the uninjured leg and supports himself against a tree. I take up the wounded leg carefully, then he gives a jump and I take the knee of the sound leg also under my arm.

The going is more difficult. Often a shell whistles across. I go as quickly as I can, for the blood from Kat's wound drips to the ground. We cannot shelter ourselves properly from the explosions; before we can take cover the danger is all over.

We lie down in a small hole to wait till the shelling is over. I give Kat some tea from my water bottle. We smoke a cigarette. "Well, Kat," I say gloomily, "We are going to be separated at last."

◀ What is Paul gloomy about? What does he remind Kat about?

He is silent and looks at me.

"Do you remember, Kat, how we commandeered[19] the goose? And how you brought me out of the barrage when I was still a young recruit and was wounded for the first time? I cried then. Kat, that is almost three years ago."

He nods.

The anguish of solitude rises up in me. When Kat is taken away I will not have one friend left.

"Kat, in any case we must see one another again, if it is peace-time before you come back."

"Do you think that I will be marked A1 again with this leg?" he asks bitterly.

"With rest it will get better. The joint is quite sound. It may get all right again."

"Give me another cigarette," he says.

"Perhaps we could do something together later on, Kat." I am very miserable, it is impossible that Kat—Kat my friend, Kat with the drooping shoulders and the poor, thin moustache, Kat, whom I know as I know no other man, Kat with whom I have shared these years—it is impossible that perhaps I shall not see Kat again.

◀ What does Paul suggest they might do? What seems impossible to Paul?

"In any case give me your address at home, Kat. And here is mine, I will write it down for you."

I write his address in my pocket book. How forlorn I am already, though he still sits here beside me. Couldn't I shoot myself quickly in the foot so as to be able to go with him.

Suddenly Kat gurgles and turns green and yellow, "Let us go on," he stammers.

I jump up, eager to help him, I take him up and start off at a run, a slow, steady pace, so as not to jolt his leg too much.

My throat is parched; everything dances red and black before my eyes, I stagger on <u>doggedly</u> and pitilessly and at last reach the dressing station.[20]

---

19. **commandeered.** Forcibly took
20. **dressing station.** Place where wounds are bandaged and first examined on the field

---

**words for everyday use**
dog • ged • ly (dòg' id lē) adv., stubbornly; persistently. *Although the other wrestler was bigger and stronger, Warren was <u>doggedly</u> determined to beat him in the match.*

▶ Why does Paul smile?

▶ What does the orderly tell Paul?

▶ What killed Kat?

There I drop down on my knees, but have still enough strength to fall on to the side where Kat's sound leg is. After a few minutes I straighten myself up again. My legs and my hands tremble. I have trouble in finding my water bottle, to take a pull. My lips tremble as I try to think. But I smile—Kat is saved.

After a while I begin to sort out the confusion of voices that falls on my ears.

"You might have spared yourself that," says an orderly.

I look at him without comprehending.

He points to Kat. "He is stone dead."

I do not understand him. "He has been hit in the shin," I say.

The orderly stands still. "That as well."

I turn round. My eyes are still dulled, the sweat breaks out on me again, it runs over my eyelids. I wipe it away and peer at Kat. He lies still. "Fainted," I say quickly.

The orderly whistles softly. "I know better than that. He is dead. I'll lay any money on that."

I shake my head: "Not possible. Only ten minutes ago I was talking to him. He has fainted."

Kat's hands are warm, I pass my hand under his shoulders in order to rub his temples with some tea. I feel my fingers become moist. As I draw them away from behind his head, they are bloody. "You see—" The orderly whistles once more through his teeth.

On the way without my having noticed it, Kat has caught a splinter in the head. There is just one little hole, it must have been a very tiny, stray splinter. But it has <u>sufficed</u>. Kat is dead.

Slowly I get up.

"Would you like to take his paybook and his things?" the lance-corporal asks me.

I nod and he gives them to me.

The orderly is mystified. "You are not related, are you?"

No, we are not related. No, we are not related.

Do I walk? Have I feet still? I raise my eyes, I let them move round, and turn myself with them, one circle, one circle, and I stand in the midst. All is as usual. Only the Militiaman Stanislaus Katczinsky has died.

Then I know nothing more.

---

**words for everyday use**

suf • fice (sə fīs′) vi., be enough; be adequate. *Patching the hole in the tent <u>sufficed</u> during the trip, but we had to get it professionally mended when we got back from camping.*

# Chapter XII

It is autumn. There are not many of the old hands left. I am the last of the seven fellows from our class.

◀ Of what is Paul the last?

Everyone talks of peace and armistice. All wait. If it again proves an illusion, then they will break up; hope is high, it cannot be taken away again without an upheaval. If there is not peace, then there will be revolution.

I have fourteen days rest, because I have swallowed a bit of gas; in the little garden I sit the whole day long in the sun. The armistice is coming soon, I believe it now too. Then we will go home.

◀ What does Paul now believe?

Here my thoughts stop and will not go any farther. All that meets me, all that floods over me are but feelings—greed of life, love of home, yearning for the blood, intoxication of deliverance. But no aims.

Had we returned home in 1916, out of the suffering and the strength of our experiences we might have unleashed a storm. Now if we go back we will be weary, broken, burnt out, rootless, and without hope. We will not be able to find our way any more.

◀ What might the soldiers have done if they returned earlier? What will they do now when they return from the war?

And men will not understand us—for the generation that grew up before us, though it has passed these years with us already had a home and a calling; now it will return to its old occupations, and the war will be forgotten—and the generation that has grown up after us will be strange to us and push us aside. We will be <u>superfluous</u> even to ourselves, we will grow older, a few will adapt themselves, some others will merely submit, and most will be bewildered;—the years will pass by and in the end we shall fall into ruin.

But perhaps all this that I think is mere melancholy and dismay, which will fly away as the dust, when I stand once again beneath the poplars and listen to the rustling of their leaves. It cannot be that it has gone, the yearning that made our blood unquiet, the unknown, the perplexing, the oncoming things, the thousand faces of the future, the melodies from dreams and from books, the whispers and divinations of women; it cannot be that this has vanished in bombardment, in despair, in brothels.

Here the trees show gay and golden, the berries of the rowan stand red among the leaves, country roads run

---

**words for everyday use**

su • per • flu • ous (sə pu̇r′ flü əs) *adj.,* unnecessary; irrelevant. *"Boy, is it wet out,"* was Adam's <u>superfluous</u> remark as we trudged through the mud in the rain.

white out to the sky line, and the canteens hum like bee-hives with rumours of peace.

I stand up.

▶ What cannot the months and years do to Paul? Why can he confront the years ahead without fear?

I am very quiet. Let the months and years come, they can take nothing from me, they can take nothing more. I am so alone, and so without hope that I can confront them without fear. The life that has borne me through these years is still in my hands and my eyes. Whether I have subdued it, I know not. But so long as it is there it will seek its own way out, heedless of the will that is within me.

\*   \*   \*

▶ What happened to Paul? What did the army report say that day?

He fell in October 1918, on a day that was so quiet and still on the whole front, that the army report confined itself to the single sentence: All quiet on the Western Front.

He had fallen forward and lay on the earth as though sleeping. Turning him over one saw that he could not have suffered long; his face had an expression of calm, as though almost glad the end had come.

## Respond to the Selection

Explain whether you were shocked by the end of this novel. Did you foresee Paul's death, or did it come as a surprise to you?

## Investigate, Inquire, and Imagine

**Recall:** GATHERING FACTS

1a. In Chapter 11, what signs are there that the war is going badly for Germany?

2a. What happens to Kat in the summer of 1918? What does Paul do to try to help Kat? What does he discover just when he thinks he has brought Kat to safety?

3a. In Chapter 12, what does Paul say the months and years cannot do to him? How does he describe himself? What happens in October 1918? What does Paul's appearance after this event seem to indicate?

**Interpret:** FINDING MEANING

1b. In Chapter 11, what signs are there that the war is also going much worse for the soldiers mentally and emotionally? Explain the way in which the soldiers have been transformed by the war. In other words, how are they different now than they were at the war's very beginning? According to Paul, what characteristics have they adopted and what purpose do theses characteristics serve?

2b. How does Paul feel about what has happened to Kat? What details let you know he feels this way? What does Paul mean when he says, "All is as usual. Only the Militiaman Stanislaus Katczinsky has died"? In what way do you think this event forever changes the war for Paul?

3b. How would you characterize how Paul feels about life after the war in Chapter 12? Why might Paul appear as he does at the story's end?

## Analyze: TAKING THINGS APART

4a. What conflicts and issues are resolved in the last chapters of this novel? Think about both political issues and more personal ones.

## Synthesize: BRINGING THINGS TOGETHER

➤ 4b. Explain whether the ending of this story is fitting. Would you have preferred a story where conflicts and issues were resolved more happily? What would the effect of a happy ending be on this novel?

## Evaluate: MAKING JUDGMENTS

5a. Explain the significance of the title of this novel. What does it refer to? What does the title indicate about war?

## Extend: CONNECTING IDEAS

➤ 5b. If you could title the story of your own life, what would that title be?

## Understanding Literature

REPETITION AND PARALLELISM. **Repetition** is a writer's conscious reuse of a sound, word, phrase, sentence, or other element. **Parallelism** is a rhetorical technique in which a writer emphasizes the equal value or weight of two or more ideas by expressing them in the same grammatical form. Look at the following lines from Chapter 11: "Shells, gas clouds, and flotillas of tanks—shattering, corroding, death. Dysentery, influenza, typhus—scalding, choking, death. Trenches, hospitals, the common grave—there are no other possibilities." What words are repeated? How are the sentences parallel? What ideas are given equal weight by the use of parallelism? What other examples of repetition and parallelism can you find in Chapter 11?

SYMBOL. A **symbol** is a thing that stands for or represents both itself and something else. What do Kemmerich's boots symbolize in this novel?

POINT OF VIEW. **Point of view** is the vantage point from which a story is told. Stories are typically told from a first-person point of view, in which the narrator uses such words as *I* and *we;* from a second-person point of view, in which the narrator uses *you;* or from a third-person point of view, in which the narrator uses such words as *he, she, it,* and *they.* From what point of view is most of the story told? To what point of view does the story suddenly shift at the end? Why do you think the author shifted the point of view at this point in the story?

# Plot Analysis of
## *All Quiet on the Western Front*

A **plot** is a series of events related to a **central conflict**, or struggle. The following plot pyramid illustrates the main parts of a plot.

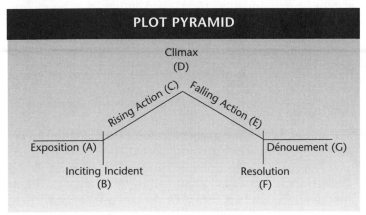

PLOT PYRAMID

Climax
(D)

Rising Action (C)    Falling Action (E)

Exposition (A)    Dénouement (G)

Inciting Incident
(B)

Resolution
(F)

The parts of a plot are as follows:

The **exposition** is the part of a plot that provides the background information, often about the characters, setting, or conflict.

The **inciting incident** is the event that introduces the central conflict.

The **rising action**, or complication, develops the conflict to a high point of intensity.

The **climax** is the high point of interest or suspense in the plot.

The **falling action** is all the events that follow the climax.

The **resolution** is the point at which the central conflict is ended, or resolved.

The **dénouement** is any material that follows the resolution and that ties up any loose ends.

## Exposition (A)

The narrator, nineteen-year-old Paul Baümer, is five miles behind enemy lines with his fellow soldiers. About half of his company has died in battle, so he and his friends get double rations. Paul's friends and companions are introduced to the reader—his classmates Albert Kropp, Müller, and Leer; Tjaden; Stanislaus Katczinsky or "Kat"; Haie Westhus; and Detering. Paul and his former classmates recall how their former teacher Kantorek encouraged them to enlist in the war. Paul, Kropp, and Müller visit another classmate and fellow soldier named Kemmerich. Kemmerich has been wounded and is dying. Müller schemes to get Kemmerich's boots as Kemmerich won't need them anymore and the hospital workers will steal them. Paul visits his friend Kemmerich the next day and watches his friend die. He takes Kemmerich's boots and gives them to Müller. Paul's group is sent new recruits, and Paul and his friends recall how they were treated cruelly by Colonel Himmelstoss during their basic training and how they plotted revenge on Himmelstoss.

## Inciting Incident (B)

Paul and his fellow soldiers are sent on a mission to lay wire at the front. They are bombarded and try to teach the new recruits what to do to survive when they are being shelled. Some horses are wounded in the attack, and their cries upset the soldiers before the horses can be shot. Then, on their way back from laying wire, the soldiers are again bombarded. They seek cover in a cemetery, using the coffins and corpses to protect themselves. They are also attacked with poison gas. After the attack, Paul and Kat find that one of the new recruits is injured badly. They know he will not survive and will only experience great pain. Paul and Kat decide to shoot their fellow soldier to put him out of his misery, just like what happened to the horses. Before they can shoot the injured man, other soldiers arrive so they go to get a stretcher.

## Rising Action (C)

The men return to their quarters behind the front. Himmelstoss has been sent to the front. Tjaden insults him and Kropp defends Tjaden, but the two are punished lightly. Kat and Paul cook a roast goose together and take some of the meat to Tjaden and Kropp. The soldiers are sent to the front again. There, they are bombarded in their trenches and have inadequate food. The enemy attacks and then Paul and his friends counterattack. Paul forces a terrified Himmelstoss to leave the trenches and fight. Haie dies. Out of Paul's company of 150 men, only 32 are left when the fighting is over. Behind the front lines, Paul and his friends meet up with three French girls. Paul then gets leave to go home. He finds that his mother is sick and that he cannot talk to anyone about what he has experienced at the front. He tells Kemmerich's mother that Kemmerich died immediately with no pain. Before he returns to the front, Paul is sent for more training. There, he sees Russian prisoners of war who live in miserable conditions. Paul then returns to the front and is reunited with his friends.

## Climax, Crisis/Turning Point (D)

Returning to battle for the first time since his leave, Paul is filled with fear. He gets separated from his friends behind enemy lines and hides in a crater. A French soldier falls into the crater and Paul stabs him. He must watch the soldier slowly die. Paul tries to comfort the soldier he stabbed, binding his wounds and giving him water. When the soldier dies, Paul goes through his wallet and learns the soldier's name and that he had a family. Paul realizes that the Frenchman is not really his enemy at all but could have been one of his friends. Paul talks to the dead soldier, promising at first that he will help his wife and daughter and later that he will struggle against the war that killed the French soldier and that is destroying Paul. Kat and Albert then find Paul. When Paul tells him of his experience, they remind him of the realities of war by showing them a soldier shooting the enemy for medals.

## Falling Action (E)

Paul and his friends are sent to guard a supply dump, where they live like kings, holding elaborate feasts and even finding fancy furniture and a pet cat. Once they leave the supply dump, they are sent to guard an evacuating village. They are attacked, and Paul and Albert Kropp are injured. They manage to get to safety and are taken by train to a hospital. They find the doctors to be cruel and indifferent to their patients' suffering. Albert's leg is amputated, and once Paul recovers he is sent back to the front alone.

## Resolution (F)

The war is going badly for the Germans. Their equipment is shoddy now, and they fight from crater to crater. One by one, Paul's friends fall. Detering deserts and is court-martialed. Müller dies and gives Kemmerich's boots to Paul. Paul decides to give them to Tjaden if he dies. Then, Kat is injured in the shin. Paul tries to carry Kat to safety, but Kat is wounded in the head as Paul carries him. By the time Paul gets Kat to a medic, he is already dead.

## Dénouement (G)

Paul is given leave after inhaling poison gas. He is now the only one of his group of friends left. He feels that the war will end soon but is not sure how he can return to civilian life. He says he is completely alone and without hope. Paul returns to the front and dies in October 1918.

# "Otto Dix: An Artist's View of World War I"
### by Paul Spencer

## ABOUT THE RELATED READING

This article discusses the life and work of a famous German artist, Otto Dix, whose experiences in World War I parallel those of the writer Erich Maria Remarque and the characters in *All Quiet on the Western Front*. Although Remarque's and Dix's modes of expression are very different, each of their works stands as a strong antiwar statement that reached a wide audience. Both suffered the same persecution and censorship under the Nazi government fifteen years after the war.

Paul Spencer (1960– ) is an art historian who lives in St. Paul, Minnesota. He is a former museum curator who writes and lectures on art. His primary interest is the history of Modern art, particularly in Europe around the time of World War I. Spencer notes that the rapid technological and social changes in those early years of the twentieth century had a radical effect on the arts that still reverberates today.

## Otto Dix: An Artist's View of World War I

Otto Dix (1891–1969) was a German artist whose experiences in World War I were like those of many young men on both sides of the conflict. Dix was initially enthusiastic about going into battle. Full of dreams of adventure and heroism, he volunteered for the German army in 1914. He was sent to the Western Front in the autumn of 1915, where he served as a machine-gunner. Dix was involved in some of the fiercest fighting and was wounded several times during the war.

◀ *How does Dix's attitude toward the war change?*

As the war dragged on, Dix became disillusioned; the fighting seemed to have no purpose and no end. By the time the end of the war did come, he was expressing his revulsion for it in paintings and drawings that assault the viewer with the ugliest aspects of the soldier's experience. Dix's art shows the animalistic behavior of men in battle, but more often he depicts shabby soldiers simply carrying on with numbed indifference to the horror around them. At the time, Dix's style and subject matter were called the New Objectivity, but he is also identified with a larger movement known as German Expressionism. The German Expressionists used harsh colors, or stark black and white, along with jagged, distorted forms to represent their emotional response to the chaotic world around them. In 1924, Dix joined with other Expressionists who had fought in the war to put on an art exhibition called "No More War!" That same year Dix produced the series *Der Krieg* (The War) from which the drawings on the following pages come. Dix made the drawings as prints so that many copies could be widely distributed, and the series was well known throughout Germany.

These pictures are excellent examples of the Expressionist drawing style, which deliberately lacked the grace that viewers of the time expected in art. The deep, jagged lines give the impression of the artist's hand slashing violently across the surface. Most of the drawings are very dense, such as *Disintegrating Trench*. Dix piled detail on detail so that it is hard to determine just what is being shown. In this way he captures the physical clutter of the trenches, but, moreover, suggests the moral and emotional confusion felt by the soldiers. *Battle-weary troops retreat* is drawn differently for another effect. The figures are suggested with just bare outlines, and the defeated army is literally and metaphorically empty and flattened against the picture plane. Some aspects of the pictures are oddly humorous, such as *Mealtime in the trench* in which a soldier greedily gobbles his food, oblivious to the skeleton beside him. Dix shows us not only the horror of the war, but also its absurdity and its irony.

▶ *What aspects of war does Dix's art express?*

In 1933, Adolf Hitler and the Nazi Party came to power in Germany and began preparing the nation for the next war. They wished to erase the memory of the disaster of World War I and attacked anyone who was critical of the military. The Nazis destroyed many of Dix's artworks and he was fired from his teaching position at the Dresden Academy art school. Nonetheless, from 1934 to 1936 he worked in secret on another antiwar statement, the painting *Flanders* [which appears on the cover of this book]. It was exhibited in Switzerland, beyond the reach of the Nazis.

The Nazi government was so suspicious of Dix that in 1939 he was arrested for a plot to assassinate Hitler. Dix was eventually acquitted and even pressed into service in the army near the end of World War II. He was captured and spent time in a French prisoner of war camp. After Germany's defeat, he returned to Dresden, which had once been a great center of arts and culture, but was now completely destroyed.

**Otto Dix:** *Disintegrating Trench*, **1924.** © Artists Rights Society (ARS), New York / VG Bild-Kunst, Bonn.

## Critical Thinking

1.  Why do you think the Nazi authorities objected to Dix's depictions of the war?
2.  Choose one of the drawings and compare it to the painting on the cover. What are the similarities or differences in the style, the subject matter, and the effect each picture has on you?
3.  Find a corresponding scene in *All Quiet on the Western Front* for one or more of Dix's drawings that appear on the following pages. The titles may help you. Explain any similarities or differences between the drawings and the scenes in the book.

Otto Dix: *Near Langemarck, February 1918*. 1924. © Artists Rights Society (ARS), New York / VG Bild-Kunst, Bonn.

Otto Dix: *The outposts in the trenches must maintain the bombardment at night*. 1924. © Artists Rights Society (ARS), New York / VG Bild-Kunst, Bonn.

**Otto Dix:** *Battle-weary troops retreat, battle of the Somme.* **1924.** © Artists Rights Society (ARS), New York / VG Bild-Kunst, Bonn.

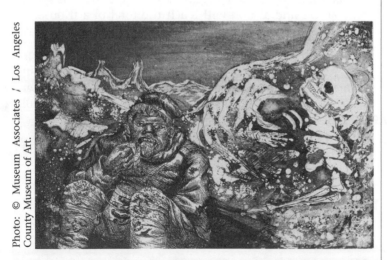

**Otto Dix:** *Mealtime in the trench; Loretta heights.* **1924.** © Artists Rights Society (ARS), New York / VG Bild-Kunst, Bonn.

# From *The Art of War*
## by Sun Tzu,
### translated by Lionel Giles

## ABOUT THE RELATED READING

Little is known about Sun Tzu's (c.500 BC) life, but he was a military leader and probably a member of the Chinese aristocracy. Sun Tzu's *The Art of War* is the earliest known treatise on military strategy. People have also applied the treatise's principles to other aspects of life, such as business and sports. Although *The Art of War* was written thousands of years before World War I, some of the principles Sun Tzu presents help explain why World War I caused so much devastation. As you read the chapter, think about how trench warfare relates to Sun Tzu's advice.

## Chapter 2

1. Sun Tzu said: In the operations of war, where there are in the field a thousand swift chariots,[1] as many heavy chariots, and a hundred thousand mail-clad soldiers, with provisions enough to carry them a thousand li,[2] the expenditure at home and at the front, including entertainment of guests, small items such as glue and paint, and sums spent on chariots and armor, will reach the total of a thousand ounces of silver per day. Such is the cost of raising an army of 100,000 men.

▶ *What will happen if victory is long in coming?*

2. When you engage in actual fighting, if victory is long in coming, then men's weapons will grow dull and their <u>ardor</u> will be damped. If you lay siege to a town, you will exhaust your strength.

▶ *What will happen in a protracted campaign?*

3. Again, if the campaign is <u>protracted</u>, the resources of the State will not be equal to the strain.

4. Now, when your weapons are dulled, your ardor damped, your strength exhausted and your treasure spent,

---

1. **chariots.** Horse-drawn, two-wheeled carts used in ancient times for war
2. **li.** Chinese unit of measurement equal to about one-third of a mile

---

**words for everyday use**

**ar • dor** (är' dər) *n.*, eagerness; enthusiasm; zeal. *Ona always tried to share with others her <u>ardor</u> for horses and riding.*

**pro • tract** (prō trakt') *vt.*, draw out; lengthen in duration; prolong. *Kaylie was having so much fun visiting her grandparents, she called her parents begging them to allow her visit to be <u>protracted</u>.*

other chieftains will spring up to take advantage of your extremity.[3] Then no man, however wise, will be able to avert the consequences that must <u>ensue</u>.

5. Thus, though we have heard of stupid haste in war, cleverness has never been seen associated with long delays.

6. There is no instance of a country having benefited from prolonged warfare.

◀ Of what is there no instance?

7. It is only one who is thoroughly acquainted with the evils of war that can thoroughly understand the profitable way of carrying it on.

8. The skillful soldier does not raise a second levy,[4] neither are his supply-wagons loaded more than twice.

9. Bring war material with you from home, but forage[5] on the enemy. Thus the army will have food enough for its needs.

10. Poverty of the State exchequer[6] causes an army to be maintained by contributions from a distance. Contributing to maintain an army at a distance causes the people to be impoverished.

11. On the other hand, the proximity of an army causes prices to go up; and high prices cause the people's substance to be drained away.

12. When their substance is drained away, the peasantry will be afflicted by heavy exactions.[7]

13,14. With this loss of substance and exhaustion of strength, the homes of the people will be stripped bare, and three-tenths of their income will be <u>dissipated</u>; while government expenses for broken chariots, worn-out horses, breast-plates and helmets, bows and arrows, spears and shields, protective mantles, draught-oxen and heavy wagons, will amount to four-tenths of its total revenue.

◀ What will happen to the people when they are taxed and must pay high prices because of war? What expenses does the government have in wartime?

---

3. **extremity.** State of extreme necessity or danger
4. **levy.** Calling up people for required military service
5. **forage.** Search for food or provisions
6. **exchequer.** Treasury or finances
7. **exactions.** Taxes

---

**words for everyday use**

en • sue (en sü′) vi., come afterward; follow. *Our guide told us that sunshine would* ensue *the brief tropical downpour.*

dis • si • pate (dis′ ə pāt′) vt., break up and scatter; dispel; disperse. *As the winds* dissipated, *the sail of our boat hung slack.*

15. Hence a wise general makes a point of foraging on the enemy. One cartload of the enemy's provisions is equivalent to twenty of one's own, and likewise a single picul[8] of his provender is equivalent to twenty from one's own store.

16. Now in order to kill the enemy, our men must be roused to anger; that there may be advantage from defeating the enemy, they must have their rewards.

17. Therefore in chariot fighting, when ten or more chariots have been taken, those should be rewarded who took the first. Our own flags should be substituted for those of the enemy, and the chariots mingled and used in conjunction with ours. The captured soldiers should be kindly treated and kept.

18. This is called, using the conquered foe to augment one's own strength.

19. In war, then, let your great object be victory, not lengthy campaigns.

20. Thus it may be known that the leader of armies is the <u>arbiter</u> of the people's fate, the man on whom it depends whether the nation shall be in peace or in peril.

## Critical Thinking

1. What does Sun Tzu warn against doing in war? What does he say you should do instead?
2. If Sun Tzu examined World War I, what might he find fault with?
3. Explain whether Paul would agree or disagree with the following statement: "The leader of armies is the arbiter of the people's fate, the man on whom it depends whether the nation shall be in peace or in peril."

---

8. **picul.** Unit of weight equal to 133 pounds

**words for everyday use**   ar • bi • ter (är′ bət ər) *n.*, person fully authorized or qualified to judge or decide. *You must respect the umpire's decisions because he or she is the <u>arbiter</u> of the game.*

# "The Soldier"
## by Rupert Brooke

### ABOUT THE RELATED READING

Rupert Brooke (1887–1915) was an Englishman who was considered a hero by many in his country. He enlisted in the Royal Navy when the war began. "The Soldier" is one of a group of patriotic and idealistic sonnets he published about the war. Brooke died of blood poisoning during the war. Brooke's patriotic sonnet "The Soldier" was written early in World War I, when people still had romantic notions about the war. It stands in contrast with many of the ideas expressed in *All Quiet on the Western Front.*

## The Soldier

If I should die, think only this of me:
That there's some corner of a foreign field
That is for ever England. There shall be
In that rich earth a richer dust concealed;
A dust whom England bore, shaped, made aware,
Gave, once, her flowers to love, her ways to roam,
A body of England's, breathing English air,
Washed by the rivers, blest by suns of home.
And think, this heart, all evil shed away,
A pulse in the eternal mind, no less
Gives somewhere back the thoughts by England given;
Her sights and sounds; dreams happy as her day;
And laughter, learnt of friends; and gentleness,
In hearts at peace, under an English heaven.

◀ *What does the speaker ask the audience to think of him if he dies?*

◀ *What type of heaven does the speaker believe he will go to?*

### Critical Thinking

1. How does the speaker in "The Soldier" feel about his country?
2. How does the speaker feel about dying? Why isn't he afraid?
3. Who in *All Quiet on the Western Front* shares ideas about war most similar to those of the speaker in "The Soldier"?
4. Compare and contrast Paul Bäumer's ideas about dying for his country to those of the speaker in "The Soldier."

# "Dulce et Decorum Est"
## by Wilfred Owen

## ABOUT THE RELATED READING

Like Rupert Brooke, Wilfred Owen (1893–1918) fought for England during World War I. Unlike Brooke, Owen wrote angrily about the war and its horrors in his poetry. Owen died in action in France just a week before the war's end. Although Owen was on a different side of the conflict than Remarque, the two authors write in the same scathing manner, condemning the horrors of war by describing them so realistically.

# Dulce et Decorum Est

Bent double, like old beggars under sacks,
Knock-kneed, coughing like hags, we cursed through sludge,
Till on the haunting flares we turned our backs
And towards our distant rest began to trudge.
Men marched asleep. Many had lost their boots
But limped on, blood-shod. All went lame; all blind;
Drunk with fatigue; deaf even to the hoots
Of tired, outstripped Five-Nines[1] that dropped behind.

Gas! Gas! Quick, boys!—An ecstasy of fumbling,
Fitting the clumsy helmets just in time;
But someone still was yelling out and stumbling
And flound'ring like a man in fire or lime...[2]
Dim, through the misty panes and thick green light,
As under a green sea, I saw him drowning.

In all my dreams, before my helpless sight,
He plunges at me, guttering,[3] choking, drowning.

If in some smothering dreams you too could pace
Behind the wagon that we flung him in,
And watch the white eyes writhing in his face,
His hanging face, like a devil's sick of sin;
If you could hear, at every jolt, the blood
Come gargling from the froth-corrupted lungs,

*▶ Where are the soldiers marching? What condition are they in?*

*▶ What alarm do the soldiers hear? What do they do to protect themselves? What does the speaker see one soldier doing?*

*▶ Where do the others put the injured soldier? What has the gas attack done to the soldier?*

1. **Five-Nines.** Artillery shells
2. **lime.** Sticky substance used to snare birds
3. **guttering.** Gurgling and sputtering

Obscene as cancer, bitter as the cud
Of vile, incurable sores on innocent tongues,—
My friend, you would not tell with such high zest
To children <u>ardent</u> for some desperate glory,
The old Lie: Dulce et decorum est
Pro patria mori. [4]

◄ According to the speaker, what would you not do if you saw the soldier who had been gassed?

## Critical Thinking

1. What view of warfare is expressed in this poem?
2. What is the old lie? To whom should this lie not be told, according to the speaker? Why might the speaker be especially concerned with this group hearing the lie?
3. Compare and contrast Owen's descriptions of battle to Remarque's. What same things did soldiers on both side of the conflict suffer?

4. **Dulce . . . mori.** Latin phrase from the Roman poet Horace's Odes, meaning, "It is sweet and proper to die for one's country."

**words for everyday use**

ar • dent (ärd' 'nt) *adj.*, intensely enthusiastic or devoted; zealous. *Aimee was an <u>ardent</u> inline skater who could be found skating in the park every weekend, rain or shine.*

# From *Testament of Youth*
## by Vera Brittain

## ABOUT THE RELATED READING

Vera Brittain (1896–1970) was an English woman who lost her fiancé, her best friend, and her brother in World War I and worked as a volunteer nurse throughout the war. *Testament of Youth* is her memoir about her experience of the war. Unlike Remarque, she thought it best to address her war experiences in a work of nonfiction rather than in a novel. Brittain's thoughts and experiences have much in common with those of the German soldier Paul Bäumer in *All Quiet on the Western Front*. This excerpt also shows that women's lives were as endangered and altered by the war as those of men.

## Chapter VIII: 14

As the German offensive rolled heavily on without appearing to <u>slacken</u>, the men who came into hospital after two or three weeks of continuous fighting no longer seemed to be weighed down with the sombre depression of the first batches of wounded; instead, they were light-headed and often strangely *exaltés*.[1] After the first shock of defeat, certain units of the British Army began to suffer from a curious masochism,[2] and, as in 1914, turned from their usual dogged reliance upon their own strength to the consolations of superstition and the illusions of fatigue.

There was little chance to get to know patients who arrived in the morning and left before the evening, and in the daily rush of dressings and convoys I had not much time for talking, but once or twice I became aware of strange discussions being carried on by the men. On one occasion I stopped to listen, and was impelled to remain; I wrote down the conversation a few weeks afterwards, and though it cannot have been verbally exact, I reproduce it as it appeared in my 1918 "novel" of nursing in France:

---

1. *exaltés.* Exalted or elevated
2. **masochism.** Perverse enjoyment from being hurt or injured

**words for everyday use**

slack • en (slak′ ən) *vi.,* become less active or intense. *Wendall took a deep drink of water to <u>slacken</u> his thirst.*

" 'Ave yer come down from Albert way?" inquired a sergeant of a corporal in the next bed, who, like himself, wore a 1914 ribbon.

"Yus," was the reply, "I have. There's some mighty queer things happenin' on the Somme just now, ain't there, mate?"

"That there be," said the sergeant. "I can tell yer of one rum[3] thing that 'appened to me, meself."

"Git on then, chum, let's hear it."

"Well, when the old regiment first came out in '16, we had a Captain with us—O.C.[4] of our company, 'e was—a might fine chap. One day at the beginning of the Somme battle some of the boys got into a tight place—a bit fool-ishlike, maybe, some of them was—and 'e comes along and pulls 'em out of it. One or two of 'em had got the wind up a bit,[5] and 've tells 'em then not to lose 'eart if they gets into difficulties, for 'e sorter knows, 'e says, when the boys 'as need of 'im, and wherever 'e is, 'e says, 'e'll do 'is best to be there. Well 'e was killed, 'elpin' the boys as usual, at the end of the fightin' on the Somme, and we mourned for 'im like a brother, as you might say. . . . 'E were a tall fine chap, no mistakin' 'im, there wasn't. Well, the other day, just before the Boches[6] got into Albert,[7] we was in a bit of a fix, and I was doin' all I knew to get us out. Suddenly I turns round, and there I sees 'im with 'is bright eyes and 'is old smile bringin' up the rear.

" 'Well, Willis, it's been a narrow shave[8] this time,' 'e says. 'But I think we've pulled it off.'

"An' forgettin' 'ow it was, I makes as if to answer 'im, and all of a sudden 'e ain't there at all. Struck me all of a heap for a bit, like. What do you make of it, mate?"

"It's more nor I can tell," answered the corporal. " 'Cos another very queer thing happened to some chaps in our company. In the old days on the Somme we had a tophole party of stretcher-bearers, and one day a coal-box[9] comes and wipes out the lot. But last week some of our chaps sees 'em again, carrying the wounded down the communica-tion trench. And I met a chum in the train who swears he was carried out by two of 'em."

A Lancashire boy from an opposite bed leaned forward eagerly.

◀ Whom does the soldier claim he saw?

◀ What happened to the stretcher-bearers? What have some people seen them doing?

---

3. **rum.** Odd
4. **O.C.** Officer commanding
5. **got the wind up a bit.** Became a little nervous
6. **Boches.** German soldiers
7. **Albert.** Albert I (1875–1934), king of Belgium
8. **narrow shave.** Close escape from danger
9. **coal-box.** German shell

"I can tell yer summat[10] that'll beat that," he said. "T'other day when we was gettin' clear of Péronne, I found a chap beside me lookin' very white and done-up, like, as if 'e could scarcely walk; fair clemmed,[11] 'e seemed to me. I found I'd got one or two of them 'ard biscuits in me pocket, an' I pulls one out and hands it to 'im. ' 'Ave a biscuit, mate,' sez I.

" 'Thank you, chum,' 'e sez, 'I don't mind if I do.'

"And 'e takes the biscuit and gives it a bite. As 'e puts out 'is 'and for it I sees 'e's got one o' them <u>swanky</u> identity-disks[12] on 'is wrist, and I reads 'is number as plain as anythink. Then 'e gets mixed up wi' t'others, and I don't see 'im no more. And it's not till I gets back to billets that I remembers.

" 'Lawks,' I sez to myself, 'if that ain't the chap I 'elped Jim to bury more'n a week agone, my name ain't Bill Bennett.'

"An' sure enough, mates, I remember takin' the silver identity-disk off 'is wrist, an' readin' the number on it as plain as plain. An' it were the number of the man I gave the biscuit."

There was an awed silence in the ward, and I turned from the dressing I was doing to ask rather breathlessly:

▶ What does the narrator ask the sergeant? What is his reply?

"Do you really mean that in the middle of the battle you met those men again whom you'd thought were dead?"

The sergeant's reply was insistent.

"Aye, Sister, they're dead right enough. They're our mates as was knocked out on the Somme in '16. And it's our belief they're fightin' with us still."

Not long afterwards I was reminded of this conversation by some lines from E. A. Mackintosh's "Cha Till Maccruimein," in his volume of poems *A Highland Regiment*, which Roland's mother and sister had sent me for Christmas:

> *And there in front of the men were marching,*
> *With feet that made no mark,*
> *The grey old ghosts of the ancient fighters*
> *Come back again from the dark. . . .*

---

10. **summat.** Something
11. **clemmed.** In bad shape
12. **identity-disks.** Similar to dog tags but worn on the wrist

**words for everyday use**    swank • y (swaŋ' kē) *adj.*, ostentatiously stylish; showy. *Jules felt out of place at the swanky party in just his jeans and a T-shirt.*

But at the time I merely felt cold and rather sick, and when I had finished the dressing I put down my tray and stood for a moment at the open door of the hut. I saw the Sisters in their white overalls hurrying between the wards, the tired orderlies toiling along the paths with their loaded stretchers, the usual crowd of Red Cross ambulances outside the reception hut, and I recognised my world for a kingdom of death, in which the poor ghosts of the victims had no power to help their comrades by breaking nature's laws.

Angels of Mons[13] still roaming about, I thought. Well, let them roam, if it cheers the men to believe in them! No doubt the Germans, too, had their Angels of Mons; I have often wondered what happened when the celestial backers of one Army encountered their angelic opponents in the nocturnal neutrality of No Man's Land. Michael's[14] war in heaven was nothing, I feel certain, to what happened then.

Certainly no Angels of Mons were watching over Étaples, or they would not have allowed mutilated men and exhausted women to be further oppressed by the series of noctural air-raids which for over a month supplied the camps beside the railway with periodic intimations[15] of the less pleasing characteristics of a front-line trench. The offensive seemed to have lasted since the beginning of creation, but must actually have been on for less than a fortnight, when the lights suddenly went out one evening as the daystaff was finishing its belated supper. Instead of the usual interval of silence followed by the return of the lights, an almost immediate series of crashes showed this alarm to be real.

◀ *How long has the offensive lasted? How long does it seem to last?*

After days of continuous heavy duty and scamped, inadequate meals, our nerves were none too reliable, and I don't suppose I was the only member of the staff whose teeth chattered with sheer terror as we groped our way to our individual huts in response to the order to scatter. Hope Milroy and I, thinking that we might as well be killed together, sat glassy-eyed in her small, pitch-black room. Suddenly, intermittent flashes half blinded us, and we listened frantically in the deafening <u>din</u> for the bugle-call

---

13. **Mons.** Scottish or North English term for men
14. **Michael's.** Michael is one of the archangels in the Bible.
15. **intimations.** Hints, implications

---

**words for everyday use**
    din (din) *n.,* loud, continuous noise. *As the students changed classes, the hallways were filled with the* <u>din</u> *of cheerful students calling out to one another.*

which we knew would summon us to join the night-staff in the wards if bombs began to fall on the hospital.

▶ What does one sister do during the attack? Why is the narrator proud?

One young Sister, who had previously been shelled at a Casualty Clearing Station, lost her nerve and rushed screaming through the Mess; two others seized her and forcibly put her to bed, holding her down while the raid lasted to prevent her from causing a panic. I knew that I was more frightened than I had ever been in my life, yet all the time a tense, triumphant pride that I was not revealing my fear to the others held me to the semblance of self-control.

When a momentary lull came in the booms and the flashes, Hope, who had also been under fire at a C.C.S., gave way to the sudden <u>bravado</u> of rushing into the open to see whether the raiders had gone; she was still wearing her white cap, and a dozen trembling hands instantly pulled her indoors again, a dozen shakily shrill voices scolded her indiscretion. Gradually, after another brief burst of firing, the camp became quiet, though the lights were not turned on again that night. Next day we were told that most of the bombs had fallen on the village; the bridge over the Canche, it was reported, had been smashed, and the train service had to be suspended while the engineers performed the exciting feat of mending it in twelve hours.

For a day or two after the raid I felt curiously light-hearted; like the hero of Hugh Walpole's *The Dark Forest*—one of the few novels that I read that winter—"I was happy . . . with a strange exultation that was unlike any emotion that I had known before. It was . . . something of the happiness of danger or pain that one has dreaded and finds, in actual truth, give way before one's resolution."

But that vital sense of self-conquest soon vanished, for within the next few weeks a good night's rest proved impossible for most of us. The liability to be called up for late convoys had already induced a habit of light, restless dozing, and the knowledge that the raiders meant business and might return at any moment after sunset did not help us to settle down quietly and confidently during the hours of darkness. Whenever a particularly tiring day had battered our exhausted nerves into indifference, the lights

---

**words for everyday use**

**bra • va • do** (brə vä′ dō) *n.,* pretended courage or defiant confidence where there is really little or none. *Lawrence's calm was an act of <u>bravado</u> because he was as frightened as we were by the mild earthquake.*

went out as the result of alarming reports from Abbeville or Camiers and revived our apprehensions. Rumour declared that we were all to be issued with steel helmets, and further spasmodic efforts were made to provide us with trenches in case of emergency.

Three weeks of such days and nights, lived without respite or off-duty time under the permanent fear of defeat and flight, reduced the staffs of the Étaples hospitals to the negative conviction that nothing mattered except to end the strain. England, panic-stricken, was frantically raising the military age to fifty and agreeing to the appointment of Foch[16] as Commander-in-Chief, but to us with our blistered feet, our swollen hands, our wakeful, reddened eyes, victory and defeat began—as indeed they were afterwards to prove—to seem very much the same thing. On April 11th, after a dizzying rush of wounded from the new German offensive at Armentières, I stumbled up to the Sisters' quarters for lunch with the certainty that I could not go on—and saw, pinned upon the notice-board in the Mess,[17] Sir Douglas Haig's[18] "Special Order of the Day." Standing there spellbound, with fatigue and despair forgotten, I read the words which put courage into so many men and women whose need of endurance was far greater than my own:

◀ *How does the staff feel after three weeks of attacks?*

◀ *How does Douglas's writing make the narrator feel?*

"TO ALL RANKS OF THE BRITISH ARMY IN FRANCE AND FLANDERS

"Three weeks ago to-day the enemy began his terrific attacks against us on a fifty-mile front. His objects are to separate us from the French, to take the Channel Ports and destroy the British Army.

"In spite of throwing already 106 Divisions into the battle and enduring the most reckless sacrifice of human life, he has as yet made little progress toward his goals.

"We owe this to the determined fighting and self-sacrifice of our troops. Words fail me to express the admiration

---

16. **Foch.** Ferdinand Foch (1851–1929) was appointed commander-in-chief of Allied forces in 1918.
17. **Mess.** Mess hall, or place where food is served
18. **Douglas Haig's.** Douglas Haig (1861–1928) was the British commander-in-chief during World War I.

---

**words for everyday use**

spas • mod • ic (spaz mäd' ik) *adj.*, sudden, violent, and temporary. *The wind blew in spasmodic gusts along the shore— one minute it would be calm and the next we would be blasted by sand.*

res • pite (res' pit) *n.*, interval of temporary relief or rest. *After mowing the lawn all day in the hot sun, Julie was happy to come inside for a brief respite before she had to return to work.*

which I feel for the splendid resistance offered by all ranks of our Army under the most trying circumstances.

"Many amongst us now are tired. To those I would say that Victory will belong to the side which holds out the longest. The French Army is moving rapidly and in great force to our support.

▶ What does the writer call on others to do?

"There is no course open to us but to fight it out. Every position must be held to the last man: there must be no retirement. With our backs to the wall and believing in the justice of our cause each one of us must fight on to the end. The safety or our homes and the Freedom of mankind alike depend upon the conduct of each one of us at this critical moment.

"General Headquarters,        "D. HAIG, F.M.,
"Thursday, April 11th, 1918."     "Commander-in-Chief
                                   "British Armies in France.

Although, since that date, the publication of official "revelations" has stripped from the Haig myth much of its glory, I have never been able to visualise Lord Haig as the colossal blunderer, the self-deceived optimist, of the Somme massacre in 1916. I can think of him only as the author of that Special Order, for after I had read it I knew that I should go on, whether I could or not. There was a braver spirit in the hospital that afternoon, and though we only referred briefly and brusquely to Haig's message, each one of us had made up her mind that, though enemy airmen blew up our huts and the Germans advanced upon us from Abbeville, so long as wounded men remained in Étaples, there would be "no retirement."

Only a day or two afterwards I was leaving quarters to go back to my ward, when I had to wait to let a large contingent of troops march past me along the main road that ran through our camp. They were swinging rapidly towards Camiers, and though the sight of soldiers marching was now too familiar to arouse curiosity, an unusual quality of bold vigour in their swift stride caused me to stare at them with puzzled interest.

▶ In what way do these soldiers seem different to the narrator?

They looked larger than ordinary men; their tall, straight figures were in vivid contrast to the under-sized armies of pale recruits to which we had grown accustomed. At first I thought their spruce, clean uniforms were those of officers, yet obviously they could not be officers, for there were too many of them; they seemed, as it were, Tommies[19] in heaven. Had yet another regiment been conjured out of our

---

19. **Tommies.** English soldiers

depleted Dominions? I wondered, watching them move with such rhythm, such dignity, such serene consciousness of self-respect. But I knew the colonial troops so well, and these were different; they were assured where the Australians were aggressive, self-possessed where the New Zealanders were turbulent.

Then I heard an excited exclamation from a group of Sisters behind me.

"Look! Look! Here are the Americans!"

◀ Who were the soldiers?

I pressed forward with the others to watch the United States physically entering the War, so god-like, so magnificent, so splendidly unimpaired in comparison with the tired, nerve-racked men of the British Army. So these were our deliverers at last, marching up the road to Camiers in the spring sunshine! There seemed to be hundreds of them, and in the fearless swagger of their proud strength they looked a formidable bulwark against the peril looming from Amiens.

Somehow the necessity of packing up in a hurry, the ignominious fight to the coast so long imagined, seemed to move further away. An uncontrollable emotion seized me—as such emotions often seized us in those days of insufficient sleep; my eyeballs pricked, my throat ached, and a mist swam over the confident Americans going to the front. The coming of relief made me realise all at once how long and how intolerable had been the tension, and with the knowledge that we were not, after all, defeated, I found myself beginning to cry.

◀ How does the narrator feel about the Americans entering the war?

• • •

## Chapter IX: 10

When the sound of victorious guns burst over London at 11 a.m. on November 11th, 1918, the men and women who looked <u>incredulously</u> into each other's faces did not cry <u>jubilantly</u>: "We've won the War!" They only said: "The War is over."

◀ What didn't people do when the war ended?

From Millbank I heard the maroons[20] crash with terrifying clearness, and, like a sleeper who is determined to go on dreaming after being told to wake up, I went on

---

20. **maroons.** Firecrackers

**words for everyday use**
in • cred • u • lous • ly (in krej′ ū ləs lē) *adv.*, in a manner that shows doubt or disbelief. *We looked at Shawna incredulously when she told us she had met the movie star.*

ju • bi • lant • ly (jü′ bə lənt lē) *adv.*, in a joyful manner. *The children jubilantly celebrated the start of summer by going to the town festival.*

automatically washing the dressing bowls in the annex[21] outside my hut. Deeply buried beneath my consciousness there stirred the vague memory of a letter that I had written to Roland in those legendary days when I was still at Oxford, and could spend my Sundays in thinking of him while the organ echoed grandly through New College Chapel. It had been a warm May evening, when all the city was sweet with the scent of wallflowers and lilac, and I had walked back to Micklem Hall after hearing an Occasional Oratorio by Handel, which described the mustering of troops for battle, the lament for the fallen and the triumphant return of the victors.

▶ To whom will the jubilant celebrations at the war's end seem a mockery?

"As I listened," I told him, "to the organ swelling forth into a final triumphant burst in the song of victory, after the solemn and mournful dirge over the dead, I thought with what mockery and irony the jubilant celebrations which will hail the coming of peace will fall upon the ears of those to whom their best will never return, upon whose sorrow victory is built, who have paid with their mourning for the others' joy. I wonder if I shall be one of those who take a happy part in the triumph—or if I shall listen to the merriment with a heart that breaks and ears that try to keep out the mirthful sounds."

▶ What has come too late for the narrator?

And as I dried the bowls I thought: "It's come too late for me. Somehow I knew, even at Oxford, that it would. Why couldn't it have ended rationally, as it might have ended, in 1916, instead of all that trumpet-blowing against a negotiated peace, and the ferocious talk of secure civilians about marching to Berlin?[22] It's come five months too late—or is it three years? It might have ended last June, and let Edward, at least, be saved! Only five months—it's such a little time, when Roland died nearly three years ago."

But on Armistice Day[23] not even a lonely survivor drowning in black waves of memory could be left alone with her thoughts. A moment after the guns had subsided into sudden, palpitating silence, the other V.A.D.[24] from my ward dashed excitedly into the annex.

"Brittain! Brittain! Did you hear the maroons? It's over—it's all over! Do let's come out and see what's happening!"

Mechanically I followed her into the road. As I stood there, stupidly rigid, long after the triumphant explosions

---

21. **annex.** Building attached to a larger one
22. **Berlin.** Capital of Germany
23. **Armistice Day.** November 11, 1918, the day that marked the end of World War I, now celebrated as Veterans' Day
24. **V.A.D.** Voluntary aid detachment

from Westminster had turned into a distant crescendo[25] of shouting, I saw a taxicab turn swiftly in from the Embankment towards the hospital. The next moment there was a cry for doctors and nurses from passers-by, for in rounding the corner the taxi had knocked down a small elderly woman who in listening, like myself, to the wild noise of a world released from nightmare, had failed to observe its approach.

◄ What is wrong with Isannah?

As I hurried to her side I realised that she was all but dead and already past speech. Like Victor in the mortuary chapel, she seemed to have shrunk to the dimensions of a child with the sharp features of age, but on the tiny chalk-white face an expression of shocked surprise still lingered, and she stared hard at me as Geoffrey had stared at his orderly in those last moments of conscious silence beside the Scarpe. Had she been thinking, I wondered, when the taxi struck her, of her sons at the front, now safe? The next moment a medical officer and some orderlies came up, and I went back to my ward.

But I remembered her at intervals throughout that afternoon, during which, with a half-masochistic notion of "seeing the sights," I made a circular tour to Kensington by way of the intoxicated West End. With aching persistence my thoughts went back to the dead and the strange irony of their fates—to Roland, gifted, ardent, ambitious, who had died without glory in the conscientious performance of a routine job; to Victor and Geoffrey, gentle and <u>diffident</u>, who, conquering nature by resolution, had each gone down bravely in a big "show"; and finally to Edward, musical, serene, a lover of peace, who had fought courageously through so many battles and at last had been killed while leading a vital counter-attack in one of the few decisive actions of the War. As I struggled through the waving, shrieking crowds in Piccadilly and Regent Street on the overloaded top of a 'bus, some witty enthusiast for contemporary history symbolically turned upside down the signboard "Seven Kings."

◄ Whom does the narrator think about on Armistice Day?

Late that evening, when supper was over, a group of elated V.A.D.s who were anxious to walk through

---

25. **crescendo.** Gradually increasing in loudness

**words for everyday use**   dif • fi • dent (dif' ə dənt) *adj.*, lacking self-confidence; timid; shy. *Seamus was a <u>diffident</u> boy who always avoided the spotlight.*

► How do people greet the Red Cross volunteers?

► In what type of world does the narrator feel she has no part?

Westminster and Whitehall to Buckingham Palace prevailed upon me to join them. Outside the Admiralty a crazy group of convalescent[26] Tommies were collecting specimens of different uniforms and bundling their wearers into flagstrewn taxis; with a shout they seized two of my companions and disappeared into the clamorous crowd, waving flags and shaking rattles. Wherever we went a burst of enthusiastic cheering greeted our Red Cross uniform, and complete strangers adorned with wound stripes rushed up and shook me warmly by the hand. After the long, long blackness, it seemed like a fairy-tale to see the street lamps shining through the chill November gloom.

I detached myself from the others and walked slowly up Whitehall, with my heart sinking in a sudden cold dismay. Already this was a different world from the one that I had known during four life-long years, a world in which people would be light-hearted and forgetful, in which themselves and their careers and their amusements would blot out political ideals and great national issues. And in that brightly lit, alien world I should have no part. All those with whom I had really been intimate were gone; not one remained to share with me the heights and the depths of my memories. As the years went by and youth departed and remembrance grew dim, a deeper and ever deeper darkness would cover the young men who were once my contemporaries.

For the first time I realised, with all that full realisation meant, how completely everything that had hitherto made up my life and vanished with Edward and Roland, with Victor and Geoffrey. The War was over; a new age was beginning; but the dead were dead and would never return.

• • •

---

26. **convalescent.** Gradually recovering health

# THE WAR GENERATION: VALE[27]

We, whom the storm-winds battered, come again
Like strangers to the places we have known,
Who sought men's understanding all in vain
For hardened hearts to grief's dark image grown;
So, passing through the careless crowd alone,
Ghosts of a time no future can restore,
We desolately roam for evermore
An empty shore.

For us they live till life itself shall end,
The frailties and the follies of those years,
Their strength which only pride of loss could lend,
Their vanished hopes, their sorrows and their tears;
But slowly towards the <u>verge</u> the dim sky clears,
For nobler men may yet redeem our clay
When we and war together, one wise day,
Have passed away.

V.B.
1933.

◀ In what manner do members of the war generation come to places they have once known?

◀ What are the members of the war generation and where do they roam?

◀ What has vanished for this generation?

---

27. **Vale.** Farewell

**words for everyday use**    **verge** (vʉrj) *n.*, edge, brink, or margin (*of* something). *At eighteen, Miles felt that he was on the <u>verge</u> of adulthood and that he was leaving his adolescence behind.*

## Critical Thinking

1. Why do you think the soldiers Vera Brittain describes believe in ghosts?
2. Compare and contrast Brittain's descriptions of the hospital in which she works with Paul's descriptions of German hospitals.
3. Why doesn't Vera Brittain feel like celebrating when the war is over?
4. How do Vera Brittain's feelings after the end of the war compare with Paul Bäumer's ideas about what life will be like after the war?
5. Explain whether you think Paul would view Vera Brittain as his enemy. How do you think Vera would view Paul?

# "Soldier's Home"
## by Ernest Hemingway

### ABOUT THE RELATED READING

Ernest Hemingway (1899–1961) was an American who volunteered to serve as an ambulance driver on the Italian front during World War I. After the war, he became a well-known and critically acclaimed writer. Throughout *All Quiet on the Western Front,* Paul and his friends speculate about what life will be like for them in peacetime now that they have been mentally scarred by the war. "Soldier's Home" is a short story that shows how an American soldier feels about his life at home now that the war is over.

# Soldier's Home

Krebs went to the war from a Methodist college in Kansas. There is a picture which shows him among his fraternity brothers, all of them wearing exactly the same height and style collar. He enlisted in the Marines in 1917 and did not return to the United States until the second division returned from the Rhine[1] in the summer of 1919.

*◄ When did Krebs enlist? When did he return home?*

There is a picture which shows him on the Rhine with two German girls and another corporal. Krebs and the corporal look too big for their uniforms. The German girls are not beautiful. The Rhine does not show in the picture.

By the time Krebs returned to his home town in Oklahoma the greeting of heroes was over. He came back much too late. The men from the town who had been drafted had all been welcomed elaborately on their return. There had been a great deal of <u>hysteria</u>. Now the reaction had set in. People seemed to think it was rather ridiculous for Krebs to be getting back so late, years after the war was over.

*◄ For what did Krebs return home too late?*

---

1. **Rhine.** River in Western Europe, flowing from eastern Switzerland north through Germany, then west through the Netherlands into the North Sea

**words for everyday use**   hys • te • ri • a (hi ster′ ē ə) *n.,* any outbreak of wild, uncontrolled excitement or feeling, such as fits of laughing and crying. *The young fans shouted and cried in <u>hysteria</u> as their favorite band took the stage.*

▶ What happened
when Krebs wanted
to talk about the
war? What does he
have to do to get
people to listen
to him?

At first Krebs, who had been at Belleau Wood, Soissons, the Champagne, St. Mihiel and in the Argonne[2] did not want to talk about the war at all. Later he felt the need to talk but no one wanted to hear about it. His town had heard too many atrocity stories[3] to be thrilled by actualities. Krebs found that to be listened to at all he had to lie, and after he had done this twice he, too, had a reaction against the war and against talking about it. A distaste for everything that had happened to him in the war set in because of the lies he had told. All of the times that had been able to make him feel cool and clear inside himself when he thought of them; the times so long back when he had done the one thing, the only thing for a man to do, easily and naturally, when he might have done something else, now lost their cool, valuable quality and then were lost themselves.

His lies were quite unimportant lies and consisted in attributing to himself things other men had seen, done or heard of, and stating as facts certain <u>apocryphal</u> incidents familiar to all soldiers. Even his lies were not sensational at the pool room. His acquaintances, who had heard detailed accounts of German women found chained to machine guns in the Argonne forest and who could not comprehend, or were barred by their patriotism from interest in, any German machine gunners who were not chained, were not thrilled by his stories.

Krebs acquired the nausea in regard to experience that is the result of untruth or exaggeration, and when he occasionally met another man who had really been a soldier and they talked a few minutes in the dressing room at a dance he fell into the easy pose of the old soldier among other soldiers: that he had been badly, sickeningly frightened all the time. In this way he lost everything.

▶ What has Krebs
been doing each
day?

During this time, it was late summer, he was sleeping late in bed, getting up to walk down town to the library to get a book, eating lunch at home, reading on the front

---

2. **Belleau Wood . . . Argonne.** Belleau Wood—small forest in northern France where U.S. forces stopped a German advance on Paris during World War I; Champagne—region in northeastern France; St. Mihiel—town in northeastern France; the Argonne—wooded plateau in northeastern France. All these places were battle sites during World War I.

3. **atrocity stories.** Stories of brutal or cruel acts

---

**words
for
everyday
use**
a • poc • ry • phal (ə päk′ rə fəl) *adj.*, of doubtful authorship or authenticity. *The art expert said the painting was <u>apocryphal</u>—it could be neither proved nor disproved that it was the artist's work.*

porch until he became bored and then walking down through the town to spend the hottest hours of the day in the cool dark of the pool room. He loved to play pool.

In the evening he practised on his clarinet, strolled down town, read and went to bed. He was still a hero to his two young sisters. His mother would have given him breakfast in bed if he had wanted it. She often came in when he was in bed and asked him to tell her about the war, but her attention always wandered. His father was non-committal.

Before Krebs went away to the war he had never been allowed to drive the family motor car. His father was in the real estate business and always wanted the car to be at his command when he required it to take clients out into the country to show them a piece of farm property. The car always stood outside the First National Bank building where his father had an office on the second floor. Now, after the war, it was still the same car.

◀ What was Krebs never allowed to do before the war?

Nothing was changed in the town except that the young girls had grown up. But they lived in such a complicated world of already defined alliances and shifting feuds that Krebs did not feel the energy or the courage to break into it. He liked to look at them, though. There were so many good-looking young girls. Most of them had their hair cut short. When he went away only little girls wore their hair like that or girls that were fast.[4] They all wore sweaters and shirt waists with round Dutch collars. It was a pattern. He liked to look at them from the front porch as they walked on the other side of the street. He liked to watch them walking under the shade of the trees. He liked the round Dutch collars above their sweaters. He liked their silk stockings and flat shoes. He liked their bobbed hair and the way they walked.

◀ What has changed in the town while Krebs was away?

When he was in town their appeal to him was not very strong. He did not like them when he saw them in the Greek's ice cream parlor. He did not want them themselves really. They were too complicated. There was something else. Vaguely he wanted a girl but he did not want to have to work to get her. He would have liked to have a girl but he did not want to have to spend a long time getting her.

◀ How does Krebs feel about girls?

---

4. **fast.** Living in a reckless, immoral way

**words for everyday use** non • com • mit • tal (nän kə mit'l) *adj.*, not committing one to any point of view or course of action; not revealing one's position or purpose. *Jason was annoyed that Carol was noncommittal about coming to his party—first she said she would attend and then she said she wasn't sure.*

He did not want to get into the <u>intrigue</u> and the politics. He did not want to have to do any courting.[5] He did not want to tell any more lies. It wasn't worth it.

▶ *How does Krebs want to live the rest of his life?*

He did not want any consequences. He did not want any consequences ever again. He wanted to live along without consequences. Besides he did not really need a girl. The army had taught him that. It was all right to pose as though you had to have a girl. Nearly everybody did that. But it wasn't true. You did not need a girl. That was the funny thing. First a fellow boasted how girls mean nothing to him, that he never thought of them, that they could not touch him. Then a fellow boasted that he could not get along without girls, that he had to have them all the time, that he could not go to sleep without them.

That was all a lie. It was all a lie both ways. You did not need a girl unless you thought about them. He learned that in the army. Then soon or later you always got one. When you were really ripe for a girl you always got one. You did not have to think about it. Sooner or later it would come. He had learned that in the army.

▶ *What did Krebs like better about French and German girls?*

Now he would have liked a girl if she had come to him and not wanted to talk. But here at home it was all too complicated. He knew he could never get through it all again. It was not worth the trouble. That was the thing about French girls and German girls. There was not all this talking. You couldn't talk much and you did not need to talk. It was simple and you were friends. He thought about France and then he began to think about Germany. On the whole he had liked Germany better. He did not want to leave Germany. He did not want to come home. Still, he had come home. He sat on the front porch.

He liked the girls that were walking along the other side of the street. He liked the look of them much better than the French girls or the German girls. But the world they were in was not the world he was in. He would like to have one of them. But it was not worth it. They were such a nice pattern. He liked the pattern. It was exciting. But he would not go through all the talking. He did not want one badly enough. He liked to look at them all, though. It was not worth it. Not now when things were getting good again.

---

5. **courting.** Wooing, striving to win the love of someone

---

**words for everyday use**

in • trigue (in trēg') *n.*, secret or underhanded plot or scheme. *The film portrayed the life of a spy and her many <u>intrigues</u> to get secret information.*

He sat there on the porch reading a book on the war. It was a history and he was reading about all the engagements[6] he had been in. It was the most interesting reading he had ever done. He wished there were more maps. He looked forward with a good feeling to reading all the really good histories when they would come out with good detail maps. Now he was really learning about the war. He had been a good soldier. That made a difference.

One morning after he had been home about a month his mother came into his bedroom and sat on the bed. She smoothed her apron.

◀ What does Krebs read about?

"I had a talk with your father last night, Harold," she said, "and he is willing for you to take the car out in the evenings."

◀ What does Krebs's mother say he can now do?

"Yeah?" said Krebs, who was not fully awake. "Take the car out? Yeah?"

"Yes. Your father has felt for some time that you should be able to take the car out in the evenings whenever you wished but we only talked it over last night."

"I'll bet you made him," Krebs said.

"No. It was your father's suggestion that we talk the matter over."

"Yeah. I'll bet you made him," Krebs sat up in bed.

"Will you come down to breakfast, Harold?" his mother said.

"As soon as I get my clothes on," Krebs said.

His mother went out of the room and he could hear her frying something downstairs while he washed, shaved and dressed to go down into the dining-room for breakfast. While he was eating breakfast his sister brought in the mail.

"Well, Hare," she said. "You old sleepy-head. What do you ever get up for?"

Krebs looked at her. He liked her. She was his best sister.

"Have you got the paper?" he asked.

She handed him *The Kansas City Star* and he shucked off its brown wrapper and opened it to the sporting page. He folded *The Star* open and propped it against the water pitcher with his cereal dish to steady it, so he could read while he ate.

"Harold," his mother stood in the kitchen doorway, "Harold, please don't muss up the paper. Your father can't read his *Star* if it's been mussed."

"I won't muss it," Krebbs said.

His sister sat down at the table and watched him while he read.

---

6. **engagements.** Battles

"We're playing indoor[7] over at school this afternoon," she said. "I'm going to pitch."

"Good," said Krebs. "How's the old wing?"

"I can pitch better than lots of the boys. I tell them all you taught me. The other girls aren't much good."

"Yeah?" said Krebs.

"I tell them all you're my beau. Aren't you my beau, Hare?"

"You bet."

"Couldn't your brother really be your beau just because he's your brother?"

"I don't know."

"Sure you know. Couldn't you be my beau, Hare, if I was old enough and if you wanted to?"

"Sure. You're my girl now."

"Am I really your girl?"

"Sure."

"Do you love me?"

"Uh, huh."

"Will you love me always?"

"Sure."

"Will you come over and watch me play indoor?"

"Maybe."

"Aw, Hare, you don't love me. If you loved me, you'd want to come over and watch me play indoor."

Kreb's mother came into the dining-room from the kitchen. She carried a plate with two fried eggs and some crisp bacon on it and a plate of buckwheat cakes.

"You run along, Helen," she said. "I want to talk to Harold."

She put the eggs and bacon down in front of him and brought in a jug of maple syrup for the buckwheat cakes. Then she sat down across the table from Krebs.

"I wish you'd put down the paper a minute, Harold," she said.

Krebs took down the paper and folded it.

▶ What does Krebs's mother ask him about?

"Have you decided what you are going to do yet, Harold?" his mother said, taking off her glasses.

"No," said Krebs.

"Don't you think it's about time?" His mother did not say this in a mean way. She seemed worried.

"I hadn't thought about it," Krebs said.

"God has some work for every one to do," his mother said. "There can be no idle hands in His Kingdom."

"I'm not in His Kingdom," Krebs said.

"We are all of us in His Kingdom."

---

7. **indoor.** Indoor baseball

Krebs felt embarrassed and resentful as always.

"I've worried about you so much, Harold," his mother went on. "I know the temptations you must have been exposed to. I know how weak men are. I know what your own dear grandfather, my own father, told us about the Civil War and I have prayed for you. I pray for you all day long, Harold."

Krebs looked at the bacon fat hardening on his plate.

"Your father is worried, too," his mother went on. "He thinks you have lost your ambition, that you haven't got a definite aim in life. Charley Simmons, who is just your age, has a good job and is going to be married. The boys are all settling down; they're all determined to get somewhere; you can see that boys like Charley Simmons are on their way to being really a credit to the community."

Krebs said nothing.

"Don't look that way, Harold," his mother said. "You know we love you and I want to tell you for your own good how matters stand. Your father does not want to <u>hamper</u> your freedom. He thinks you should be allowed to drive the car. If you want to take some of the nice girls out riding with you, we are only too pleased. We want you to enjoy yourself. But you are going to have to settle down to work, Harold. Your father doesn't care what you start in at. All work is honorable as he says. But you've got to make a start at something. He asked me to speak to you this morning and then you can stop in and see him at his office."

"Is that all?" Krebs said.

"Yes. Don't you love your mother, dear boy?"

"No," Krebs said.

His mother looked at him across the table. Her eyes were shiny. She started crying.

"I don't love anybody," Krebs said.

It wasn't any good. He couldn't tell her, he couldn't make her see it. It was silly to have said it. He had only hurt her. He went over and took hold of her arm. She was crying with her head in her hands.

"I didn't mean it," he said. "I was just angry at something. I didn't mean I didn't love you."

His mother went on crying. Krebs put his arm on her shoulder.

◀ What does Krebs's father think about his son?

◀ What does Krebs's mother ask him? What is his response?

---

**words for everyday use**

ham • per (ham' pər) *vt.*, keep from moving or acting freely; hinder; impede. *At first Ann thought the heavy scuba gear would <u>hamper</u> her movements, but once she was in the water, the gear felt light.*

"Can't you believe me, mother?"

His mother shook her head.

"Please, please, mother. Please believe me."

"All right," his mother said chokily. She looked up at him. "I believe you, Harold."

Krebs kissed her hair. She put her face up to him.

"I'm your mother," she said. "I held you next to my heart when you were a tiny baby."

Krebs felt sick and vaguely nauseated.

"I know, Mummy," he said. "I'll try and be a good boy for you."

"Would you kneel and pray with me, Harold?" his mother asked.

They knelt down beside the dining-room table and Krebs's mother prayed.

"Now, you pray Harold," she said.

"I can't," Krebs said.

"Try, Harold."

"I can't."

"Do you want me to pray for you?"

"Yes."

So his mother prayed for him and they stood up and Krebs kissed his mother and went out of the house. He had tried so to keep his life from being complicated. Still, none of it had touched him. He had felt sorry for his mother and she had made him lie. He would go to Kansas City and get a job and she would feel all right about it. There would be one more scene maybe before he got away. He would not go down to his father's office. He would miss that one. He wanted his life to go smoothly. It had just gotten going that way. Well, that was all over now, anyway. He would go over to the schoolyard and watch Helen play indoor baseball.

▶ What does Krebs's mother ask him to do? What is his response?

▶ What does Krebs say his mother made him do?

## Critical Thinking

1. Why does Krebs find it hard to talk to people? Why doesn't he want to make the effort to find a girlfriend or get work?
2. Why might Krebs wish to live without consequences?
3. When Krebs tells his mother that he doesn't love her or anybody else, does he mean it?
4. Why does Krebs tell his mother that he doesn't love her and that he cannot pray? What might he be trying to share with her? In what way has the war changed him?
5. Explain how you think Paul would be similar to or different from Krebs if he returned home from the war.

# From Presidential Address to the Nation, October 7, 2001
## by George W. Bush

## ABOUT THE RELATED READING

On September 11, 2001, the United States was attacked at home for the first time since the Japanese bombed Pearl Harbor on December 7, 1941. On the morning of September 11, two hijacked passenger jets from Boston struck the north and south towers of the World Trade Center. Both buildings collapsed. Another passenger jet struck the Pentagon in Washington, DC. A fourth flight crashed in Somerset, Pennsylvania, apparently after a group of brave passengers learned of what happened with the other flights and chose to confront the hijackers. About three thousand lives were lost. In the speech that follows, George W. Bush (1946–    ), forty-third president of the United States, outlines a plan of action for the nation following these events. Prior to this speech, the President had demanded that the Taliban government of Afghanistan close the al Qaeda terrorist camps believed to be responsible for the attacks and turn over to the United States al Qaeda's military leaders, including Osama bin Laden.

The war on terrorism that the United States declared after the attacks of September 11 is different than the other wars the country has fought. In World War I, allies and enemies were clearly delineated, with Great Britain, France, Russia, and later the United States joining in alliance to fight Germany and Austria-Hungary. In the war on terrorism, the United States' enemies are the many terrorist groups that act within many different countries, some of them U.S. allies.

## From Presidential Address to the Nation, October 7, 2001

Good afternoon. On my orders, the United States military has begun strikes against al Qaeda terrorist training camps and military installations of the Taliban regime in Afghanistan.[1] These carefully targeted actions are designed

◀ *What does the President say has already taken place? What are the attacks meant to accomplish?*

---

1. **al Qaeda . . . Afghanistan.** Al Qaeda is the terrorist group held responsible for the attacks on the World Trade Center and the Pentagon on September 11, 2001. The terrorist group had training camps in Afghanistan, which at the time was under the rule of a group of fundamentalist Muslims called the Taliban.

to disrupt the use of Afghanistan as a terrorist base of operations, and to attack the military capability of the Taliban <u>regime</u>.

We are joined in this operation by our <u>staunch</u> friend, Great Britain. Other close friends, including Canada, Australia, Germany and France, have pledged forces as the operation unfolds. More than 40 countries in the Middle East, Africa, Europe and across Asia have granted air transit or landing rights. Many more have shared intelligence. We are supported by the collective will of the world.

▶ *What did the president demand? According to the President, what was the Taliban's response? What does the President say the Taliban will do now?*

More than two weeks ago, I gave Taliban leaders a series of clear and specific demands: Close terrorist training camps; hand over leaders of the al Qaeda network; and return all foreign nationals, including American citizens, unjustly detained in your country. None of these demands were met. And now the Taliban will pay a price. By destroying camps and disrupting communications, we will make it more difficult for the terror network to train new recruits and coordinate their evil plans.

Initially, the terrorists may burrow deeper into caves and other entrenched hiding places. Our military action is also designed to clear the way for sustained, comprehensive and relentless operations to drive them out and bring them to justice.

▶ *What will the United States do as it strikes military targets?*

At the same time, the oppressed people of Afghanistan will know the generosity of America and our allies. As we strike military targets, we'll also drop food, medicine and supplies to the starving and suffering men and women and children of Afghanistan.

▶ *To whom is the United States a friend? To whom is it an enemy?*

The United States of America is a friend to the Afghan people, and we are the friends of almost a billion worldwide who practice the Islamic faith. The United States of America is an enemy of those who aid terrorists and of the barbaric criminals who <u>profane</u> a great religion by committing murder in its name.

This military action is a part of our campaign against terrorism, another front in a war that has already been joined through diplomacy, intelligence, the freezing of financial assets and the arrests of known terrorists by law enforcement agents in 38 countries. Given the nature and

---

**words for everyday use**

re • gime (rə zhēm') *n.*, particular administration or government. *The United States stopped trading with Cuba under Fidel Castro's <u>regime</u>.*

staunch (stônch) *adj.*, firm; steadfast; loyal. *As a <u>staunch</u> supporter of the mayor,* *Miguel helped work in the mayor's reelection campaign.*

pro • fane (prō fān') *adj.*, put to a base or improper use; debase; defile. *Margie was on a kosher diet and would not eat pork because it would <u>profane</u> her religion.*

---

reach of our enemies, we will win this conflict by the patient accumulation of successes, by meeting a series of challenges with determination and will and purpose.

Today we focus on Afghanistan, but the battle is broader. Every nation has a choice to make. In this conflict, there is no neutral ground. If any government sponsors the outlaws and killers of innocents, they have become outlaws and murderers, themselves. And they will take that lonely path at their own peril.

◀ What choice does every nation have to make, according to the President?

I'm speaking to you today from the Treaty Room of the White House, a place where American Presidents have worked for peace. We're a peaceful nation. Yet, as we have learned, so suddenly and so tragically, there can be no peace in a world of sudden terror. In the face of today's new threat, the only way to pursue peace is to pursue those who threaten it.

◀ What is the only way to pursue peace, according to the President?

We did not ask for this mission, but we will fulfill it. The name of today's military operation is Enduring Freedom. We defend not only our precious freedoms, but also the freedom of people everywhere to live and raise their children free from fear.

I know many Americans feel fear today. And our government is taking strong precautions. All law enforcement and intelligence agencies are working aggressively around America, around the world and around the clock. At my request, many governors have activated the National Guard to strengthen airport security. We have called up Reserves to reinforce our military capability and strengthen the protection of our homeland.

In the months ahead, our patience will be one of our strengths—patience with the long waits that will result from tighter security; patience and understanding that it will take time to achieve our goals; patience in all the sacrifices that may come.

Today, those sacrifices are being made by members of our Armed Forces who now defend us so far from home, and by their proud and worried families. A Commander-in-Chief sends America's sons and daughters into a battle in a foreign land only after the greatest care and a lot of prayer. We ask a lot of those who wear our uniform. We ask them to leave their loved ones, to travel great distances, to risk injury, even to be prepared to make the ultimate sacrifice of their lives. They are dedicated, they are honorable; they represent the best of our country. And we are grateful. To all the men and women in our military—every sailor, every soldier, every airman, every coastguardsman, every Marine—I say this: Your mission is defined; your objectives

◀ What do we ask of our armed forces?

are clear; your goal is just. You have my full confidence, and you will have every tool you need to carry out your duty.

▶ *What did the girl's letter say?*

I recently received a touching letter that says a lot about the state of America in these difficult times—a letter from a 4th-grade girl, with a father in the military: "As much as I don't want my Dad to fight," she wrote, "I'm willing to give him to you."

This is a precious gift, the greatest she could give. This young girl knows what America is all about. Since September 11, an entire generation of young Americans has gained new understanding of the value of freedom, and its cost in duty and in sacrifice.

▶ *According to the President, what have we gained since September 11?*

The battle is now joined on many fronts. We will not waver; we will not tire; we will not falter; and we will not fail. Peace and freedom will prevail.

Thank you. May God continue to bless America.

## Critical Thinking

1. In this speech, how does the President define the United States' friends and enemies?
2. In what way does the President try to distinguish the group he is attacking from the Afghan people as a whole and from all those of the Muslim faith?
3. Why do you think the President shares the anecdote about the fourth-grade girl who wrote him a letter?
4. What opinion do you think Paul Bäumer would have on the war on terrorism?

# Creative Writing Activities

## Brooke or Owen Poem

Rupert Brooke and Wilfred Owen were World War I poets who wrote very different poems about war. Write your own poem about World War I, using *All Quiet on the Western Front* as inspiration. You can write a poem that is positive, like Brooke's. For example, you might write a patriotic poem from Kantorek's perspective, a poem about friendship from Paul's perspective, or a poem about eating suckling pigs and roast goose from Kat's perspective. You can also write a poem that condemns the war as Wilfred Owen's "Dulce et Decorum Est" does. For example, you might write a poem about the man Paul stabs in the trenches, either from his perspective or Paul's, or you might write a poem about Kat's death from Paul's perspective.

## A Woman's Point of View

Although female characters appear in *All Quiet on the Western Front*—Paul's mother and sister, Kemmerich's mother, the French girls, the sister on the train of injured men, and the nurses in the hospitals—the novel is told only from a male point of view—Paul's. What these women think of events in the novel is often unclear. Write a retelling of a scene from the novel from a woman's point of view. Your scene need not match the mood and tone of the novel exactly. For example, a scene retold from the point of view of the French girls or the sister on the train might actually be quite humorous, while a scene retold from Kemmerich's mother's point of view might have a sadder tone. Before you begin writing, choose the character you are most interested in and the scene you would like to retell. Then, think about how this scene might have seemed different from your chosen character's perspective.

## Personal Letter/Persuasive Writing

Write a letter to George W. Bush, sharing your opinion on the war on terrorism. Your letter should be persuasive, as your goal is to make the president see your point of view and perhaps respond in some way. Remember that whether you send it or not, your letter will be addressed to the president, so it should be appropriate in tone and language. People are more likely to listen to a polite, carefully thought-out, and well-worded letter than they are to a rambling, bossy, or incoherent one.

## Science Fiction or Fantasy Story

Science fiction and fantasy writers have long been interested in writing about wars. **Fantasy** contains highly unrealistic elements. **Science fiction** writers use fantastic elements based on scientific principles, discoveries, or laws. For example, a fantasy writer might write about a war in an imaginary country in which good magicians and dragons fight against ghouls sent to Earth by some evil magician. A science fiction writer might write about a war that takes place between Earth and another planet or about how the course of World War I was alerted by a scientist who discovered the secret of time travel. Write your own fantasy or science fiction short story about a war.

## Propaganda

**Propaganda** is the intentional use of false arguments to persuade others. In *All Quiet on the Western Front,* the German soldiers mention some propaganda that has been spread about them—that German soldiers eat children. Write your own piece of propaganda about any historical war. First, choose the war you are most interested in. Then choose the side for which you want to write. You will be writing propaganda to disparage the other side of the conflict. Remember that propaganda that rings untrue is easily dismissed.

# Critical Writing Activities

## Nature

In *All Quiet on the Western Front,* Remarque uses many vivid descriptions of nature and animals. For what purpose does Remarque use nature imagery? What effect does the use of descriptions of nature and its creatures have on Remarque's message about war? Think about these questions, and write a critical essay about the significance of the use of nature imagery in the novel. Your first paragraph should contain a thesis statement explaining why Remarque uses nature imagery and how the imagery relates to Remarque's message about war. Support your thesis in following paragraphs with your own opinions and quotations from the text. In a final paragraph, come to a conclusion about the effectiveness of nature imagery in *All Quiet on the Western Front.*

## Didactic Criticism and Pacifist Ideals

**Didactic criticism** evaluates works of art in terms of the moral, ethical, or political messages they convey. Erich Maria Remarque was a **pacifist,** a person who opposes the use of force under any circumstances. Write a critical essay in which you examine *All Quiet on the Western Front* using didactic criticism. In the first paragraph, you should have a thesis in which you clearly state Remarque's political position on war. In your supporting paragraphs, you should trace how Remarque builds his pacifist ideas throughout the novel, using direct quotations to support your points. Finally, in your conclusion, argue whether Remarque's political agenda strengthens or weakens the novel.

## Biographical Criticism

**Biographical criticism** attempts to account for elements of literary works by relating them to events in the lives of their authors. Write a critical essay in which you explain how Erich Maria Remarque's own life helped shape *All Quiet on the Western Front.* Use the biography of Erich Maria Remarque that appears on pages v–vii of this book as your source for information on the author's life. In your first paragraph, clearly state in a thesis statement the extent to which you believe *All Quiet on the Western Front* was autobiographical, or based on the author's own life. In your supporting paragraphs, compare and contrast the author's own life to events from the novel, using quotations to support your opinions. In your conclusion, sum up how you feel any biographical elements in *All Quiet on the Western Front* affected the novel. Did they make it more realistic? stronger? weaker? more biased?

## Foreshadowing

**Foreshadowing** is the act of presenting materials that hint at events to occur later in a story. Write a critical essay in which you explore whether Paul's death was foreshadowed in *All Quiet on the Western Front*. You should write a thesis statement in your first paragraph in which you present your opinion on whether Paul's death was foreshadowed. In the following paragraphs, you should support your opinion using evidence from the text. In your concluding paragraph, you might suggest why Remarque did or did not choose to foreshadow Paul's death.

## Theme: The Lost Generation

The generation that fought in World War I was later called the lost generation. Write a critical essay in which you explore Paul Bäumer's character as an example of the lost generation. In your first paragraph, include a thesis statement explaining what Paul lost in this war and how he believes the war will affect his generation. Support and expand on your thesis in the following paragraphs, using evidence from the text. In a final concluding paragraph, explain what the term *lost generation* means to you and why Paul is a fitting example of this generation.

# Projects

## Honoring Veterans

As you have learned in reading *All Quiet on the Western Front,* soldiers undergo some extraordinary and terrible things in service of their country. They also have not always been treated warmly or with appreciation on their return to their home country. Work together with your classmates to plan a celebration of our country's veterans. It doesn't matter if Veterans' Day, November 11, is past. Schedule your celebration as a class and then form small groups to brainstorm different ways you might honor veterans at your celebration. Your group might choose to create a painting or other work of art celebrating veterans. You might also read poems you have written about our country's veterans, sing a song, or enact a brief drama. Your class might be interested in contacting a veterans' group or veterans that you know personally to ask them if they would like to attend to be honored at your celebration.

## Researching World War I

World War I was a complex war, with many nations involved and many fronts. Work with a partner to research a particular aspect of World War I. You and your partner should then prepare an oral report on your aspect of the war to deliver to your class. Try to use pictures, diagrams, maps, and other visual aids in your presentation. You can research any topic in which you are interested, but a list of possible topics related to World War I follows:

- Naval warfare and the role of the U-boat in World War I
- Japan's role in World War I
- The Schlieffen Plan
- The Battle of Verdun
- The First Battle of the Somme
- The Bolshevik Revolution
- The Treaty of Versailles
- The formation of a League of Nations

## Searching for World War I Art

World War I was not the first war to be photographed, but the photographs of the war certainly had a powerful influence on people. Work in small groups to find images of the war. Your school or public library is an excellent place to start looking, and you can also find images from the war on the Internet. Use the images you find and what you learned of World War I in *All Quiet on the Western Front* as your inspiration to create your own artwork. You might create a sketch or drawing, a painting, a sculpture, or a diorama.

## Enacting a Scene

Work with a small group of classmates to write and present a brief scene from *All Quiet on the Western Front*. You should work together to choose and write your scene. You will find this task easier if you choose a scene in which there is a lot of dialogue. For example, the scene in which Paul and his friends talk about the causes of war has lots of dialogue that you can use. Each member of your group should be given a part. Your group should rehearse your scene, not only delivering your lines but also planning your movements, gestures, and expressions. Then, either videotape your group's scene or deliver it live in front of your class.

## Mapmaking

Work with a group of classmates to create a large map on poster board of where the action takes place in *All Quiet on the Western Front*. You should find some historical maps of World War I and then locate sites mentioned in the novel. Your map should show these sites along with major cities and natural features such as rivers, oceans, and mountains.

# Glossary

## PRONUNCIATION KEY

### VOWEL SOUNDS

| | | | | | | |
|---|---|---|---|---|---|---|
| a | hat | ō | go | ə | extra |
| ā | play | ȯ | paw, born | | under |
| ä | star | u̇ | book, put | | civil |
| e | then | ü | blue, stew | | honor |
| ē | me | oi | boy | | bogus |
| i | sit | ou | wow | | |
| ī | my | u | up | | |

### CONSONANT SOUNDS

| | | | | | | |
|---|---|---|---|---|---|---|
| b | but | l | lip | t | sit |
| ch | watch | m | money | th | with |
| d | do | n | on | v | valley |
| f | fudge | ŋ | song, sink | w | work |
| g | go | p | pop | y | yell |
| h | hot | r | rod | z | pleasure |
| j | jump | s | see | | |
| k | brick | sh | she | | |

**ab • er • ra • tion** (ab' ər ā' shən) *n.,* deviation from the normal or the typical.

**ab • strac • tion** (ab strak' shən) *n.,* formation of an idea, as of the qualities or properties of a thing, by mental separation from particular instances.

**a • byss** (ə bis') *n.,* deep fissure in the earth; bottomless gulf.

**ac • rid** (ak' rid) *adj.,* sharp, bitter, stinging, or irritating to the taste or smell.

**af • fa • bly** (af' ə blē) *adj.,* in a pleasant and friendly manner.

**ag • i • ta • tion** (aj' ə tā' shən) *n.,* emotional disturbance or excitement.

**al • lure • ment** (ə lu̇r' mənt) *n.,* power to entice or attract; fascination.

**a • miss** (ə mis') *adv.,* in a wrong way.

**an • ni • hi • la • tion** (ə nī' ə lā' shən) *n.,* complete destruction.

**ap • a • thet • ic** (ap' ə thet' ik) *adj.,* feeling little or no emotion; indifferent.

**a • poc • ry • phal** (ə päk′ rə fəl) *adj.*, of doubtful authorship or authenticity.

**ap • pall • ing** (ə pȯl′ iŋ) *adj.*, causing horror, shock, or dismay.

**ar • bi • ter** (är′ bət ər) *n.*, person fully authorized or qualified to judge or decide.

**ar • dent** (ärd′ ′nt) *adj.*, intensely enthusiastic or devoted; zealous.

**ar • dor** (är′ dər) *n.*, eagerness; enthusiasm; zeal.

**a • skance** (ə skans′) *adv.*, with suspicion or disapproval.

**as • sur • ance** (ə shu̇r′ əns) *n.*, sureness; confidence.

**au • tom • a • ton (pl. automata)** (ȯ täm′ ə tän′) *n.*, person or animal acting in an automatic or mechanical way.

**ba • nal** (bā′ nəl) *adj.*, dull or stale because of overuse; commonplace.

**be • queath** (bē kwēth′) *vt.*, leave (property) to another by last will and testament.

**be • wil • der** (bē wil′ dər) *vt.*, confuse hopelessly.

**blus • ter** (blus′ tər) *vi.*, speak or conduct oneself in a noisy, swaggering, or bullying manner.

**bom • bard • ment** (bäm bärd′ mənt) *n.*, attack, especially by bombs or missiles.

**bra • va • do** (brə vä′ dō) *n.*, pretended courage or defiant confidence where there is really little or none.

**brood** (brüd) *vi.*, keep thinking about something in a distressed or troubled way.

**bus • tle** (bus′ əl) *vi.*, hurry busily or with much fuss and bother.

**claus • tro • pho • bi • a** (klȯs′ trə fō′ bē ə) *n.*, abnormal fear of being in an enclosed or confined place.

**con • cord** (kän′ kȯrd′) *n.*, combination of simultaneous and harmonious tones.

**con • dem • na • tion** (kän′ dem nā′ shən) *n.*, adverse judgment; disapproval.

**con • sole** (kən sōl′) *vt.*, make feel less sad or disappointed.

**con • straint** (kən strānt′) *n.*, forced, unnatural manner; awkwardness.

**cov • et** (kuv′ it) *vt.*, long for with envy.

**cul • prit** (kul′ prit) *n.*, person guilty of a crime or offense; offender.

**curt • ly** (kʉrt′ lē) *adv.*, in a manner that is brief to the point of rudeness.

**de • co • rum** (di kō′ rəm) *n.*, propriety and good behavior.

**de • fi • ance** (dē fī′ əns) *n.*, open, bold resistance to authority or opposition.

**de • gen • er • a • tion** (dē jen′ ər ā′ shən) *n.*, sinking below a former condition; deterioration; corruption.

**de • lir • i • um** (di lir′ ē əm) *n.*, temporary state of extreme mental excitement, marked by restlessness, confused speech, and hallucinations.

**de • ment** (dē ment′) *vt.*, make insane.

**de • mon • stra • tive** (di män′ strə tiv) *adj.*, showing feelings openly and frankly.

**des • ti • tute** (des′ tə tüt′) *adj.*, lacking the necessities of life; living in complete poverty.

**de • ter** (dē tʉr′) *vt.*, keep or discourage (a person, group, or nation) from doing something by instilling fear, anxiety, or doubt.

**dif • fi • dent** (dif′ ə dənt) *adj.*, lacking self-confidence; timid; shy.

**din** (din) *n.*, loud, continuous noise.

**dis • a • buse** (dis′ ə byüz′) *vt.*, rid of false ideas.

**dis • com • fi • ture** (dis kum′ fi chər) *n.*, frustration, confusion.

**dis • con • cert** (dis′ kən sʉrt′) *vt.*, upset the composure of; embarrass; confuse.

**dis • pute** (di spyüt′) *n.*, quarrel, argument.

**dis • qui • e • tude** (dis kwī ə tüd′) *n.*, disturbed or uneasy condition; restlessness; anxiety.

**dis • si • pate** (dis′ ə pāt′) *vt.*, break up and scatter; dispel; disperse.

**dis • so • lu • tion** (dis′ ə lü′ shən) *n.*, dissolving or being dissolved.

**doc • ile** (däs′ əl) *adj.*, easy to manage or discipline; submissive.

**dog • ged • ly** (dòg′ id lē) *adv.*, stubbornly; persistently.

**dol • lop** (däl′ əp) *n.*, soft mass or blob, as of some food.

**dregs** (dregz) *n. pl.,* particles of solid matter that settle at the bottom in a liquid.

**e • ma • ci • ate** (ē mā' shē āt') *vt.,* cause to become abnormally lean; cause to lose much flesh or weight, as by starvation or disease.

**en • sue** (en sü') *vi.,* come afterward; follow.

**en • tice** (en tīs') *vt.,* attract by offering hope of reward or pleasure.

**e • qua • nim • i • ty** (ek' wə nim' ə tē) *n.,* quality of remaining calm and undisturbed.

**e • vade** (ē vād') *vi.,* avoid doing or answering directly.

**ex • alt** (eg z olt') *vt.,* raise on high; elevate; lift up; specifically, raise in status, dignity, power, honor, or wealth.

**ex • as • per • ate** (eg zas' pər āt') *vt.,* irritate or annoy very much; make angry.

**ex • e • cute** (ek' si kyüt') *vt.,* follow out or carry out; do; perform.

**ex • ten • u • a • tion** (ek sten' yü ā' shən) *n.,* lessening or seeming to lessen the seriousness of (an offense, guilt, etc.) by giving excuses.

**fal • li • ble** (fal' ə bəl) *adj.,* liable to be mistaken or deceived.

**fal • ter • ing • ly** (fȯl' tər iŋ lē) *adv.,* hesitantly; showing uncertainty.

**fas • tid • i • ous** (fas tid' ē əs) *adj.,* refined in a too dainty or oversensitive way, so as to be easily disgusted.

**fat • u • ous** (fach' ü əs) *adj.,* complacently stupid or inane; silly; foolish.

**flit** (flit) *vi.,* pass lightly and rapidly.

**for • age** (fȯr' ij) *vi.,* search for food or provisions.

**for • lorn** (fȯr l orn') *adj.,* without hope; desperate.

**fore • bod • ing** (fōr bōd' iŋ) *n.,* prediction, especially of something bad or harmful.

**fur • tive • ly** (fʉr' tiv lē) *adv.,* in a stealthy or sneaky manner.

**gait** (gāt) *n.,* manner of walking or running.

**gam • ut** (gam' ət) *n.,* entire range or extent, as of emotions.

**glow • er** (glou' ər) *vi.,* stare with sullen anger; scowl.

**griev • ous** (grēv' əs) *adj.,* causing grief.

**ground • less** (ground' lis) *adj.,* without reason or cause; unjustified.

**grov • el** (gruv' əl) *vi.,* behave humbly; debase oneself in a servile fashion.

**ham • per** (ham' pər) *vt.,* keep from moving or acting freely; hinder; impede.

**hap • haz • ard** (hap' haz' ərd) *adv.,* by chance; casually.

**head • long** (hed' lòŋ') *adv.,* with uncontrolled speed and force.

**heart • en** (härt' 'n) *vt.,* cheer up; encourage.

**hel • ter-skel • ter** (hel' tər skel' tər) *adv.,* in a disorderly, hurried manner.

**hy • gi • en • ic** (hī jē en' ik) *adj.,* sanitary, clean.

**hys • te • ri • a** (hi ster' ē ə) *n.,* any outbreak of wild, uncontrolled excitement or feeling, such as fits of laughing and crying.

**i • dyll** (īd' 'l) *n.,* simple, peaceful scene of rural or pastoral life.

**im • ma • te • ri • al** (im' mə tir' ē əl) *adj.,* unimportant.

**im • meas • ur • a • bly** (im mezh' ər ə blē) *adv.,* without bounds; vastly.

**im • mense** (im mens') *adj.,* very large; vast; huge.

**im • per • cep • ti • bly** (im' pər sep' tə blē) *adv.,* in a manner so slight, gradual, or subtle as not to be easily perceived.

**im • pinge** (im pinj') *vi.,* strike, hit, or dash (*on, upon,* or *against* something).

**im • pla • ca • ble** (im plā' kə bəl) *adj.,* that cannot be appeased or pacified; relentless.

**im • por • tune** (im' pȯr tün') *vt.,* trouble with requests or demands; urge or entreat persistently or repeatedly.

**in • ap • pre • hen • si • ble** (in' ap' rē hen' sə bəl) *adj.,* that cannot be apprehended, or understood.

**in • cli • na • tion** (in' klə nā' shən) *n.,* particular disposition or bent of mind.

**in • cred • u • lous • ly** (in krej' ù ləs lē) *adv.,* in a manner that shows doubt or disbelief.

**in • de • fat • i • ga • ble** (in' di fat' i gə bəl) *adj.,* cannot be tired out; untiring.

**in • dif • fer • ent** (in dif' ər ənt) *adj.,* having or showing no interest, concern, or feeling.

**in • di • gent** (in' di jənt) *adj.*, in poverty; poor; needy.

**in • duce • ment** (in düs' mənt) *n.*, motive; incentive.

**in • fu • ri • ate** (in fy ur' ē āt') *vt.*, cause to become very angry; enrage.

**in • sa • ti • a • ble** (in sā' shə bəl) *adj.*, constantly wanting more.

**in • sen • sate** (in sen' sāt') *adj.*, without sense or reason; foolish; stupid.

**in • sen • si • ble** (in sen' sə bəl) *adj.*, lacking sensation; unaware; indifferent.

**in • sub • or • di • na • tion** (in' sə bȯrd' 'n ā shən) *n.*, disobedience.

**in • suf • fer • a • ble** (in suf' ər ə bəl) *adj.*, intolerable; unbearable.

**in • ter • val** (in' tər vəl) *n.*, period of time between two points of time.

**in • tol • er • a • ble** (in täl' ər ə bəl) *adj.*, too severe, painful, or cruel to be endured.

**in • trigue** (in trēg') *n.*, secret or underhanded plot or scheme.

**ir • res • o • lute • ly** (ir rez' ə lüt' lē) *adv.*, indecisively.

**jest** (jest) *n.*, joke; witticism.

**jo • vi • al** (jō' vē əl) *adj.*, full of hearty, playful good humor.

**ju • bi • lant • ly** (jü' bə lənt lē) *adv.*, in a joyful manner.

**la • con • i • cal • ly** (lə kän' ik ə lē) *adv.*, using few words; concisely.

**list • less** (list' lis) *adj.*, having no interest in what is going on about one, as a result of illness, weariness, or dejection.

**loaf** (lōf) *vi.*, spend time idly; loiter or lounge about.

**loft • i • ly** (lȯf' tə lē) *adv.*, in a haughty, arrogant manner.

**lull** (lul) *n.*, short period of quiet or of comparative calm.

**lu • mi • nous** (lü' mə nəs) *adj.*, giving off light; shining; bright.

**lurch** (lŭrch) *vi.*, roll or sway suddenly forward or to one side.

**ma • lev • o • lent** (mə lev' ə lənt) *adj.*, wishing evil or harm to others; having or showing ill will.

**ma • li • cious** (mə lish' əs) *adj.*, spiteful; intentionally mischievous or harmful.

**mar • tyr** (märt' ər) *vt.*, torture; make suffer greatly; persecute.

**me • di • a • tor** (mē' dē āt' ər) *n.*, person who intervenes to resolve a matter.

**meek** (mēk) *adj.*, too submissive; easily imposed on; spineless; spiritless.

**mel • an • chol • y** (mel' ən käl' ē) *adj.*, sad and depressed; gloomy.

**men • ace** (men' əs) *n.*, threat or the act of threatening.

**mere** (mir) *adj.*, nothing more or other than; only.

**mo • not • o • nous • ly** (mə nät' 'n əs lē) *adv.*, going on in the same tone without variation.

**mot • tled** (mät' 'ld) *adj.*, marked with blotches, streaks, and spots of different colors or shades.

**mu • ti • neer** (myü̇ 'n ir') *n.*, person who revolts against authority.

**nerve-wrack • ing** (nŭrv rak' iŋ) *adj.*, very trying to one's patience or calm.

**non • com • mit • tal** (nän kə mit'l) *adj.*, not committing one to any point of view or course of action; not revealing one's position or purpose.

**ob • lit • er • ate** (ə blit' ər āt') *vt.*, blot out or wear away, leaving no traces.

**ob • tuse** (äb tüs') *adj.*, slow to understand or perceive.

**os • tra • cize** (äs' trə sīz') *vt.*, exclude or banish.

**pal • lid** (pal' id) *adj.*, faint in color; pale; wan.

**pa • tron • iz • ing • ly** (pā' trən īz' iŋ lē) *adv.*, in a helpful but snobbish way, as if dealing with an inferior.

**pee • vish** (pēv' ish) *adj.*, showing ill humor or impatience.

**pen • sive • ness** (pen' siv nəs) *n.*, filled with deep or serious thoughts, often of sad or melancholy things.

**per • plex • ing** (pər pleks' iŋ) *adj.*, confusing; puzzling.

**pi • thi • ly** (pi' thi lē) *adv.*, having substance and point.

**pla • cate** (plā' kāt') *vt.*, stop from being angry; appease.

**pre • dom • i • nant** (prē däm' ə nənt) *adj.*, most frequent, noticeable, etc.

**pre • oc • cu • pied** (prē äk′ yü pīd′) *adj.,* wholly occupied with or absorbed in one's thoughts.

**pre • tense** (prē tens′) *n.,* false show of something.

**pro • fane** (prō fān′) *adj.,* put to a base or improper use; debase; defile.

**prof • fer** (präf′ ər) *vt.,* offer (usually something intangible).

**pro • found • ly** (prō found′ lē) *adv.,* deeply.

**pro • tract** (prō trakt′) *vt.,* draw out; lengthen in duration; prolong.

**pro • trude** (prō trüd′) *vt.,* thrust or jut out.

**pro • vi • sions** (prō vizh′ əns) *n.,* stock of food and other supplies assembled for future needs.

**prov • o • ca • tion** (präv′ ə kā′ shən) *n.,* something that angers, irritates, or annoys.

**pu • tre • fac • tion** (pyü′ trə fak′ shən) *n.,* decomposition of organic matter by bacteria, fungi, and oxidation, resulting in the formation of foul-smelling products.

**qual • i • fi • ca • tion** (kwȯl′ i fi kā′ shən) *n.,* any quality, skill, knowledge, or experience that fits a person for a position, office, or profession.

**queue** (kyü) *n.,* line or file of persons, vehicles, etc. waiting as to be served.

**quix • ot • ic** (kwiks ät′ ik) *adj.,* extravagantly chivalrous or foolishly idealistic; visionary; impractical.

**rapt** (rapt) *adj.,* completely absorbed or engrossed.

**rap • ture** (rap′ chər) *n.,* state of being carried away with joy or love.

**ra • tion** (rash′ ən) *n.,* fixed allowance or allotment of food or provisions.

**rave** (rāv) *vi.,* speak out wildly; talk irrationally.

**re • gen • er • a • tion** (ri jen′ ə rā shən) *n.,* being renewed, reformed, or reconstituted.

**re • gime** (rə zhēm′) *n.,* particular administration or government.

**rem • i • nis • cence** (rem′ ə nis′ əns) *n.,* act of remembering past experiences.

**rem • nant** (rem′ nənt) *n.,* what is left over; remainder; residue.

**re • mon • strance** (ri män' strəns) *n.,* protest or complaint.

**rent** (rent) *adj.,* pierced with sound.

**req • ui • si • tion** (rek' wə zish' ən) *vt.,* submit a written order or request for (equipment, etc.).

**re • proach • ful • ly** (ri prōch' fəl lē) *adv.,* in a manner that expresses blame or criticism.

**res • pite** (res' pit) *n.,* interval of temporary relief or rest.

**res • tive** (res' tiv) *adj.,* nervous or impatient under pressure or restraint.

**re • tal • i • ate** (ri tal' ē āt') *vi.,* return like for like, especially to pay back injury for injury.

**re • tort** (ri tȯrt') *vi.,* reply, esp. in a sharp, quick, or witty way.

**re • ver • ber • a • tion** (ri vʉr' bə rā' shən) *n.,* reechoing or reflection of light or sound waves, deflection of heat or flame.

**re • vile** (ri vīl') *vt.,* use abusive or scolding language in speaking to or about.

**row** (rou) *n.,* noisy quarrel, dispute, or disturbance.

**scaf • fold** (skaf' əld) *n.,* raised platform on which criminals are executed, as by hanging.

**sheep • ish** (shēp' ish) *adj.,* embarrassed.

**shrap • nel** (shrap' nəl) *n.,* artillery shell filled with an explosive charge and many small metal balls designed to explode in the air over the objective; any fragments scattered by such an explosion.

**shrewd** (shrüd) *adj.,* keen-witted, clever, or sharp in practical affairs.

**sim • u • late** (sim' yü lāt') *vt.,* have or take on the external appearance of; look or act like.

**slack • en** (slak' ən) *vi.,* become less active or intense.

**slink** (sliŋk) *vi.,* move in a quiet, furtive, or sneaking manner, as from fear or guilt.

**sol • ace** (säl' is) *n.,* something that eases or relieves; comfort.

**spar • ing** (sper' iŋ) *adj.,* careful in spending or using; frugal.

**spas • mod • ic** (spaz mäd' ik) *adj.,* sudden, violent, and temporary.

**spry** (sprī) *adj.,* full of life; active, nimble.

**stag • ger** (stag′ ər) *vi.*, move unsteadily, as though about to collapse.

**stag • nant** (stag′ nənt) *adj.*, foul from lack of movement.

**stark** (stärk) *adj.*, sharply outlined or prominent.

**staunch** (stȯnch) *adj.*, firm; steadfast; loyal.

**sti • fle** (stī′ fəl) *vt.*, repress; hold back.

**storm** (stȯrm) *vt.*, attack or direct something at (someone) in a vigorous or angry outburst.

**strat • a • gem** (strat′ ə jəm) *n.*, any trick or scheme for achieving some purpose.

**su • per • fi • cial** (sü′ pər fish′ əl) *adj.*, concerned with and understanding only the easily apparent and obvious; shallow.

**su • per • fi • ci • al • i • ty** (sü′ pər fish′ ē al′ ə tē) *adj.*, something that is only on the surface or that is shallow and not profound.

**su • per • flu • ous** (sə pʉr′ flü əs) *adj.*, unnecessary; irrelevant.

**sub • side** (səb sīd′) *vi.*, become less active or intense.

**suf • fice** (sə fīs′) *vi.*, be enough; be adequate.

**sul • len** (sul′ ən) *adj.*, showing resentment and ill humor by morose, unsociable withdrawal.

**sul • try** (sul′ trē) *adj.*, oppressively hot and moist.

**sur • rep • ti • tious • ly** (sʉr′ əp tish′ əs lē) *adv.*, in a secret, stealthy way.

**swank • y** (swaŋ′ kē) *adj.*, ostentatiously stylish; showy.

**syn • thet • ic** (sin thet′ ik) *adj.*, human-made, not natural.

**tax** (taks) *vt.*, impose a burden on; put a strain on.

**tri • fling** (trī′ fliŋ) *adj.*, having little value or importance.

**tru • ant** (trü′ ənt) *n.*, pupil who stays away from school without permission.

**trudge** (truj) *vi.*, walk wearily or laboriously.

**trun • dle** (trun′ dəl) *vt.*, move along in a wheeled vehicle.

**un • can • ny** (un kan′ ē) *adj.*, so remarkable or acute as to seem supernatural.

**u • ni • son** (yün′ ə sən) *adj.*, uttering the same words, or producing the same sound, at the same time.

**un • scathed** (un skāthd') *adj.,* not hurt; unharmed.

**up • roar • i • ous • ly** (up rôr' ē əs lē) *adv.,* in a loud and boisterous manner.

**ut • ter** (ut' ər) *adj.,* complete; total.

**ven • ture** (ven' chər) *vt.,* express at the risk of criticism, objection, or denial.

**verge** (vʉrj) *n.,* edge, brink, or margin (*of* something).

**vile** (vīl) *adj.,* morally base or evil; wicked.

**vo • rac • i • ty** (vȯ ras' ə tē) *n.,* greediness in eating.

**vor • tex** (vȯr' teks') *n.,* whirling mass of water forming a vacuum at its center, into which anything caught in the motion is drawn.

**wage** (wāj) *vt.,* engage in or carry on (a war, struggle, campaign, etc.).

**whim • per** (hwim' pər) *vi.,* make low, whining, broken sounds, as in crying or in fear.

**wind • fall** (wind' fȯl') *n.,* any unexpected gain.

**wrath • ful • ly** (rath' fəl lē) *adv.,* in a very angry manner.

**zeal • ous • ly** (zel' əs lē) *adv.,* in an intensely enthusiastic manner.

# Handbook of Literary Terms

**AIM.** A writer's **aim** is his or her purpose or goal. People may write with the following aims:

- to inform (expository/informational writing)
- to entertain, enrich, enlighten, and/or use an artistic medium to share a perspective (imaginative writing)
- to make a point by sharing a story about an event (narrative writing)
- to reflect (personal/expressive writing)
- to persuade readers or listeners to respond in some way (persuasive/argumentative writing)

**ALLUSION.** An **allusion** is a rhetorical technique in which reference is made to a person, event, object, or work from history or literature.

**CARPE DIEM.** **Carpe diem** is a Latin term meaning "seize the day." The *carpe diem* theme, telling people not to waste time but rather to enjoy themselves while they have a chance, was common in Renaissance English poetry.

**CHIVALRY.** See *Hero and Chivalry.*

**COMIC RELIEF.** Writers sometimes insert into a serious work of fiction or drama a humorous scene that is said to provide **comic relief**, because it relieves the seriousness or emotional intensity felt by the audience. Paradoxically, a scene introduced for comic relief can sometimes, because of the contrast it provides, increase the perceived intensity or seriousness of the action around it.

**CONFLICT AND CENTRAL CONFLICT.** A **conflict** is a struggle between two forces in a literary work. A *plot* involves the introduction, development, and eventual resolution of a conflict. The **central conflict** is the primary struggle dealt with in the plot of a story or novel. One side of the central conflict is taken by the main character. A struggle that takes place between a character and some outside force is called an *external conflict*. A struggle that takes place within a character is called an *internal conflict.*

**CRISIS.** In the plot of a story or drama, the **crisis** is that point in the development of the conflict at which a decisive event occurs that causes the main character's situation to become better or worse.

**DESCRIPTION.** **Description** is a type of writing that portrays a character, an object, or a scene.

**Foil.** A **foil** is a character or thing whose attributes, or characteristics, contrast with and therefore throw into relief the attributes of another character or thing.

**Hero and Chivalry.** A **hero** is a character whose actions are inspiring and courageous. **Chivalry** was the code of conduct of the medieval knight. According to the code of chivalry, a knight exemplified virtues as loyalty, bravery, courage, courtesy, honesty, faith, and gentleness. Knights obeyed strict codes of behavior even in battle; for example, if a knight was unhorsed another knight might let him get back on his horse before resuming the fight, rather than pressing his advantage. Knights were often heroes in medieval writing.

**Image and Imagery.** An **image** is language that creates a concrete representation of an object or an experience. An image is also the vivid mental picture created in the reader's mind by that language. The images in a work are referred to, collectively, as the work's **imagery**.

**Irony.** **Irony** is a difference between appearance and reality. In *irony of situation,* an event occurs that violates the expectations of the characters, the reader, or the audience.

**Motif.** A **motif** is any element that recurs in one or more works of literature or art.

**Parallelism.** **Parallelism** is a rhetorical technique in which a writer emphasizes the equal value or weight of two or more ideas by expressing them in the same grammatical form.

**Personification.** **Personification** is a figure of speech in which an idea, animal, or thing is described as if it were a person.

**Point of View.** **Point of view** is the vantage point from which a story is told. Stories are typically told from a first-person point of view, in which the narrator uses such words as *I* and *we;* from a second-person point of view, in which the narrator uses *you;* or from a third-person point of view, in which the narrator uses such words as *he, she, it,* and *they.*

**Repetition.** **Repetition** is a writer's conscious reuse of a sound, word, phrase, sentence, or other element.

**Sensory Details.** **Sensory details** are words and phrases that describe how things look, sound, smell, taste, or feel.

SETTING. The **setting** of a literary work is the time and place in which it occurs, together with all the details used to create a sense of a particular time and place.

STYLE. **Style** is the manner in which something is said or written. Traditionally, critics and scholars have referred to three levels of style: high style, for formal occasions or lofty subjects; middle style, for ordinary occasions or subjects; and low style, for extremely informal occasions and subjects.

SYMBOL. A **symbol** is a thing that stands for or represents both itself and something else.

THEME. A **theme** is a central idea in a literary work.

# Acknowledgments

**Simon & Schuster.** "Soldier's Home" by Ernest Hemingway. Reprinted with permission of Scribner, a Division of Simon & Schuster, Inc., from *The Short Stories of Ernest Hemingway.* Copyright 1925 by Charles Scribner's Sons. Copyright renewed 1953 by Ernest Hemingway.

**Mark Bostridge and Rebecca Williams.** From *Testament of Youth* by Vera Brittain. Excerpts from Vera Brittain's *Testament of Youth* are included by permission of Mark Bostridge and Rebecca Williams, her literary executors.

**New Directions Publishing Corporation.** "Dulce et Decorum Est" by Wilfred Owen, from *The Collected Poems of Wilfred Owen,* copyright ©1963 by Chatto & Windus, Ltd. Reprinted by permission of New Directions Publishing Corporation.